Mathematica® for Rogawski's Calculus

2nd Edition 2011
Based on *Mathematica* Version 7

Abdul Hassen, Gary Itzkowitz, Hieu D. Nguyen, Jay Schiffman

FREEMAN
Custom Publishing

ISBN-13: 978-1-4641-0187-8
ISBN-10: 1-4641-0187-6

Printed in 2011 in the United States of America

Custom Publishing Division
W.H. Freeman and Company
41 Madison Avenue New York, NY 10010

www.whfreeman.com/custompub

Table of Contents

Chapter 1   Introduction

Welcome to *Mathematica*! This tutorial manual is intended as a supplement to Rogawski's *Calculus* textbook and aimed at students looking to quickly learn *Mathematica* through examples. It also includes a brief summary of each calculus topic to emphasize important concepts. Students should refer to their textbook for a further explanation of each topic.

■ 1.1 Getting Started

Mathematica is a powerful computer algebra system (CAS) whose capabilities and features can be overwhelming for new users. Thus, to make your first experience in using *Mathematica* as easy as possible, we recommend that you read this introductory chapter very carefully. We will discuss basic syntax and frequently used commands.

NOTE: You may need to obtain a computer account on your school's computer network in order to access the *Mathematica* software package available on campus computers. Check with your instructor or your school's IT office.

■ 1.1.1 First-Time Users of *Mathematica* 7

Launch the program *Mathematica* 7 on your computer. *Mathematica* will automatically create a new Notebook (see typical startup screen below).

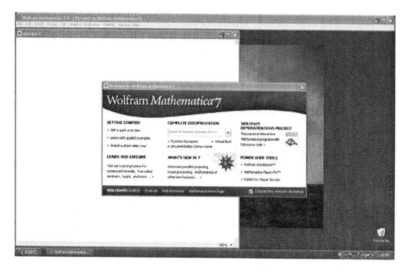

■ 1.1.2 Entering and Evaluating Input Commands

Just start typing to input commands (a cell formatted as an input box will be automatically created). For example, type 3+7. To evaluate this command or any other command(s) contained inside an input box, simultaneously press SHIFT+ENTER, that is, the keys SHIFT and ENTER at the same time. Be sure your mouse's cursor is positioned inside the input box or else select the input box(es) that you want to evaluate. The kernel application, which does all the computations, will load at the first evaluation. This is a one-time procedure whenever *Mathematica* is launched and may take a few seconds depending on the speed of your computer, so be patient.

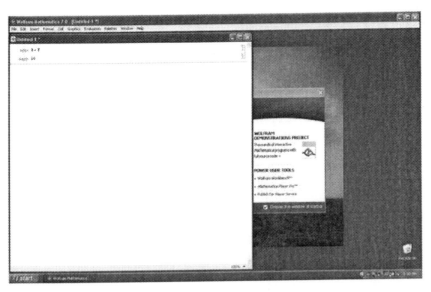

As can be seen from the screen shot above, a cell formatted as an output box and containing the value 10 is generated as a result of the evaluation. To create another input box (cell), just start typing again and an input box will be inserted at the position of the cursor (use the mouse to position the cursor where you would like to insert the new input box).

■ 1.1.3 Documentation Center (Help Menu)

Mathematica provides an online help menu to answer many of your questions about the program. One can search for a particular command expression in the Documentation Center under this menu or else just position the cursor next to the expression (for example, **Plot**) and select **Find Selected Function** (F1) under the Help menu (see screen shot that follows).

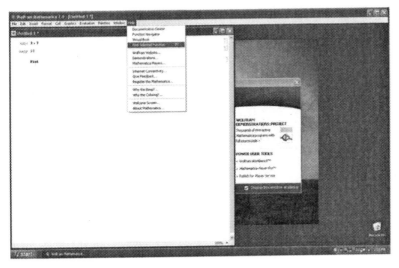

Mathematica will then display a description of **Plot**, including examples on how to use it (see screen shot below).

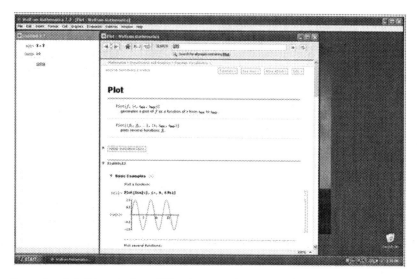

For only a brief description of **Plot** (or any other expression **expr**), just evaluate **?Plot** (or **?expr**).

In[1]:= **? Plot**

Plot[f, {x, x_{min}, x_{max}}] generates a plot of f as a function of x from x_{min} to x_{max}.

Plot[{f_1, f_2, ...}, {x, x_{min}, x_{max}}] plots several functions f_i. ≫

■ 1.2 *Mathematica*'s Conventions for Inputting Commands

■ 1.2.1 Naming

Built-in *Mathematica* commands, functions, constants, and other expressions begin with capital letters and are (for the most part) one or more full-length English words (each word is capitalized). Furthermore, *Mathematica* is case sensitive; a common cause of error is the failure to capitalize command names. For example, **Plot**, **Integrate**, and **FindRoot** are valid function names. **Sin**, **Exp**, **Det**, **GCD**, and **Max** are some of the standard mathematical abbreviations that are exceptions to the full-length English word(s) rule.

User-defined functions and variables can be any mixture of uppercase and lowercase letters and numbers. However, a name cannot begin with a number. User-defined functions may begin with a lowercase letter, but this is not required. For example, **f**, **g1**, **myPlot**, **r12**, **sOLution**, and **Method1** are permissible function names.

■ 1.2.2. Parenthesis, Brackets, and Braces

Mathematica interprets various types of delimiters (brackets) differently. Using an incorrect type of delimiter is another common source of error. *Mathematica*'s bracketing conventions are as follows:

1) Parentheses, **( )**, are used only for grouping expressions. For example, **(x-y)^2**, **1/(a+b)** and **(x^3-y)/(x+3y^2)** demonstrate proper use of parentheses. Users should realize that *Mathematica* understands **f(2)** as f multiplied with 2 and not as the function $f(x)$ evaluated at $x = 2$.

2) Square brackets, **[ ]**, are used to enclose function arguments. For example, **Sqrt[346]**, **Sin[Pi]**, and **Simplify[(x^3-y^3)/(x-y)]** are valid uses of square brackets. Therefore, to evaluate a function $f(x)$ at $x = 2$, we can type **f[2]**.

3) Braces or curly brackets, **{ }**, are used for defining lists, ranges and iterators. In all cases, list elements are separated by commas. Here are some typical uses of braces:

{1, 4, 9, 16, 25, 36}: This lists the square of the first six positive integers.

Plot[f[x],{x,-5,5}]: The list {x,-5,5} here specifies the range of values for x in plotting f.

Table[m^3,{m,1,100}]: The list {m,1,100} here specifies the values of the iterator m in generating a table of cube powers of the first 100 whole numbers.

■ 1.2.3. Lists

A *list* (or string) of elements can be defined in *Mathematica* as **List[e_1, e_2,...,e_n]** or **{e_1, e_2,...,e_n}**. For example, the following command defines $S = \{1, 3, 5, 7, 9\}$ to be the list (set) of the first five odd positive integers.

In[2]:= **S = List[1, 3, 5, 7, 9]**

Out[2]= {1, 3, 5, 7, 9}

To refer to the kth element in a list named **expr**, just evaluate **expr[[k]]**. For example, to refer to the fourth element in S, we evaluate

In[3]:= **S[[4]]**

Out[3]= 7

It is also possible to define nested lists whose elements are themselves lists, called *sublists*. Each sublist contains *subelements*. For example, the list $T = \{\{1, 3, 5, 7, 9\}, \{2, 4, 6, 8, 10\}\}$ contains two elements, each of which is a list (first five odd and even positive integers).

In[4]:= **T = {{1, 3, 5, 7, 9}, {2, 4, 6, 8, 10}}**

Out[4]= {{1, 3, 5, 7, 9}, {2, 4, 6, 8, 10}}

To refer to the kth subelement in the jth sublist of **expr**, just evaluate **expr[[j,k]]**. For example, to refer to the third subelement in the second sublist of T (or 6), we evaluate

In[5]:= **T[[2, 3]]**

Out[5]= 6

A detailed description of how to manipulate lists (e.g., to append elements to a list or delete elements from a list) can be found in *Mathematica*'s Documentation Center (under the Help menu). Search for the entry **List**.

■ 1.2.4. Equal Signs

Here are *Mathematica*'s rules regarding the use of equal signs:

1) A single equal sign (=) assigns a value to a variable. Thus, entering **q = 3** means that q will be assigned the value 3.

In[6]:= **q = 3**

Out[6]= 3

If we then evaluate **10+q^3**, *Mathematica* will return 37.

In[7]:= **10 + q^3**

Out[7]= 37

As another example, suppose the expression **y = x^2-x-1** is entered.

In[8]:= **y = x^2 - x - 1**

Out[8]= $-1 - x + x^2$

If we then assign a value for *x*, say *x* = 3, then in any future input containing *y*, *Mathematica* will use this value of *x* to calculate *y*, which would be 5 in our case.

In[9]:= **x = 3**

y

Out[9]= 3

Out[10]= 5

2) A colon-equal sign (:=) creates a delayed statement for an expression and can be used to define a function. For example, typing **f[x_]: = x^2-x-1** tells *Mathematica* to delay the assignnment of $f(x)$ as a function until f is evaluated at a particular value of *x*.

In[11]:= **f[x_] := x^2 - x - 1**

f[3]

Out[12]= 5

We will say more about defining functions in section 1.3 below.

3) A double-equal sign (= =) is a test of equality between two expressions. Since we previously set **x** = 3, then evaluating **x = = 3** returns True, whereas evaluating **x = = -3** returns False.

In[13]:= **x == 3**

x == -3

Out[13]= True

Out[14]= False

Another common usage of the double equal sign (= =) is to solve equations, such as the command **Solve[x^2-x-1= = 0, x]** (see Section 1.5). Be sure to clear the variable *x* beforehand.

In[15]:= **Clear[x]**

Solve[x^2 - x - 1 == 0, x]

Out[16]= $\left\{ \left\{ x \rightarrow \frac{1}{2} \left(1 - \sqrt{5} \right) \right\}, \left\{ x \rightarrow \frac{1}{2} \left(1 + \sqrt{5} \right) \right\} \right\}$

■ 1.2.5. Referring to Previous Results

Mathematica saves all input and output in a session. Type **In[k]** (or **Out[k]**) to refer to input (or output) line numbered *k*. One can also refer to previous output by using the percent sign **%**. A single **%** refers to *Mathematica*'s last output, **%%** refers to the next-to-last ouput, and so forth. The command **%k** refers to the output line numbered *k*. For example, **%12** refers to output line number 12.

In[17]:= **Out[12]**

Out[17]= 5

Mathematica saves all input and output in a session. Type **In[k]** (or **Out[k]**) to refer to input (or output) line numbered *k*. One can also refer to previous output by using the percent sign **%**. A single **%** refers to *Mathematica*'s last output, **%%** refers to the next-to-last ouput, and so forth. The command **%k** refers to the output line numbered *k*. For example, **%12** refers to output line number 12.

In[18]:= **%12**

Out[18]= 5

NOTE: CTRL+L reproduces the last input and CTRL+SHIFT+L reproduces the last output.

■ 1.2.6. Commenting

One can insert comments on any input line. The comments should be enclosed between the delimiters (* and *). For example,

In[19]:= **(* This command plots the graph of two functions in different colors. *)**
Plot[{Sin[x], Cos[x]}, {x, 0, 2 Pi}, PlotStyle -> {Red, Blue}]

Out[19]=

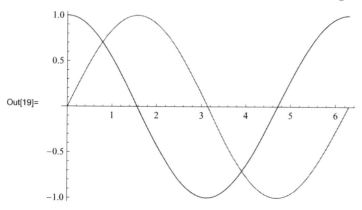

NOTE: One can also insert comments by creating a text box. First, create an input box. Then select it and format it as Text using the drop-down window menu.

■ 1.3 Basic Calculator Operations

Mathematica uses the standard symbols +, -, *, /, ^, ! for addition, subtraction, multiplication, division, raising powers (exponents), and factorials, respectively. Multiplication can also be performed by leaving a blank space between factors. Powers can also be entered by using the palette menu to generate a superscript box (or else press CTRL+6) and fractions can be entered by generating a fraction box (from palette menu or pressing CTRL+/).

To generate numerical output in decimal form, use the command **N[expr]** or **N[expr,d]**. In most cases, **N[expr]** returns six digits of **expr** by default and may be in the form $n.abcde * 10^m$ (scientific notation), whereas **N[expr,d]** attempts to return *d* digits of expr.

NOTE: *Mathematica* can perform calculations to arbitrary precision and handle numbers that are arbitrarily large or small.

Here are some examples:

In[20]:= **Pi**

Out[20]= π

In[21]:= **N[Pi]**

Out[21]= 3.14159

In[22]:= **N[Pi, 200]**

Out[22]= 3.14159265358979323846264338327950288419716939937510582097494459230781640628620899862803482534211706798214808651328230664709384460955058223172535940812848111745028410270193852110555964462294895493038 20

In[23]:= **6$^{5^4}$**

Out[23]= 2 210 708 544 304 025 665 789 890 545 869 282 983 189 550 730 342 026 817 054 484 706 923 451 925 215 263 872 221 875 601 412 877 526 055 033 568 150 952 983 731 997 599 172 762 855 409 042 386 638 455 130 114 567 918 179 610 415 056 135 043 685 865 981 465 821 197 678 998 054 981 600 364 232 459 680 450 883 986 513 397 952 866 100 532 961 319 277 446 513 221 836 325 497 685 382 494 082 501 890 188 075 860 096 650 899 943 982 604 939 901 346 570 765 022 869 199 395 889 789 728 382 946 141 484 842 179 531 904 056 612 897 175 359 078 633 987 736 867 003 878 781 857 613 656 893 578 474 392 372 463 398 376 238 316 805 554 810 164 724 551 909 376

In[24]:= **1 / 300 !**

Out[24]= 1 / 306 057 512 216 440 636 035 370 461 297 268 629 388 588 804 173 576 999 416 776 741 259 476 533 176 716 867 465 515 291 422 477 573 349 939 147 888 701 726 368 864 263 907 759 003 154 226 842 927 906 974 559 841 225 476 930 271 954 604 008 012 215 776 252 176 854 255 965 356 903 506 788 725 264 321 896 264 299 365 204 576 448 830 388 909 753 943 489 625 436 053 225 980 776 521 270 822 437 639 449 120 128 678 675 368 305 712 293 681 943 649 956 460 498 166 450 227 716 500 185 176 546 469 340 112 226 034 729 724 066 333 258 583 506 870 150 169 794 168 850 353 752 137 554 910 289 126 407 157 154 830 282 284 937 952 636 580 145 235 233 156 936 482 233 436 799 254 594 095 276 820 608 062 232 812 387 383 880 817 049 600 000 000 000 000 000 000 000 000 000 000 000 000 000 000 000 000 000 000 000 000 000 000 000

In[25]:= **(* This command returns a decimal answer of the last output *)**
N[%]

Out[25]= 3.267359761105326 × 10^{-615}

Example 1.1. How close is $e^{\sqrt{163}\,\pi}$ to being an integer?

Solution:

In[26]:= **E ^ (Pi * Sqrt[163])**

Out[26]= $e^{\sqrt{163}\,\pi}$

In[27]:= **N[%, 40]**

Out[27]= 2.625374126407687439999999999999992500725972 × 10^{17}

We can rewrite this output in non-scientific notation by moving the decimal point 17 places to the right. This shows that $e^{\sqrt{163}\,\pi}$ is very close to being an integer. Another option is to use the command **Mod[n,m]**, which returns the remainder of *n* when divided by *m*, to obtain the fractional part of $e^{\sqrt{163}\,\pi}$:

In[28]:= **Mod[%, 1]**

Out[28]= 0.999999999999992500725972

In[29]:= **1 - %**

Out[29]= $7.499274028 \times 10^{-13}$

■ 1.4 Functions

There are two different ways to represent functions in *Mathematica*, depending on how they are to be used. Consider the following example:

Example 1.2. Enter the function $f(x) = \dfrac{x^2+x+2}{x+1}$ into *Mathematica*.

Solution:

Method 1: Simply assign f the expression $\dfrac{x^2+x+2}{x+1}$, for example,

In[30]:= **Clear[f, x] (* This clears the arguments f and x *)**

In[31]:= **f = (x^2 + x + 2) / (x + 1)**

Out[31]= $\dfrac{2 + x + x^2}{1 + x}$

To evaluate $f(x)$ at $x = 10$, we use the substitution command **/.** (slash-period) as follows:

In[32]:= **f /. x -> 10**

Out[32]= $\dfrac{112}{11}$

Warning: Recall that *Mathematica* reads *f(x)* as *f* multiplied by *x*; commas are considered delimiters.

In[33]:= **f (10)**

Out[33]= $\dfrac{10 \left(2 + x + x^2\right)}{1 + x}$

Method 2: An alternative way to explicitly represent *f* as a function of the argument *x* is to enter

In[34]:= **Clear[f]**
f[x_] := (x^2 + x + 2) / (x + 1)

Evaluating the command **f[10]** now tells *Mathematica* to compute *f* at $x = 10$.

In[36]:= **f[10]**

Out[36]= $\dfrac{112}{11}$

More generally, the command **f[{a,b,c,...}]** evaluates $f(x)$ for every value of x in the list **{a,b,c,...}**:

In[37]:= **f[{-3, -2, -1, 0, 1, 2, 3}]**

Power::infy : Infinite expression $\dfrac{1}{0}$ encountered. ≫

Out[37]= $\left\{-4, -4, \text{ComplexInfinity}, 2, 2, \dfrac{8}{3}, \dfrac{7}{2}\right\}$

Here, *Mathematica* is warning us that it has encountered the undefined expression $\frac{1}{0}$ in evaluating $f(-1)$ by returning the message ComplexInfinity.

Remark: If there is no need to attach a label to the expression $\dfrac{x^2+x+2}{x+1}$, then we can directly enter this expression into *Mathematica*:

In[38]:= $\dfrac{x^2 + x + 2}{x + 1}$ **/. x -> 10**

Out[38]= $\dfrac{112}{11}$

In[39]:= $\dfrac{x^2 + x + 2}{x + 1}$ **/. x -> {-3, -2, -1, 0, 1, 2, 3}**

Power::infy : Infinite expression $\dfrac{1}{0}$ encountered. ≫

Out[39]= $\left\{-4, -4, \text{ComplexInfinity}, 2, 2, \dfrac{8}{3}, \dfrac{7}{2}\right\}$

Piece-wise functions can be defined using the command **If[cond, *p*, *q*]**, which evaluates **p** if **cond** is true; otherwise, **q** is evaluated.

Example 1.3. Enter the following piece-wise function into *Mathematica*:

$$f(x) = \begin{cases} \tan\left(\dfrac{\pi x}{4}\right), & \text{if } |x| < 1; \\ x, & \text{if } |x| \geq 1. \end{cases}$$

Solution:

In[40]:= **f[x_] := If[Abs[x] < 1, Tan[Pi * x / 4], x]**

▪ 1.5 Palettes

Mathematica allows us to enter commonly used mathematical expressions and commands from six different palettes. Palettes are calculator pads containing buttons that can be clicked on to insert the desired expression or command into a command line. These palettes can be found under the Palettes menu. If the Basic Math Assistant Palette does not appear by default, then click on Palettes from the menu and select it. One can also select more advanced math typesetting palettes such as the Basic Math Input and Algebraic Manipulate Palettes.

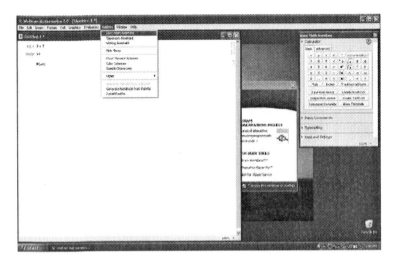

Example 1.4. Enter $\sqrt{\dfrac{3}{\pi^4}}$ into a notebook.

Solution:

Here is one set of instructions for entering this expression using the Basic Math Assistant Palette:

a) Click on the palette button $\sqrt{\Box}$.

b) Click on $\frac{\Box}{\Box}$.

c) Enter the number 3 into the highlighted top placeholder.

$$\sqrt{\dfrac{3}{\Box}}$$

d) Press the TAB key to move the cursor to the bottom placeholder.

e) Click on $\Box^{\Box}$.

f) To insert π into the base position, click on the palette button for π.

$$\sqrt{\dfrac{3}{\pi^{\Box}}}$$

g) Press the TAB key to move the cursor to the superscript placeholder.

h) Enter the number 4.

$$\sqrt{\dfrac{3}{\pi^4}}$$

∎ 1.6 Solving Equations

Mathematica has a host of built-in commands to help the user solve equations and manipulate expressions. The command **Solve[lhs == rhs, var]** solves the equation **lhs == rhs** (recall *Mathematica*'s use of the double-equal sign) for the variable **var**. For example, the command below solves the quadratic equation $x^2 - 4 = 0$ for x.

In[41]:= **Solve[x^2 - 4 == 0, x]**

Out[41]= $\{\{x \to -2\}, \{x \to 2\}\}$

A system of m equations in n unknowns can also be solved with using the same command, but formatted as **Solve[{lhs$_1$ == rhs$_1$, lhs$_2$ == rhs$_2$, ..., lhs$_m$ == rhs$_m$}, {x_1, x_2, ..., x_n}]**. In situations where exact solutions cannot be obtained (e.g., certain polynomial equations of degree 5 or higher), numerical approximations can be obtained through the command **NSolve[lhs == rhs, var]**. Here are two examples:

In[42]:= **Clear[x, y]**
        Solve[{2 x - y == 3, x + 4 y == -2}, {x, y}]

Out[43]= $\left\{\left\{x \to \dfrac{10}{9}, y \to -\dfrac{7}{9}\right\}\right\}$

In[44]:= **NSolve[x^5 - x + 1 == 0, x]**

Out[44]= $\{\{x \to -1.1673\}, \{x \to -0.181232 - 1.08395 \, i\}, \{x \to -0.181232 + 1.08395 \, i\},$
        $\{x \to 0.764884 - 0.352472 \, i\}, \{x \to 0.764884 + 0.352472 \, i\}\}$

There are many commands to algebraically manipulate expressions: **Expand, Factor, Together, Apart, Cancel, Simplify, FullSimplify, TrigExpand, TrigFactor, TrigReduce, ExpToTrig, PowerExpand**, and **ComplexExpand**.

In[45]:= **Factor[x^2 + 4 x - 21]**

Out[45]= $(-3 + x) (7 + x)$

NOTE: These commands can also be entered from the Algebraic Manipulation Palette; highlight the expression to be manipulated and click on the button corresponding to the command to be inserted. The screen shot below demonstrates how to select the **Factor** command from the Algebraic Manipulate Palette to factor the highlighted expression $x^2 + 4x - 21$.

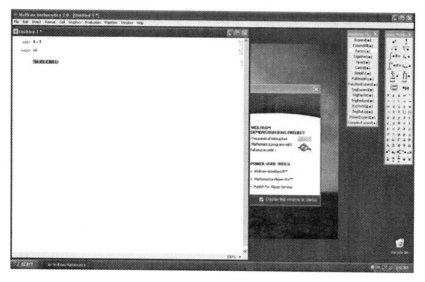

■ Exercises

In Exercises 1 through 5, evaluate the expressions:

1. 103.41+20*76   2. $\dfrac{5^2+\pi}{1+\pi}$ 3. $\dfrac{1}{1+\dfrac{1}{1+\dfrac{1}{4!}}}$ 4. $\dfrac{2.06*10^9}{0.99*10^{-8}}$ 5. What is the remainder of 1998 divided by 13?

In Exercises 6 through 8, enter the functions into *Mathematica* and evaluate each at $x = 1$:

6. $f(x) = 2\,x^3 - 6\,x^2 + x - 5$ 　　　　7. $g(x) = \frac{x^2-1}{x^2+1}$ 　　　　8. $h(x) = \left| \sqrt{x} - 3 \right|$

In Exercises 9 through 11, evaluate the functions at the given point using *Mathematica*:

9. $f(x) = 1001 + x^4$ at $x = 25$ 　　　　10. $1 + \sqrt{x} + \sqrt[3]{x} + \sqrt[4]{x}$ at $x = \pi$ 　　　　11. $1 + \cfrac{1}{2 + \cfrac{(2x+1)^2}{2 + \cfrac{(4x+1)^2}{2}}}$ at $x = 1$

In Exercises 12 through 17, enter the expressions into *Mathematica*:

12. $\sqrt[3]{80}$ 　　　　13. $\dfrac{\sqrt[5]{1024}}{2^{-3}}$ 　　　　14. $\sqrt[3]{\sqrt{125}}$

15. $\sqrt{\sqrt[3]{10\,a^7\,b}}$ 　　　　16. $\left(\dfrac{x^{-3}\,y^4}{5}\right)^{-3}$ 　　　　17. $\left(\dfrac{3\,m^{\frac{1}{6}}\,n^{\frac{1}{3}}}{4\,n^{-\frac{2}{3}}}\right)^2$

In Exercises 18 through 21, expand the expressions:

18. $(x+1)(x-1)$ 　　　　19. $(x+y-2)(2x-3)$ 　　　　20. $\left(x^2 + x + 1\right)(x-1)$ 　　　　21. $\left(x^3 + x^2 + x + 1\right)(x-1)$

In Exercises 22 through 25, factor the expressions:

22. $x^3 - 2\,x^2 - 3\,x$ 　　　　23. $4\,x^{2/3} + 8\,x^{1/3} + 3.6$ 　　　　24. $6 + 2\,x - 3\,x^3 - x^4$ 　　　　25. $x^5 - 1$

In Exercises 26 through 29, simplify the expressions using both of the commands **Simplify** and **FullSimplify** (the latter uses a wider variety of methods to simplify expressions).

26. $\dfrac{x^2 + 4\,x - 12}{3\,x - 6}$ 　　　　27. $\dfrac{\left(\frac{2}{x}-3\right)}{1-\frac{1}{x-1}}$ 　　　　28. $(x(1-2\,x))^{-3/2} + (1-2\,x)^{-1/2}$ 　　　　29. $\dfrac{x^5-1}{x-1}$

In Exercises 30 through 33, solve the equations for x (compare outputs using both the **Solve** and **NSolve** commands):

30. $x^2 - x + 1 = 0$ 　　　　31. $x(1-2\,x)^{-3/2} + (1-2\,x)^{-1/2} = 0$ 　　　　32. $x^3 - 1 = 0$ 　　　　33. $\sqrt{1 + \sqrt{x + \sqrt{x^2}}} = 5$

Chapter 2   Graphs of Functions, Limits, and Continuity

■ 2.1 Plotting Graphs

Students should read Chapter 1 of Rogawski's *Calculus* [1] for a detailed discussion of the material presented in this section.

■ 2.1.1 Basic Plot

In this section, we will discuss how to plot graphs of functions using *Mathematica* and how to utilize its various plot options. We will discuss in detail several options that will be useful in our study of calculus. The basic syntax for plotting the graph of a function $y = f(x)$ with x ranging in value from a to b is **Plot[f, {x, a, b}]**. On the other hand, **Plot[{f_1, f_2, ..., f_N}, {x, a, b}]** plots the graphs of f_1, f_2, ..., f_N on the same set of axes.

Example 2.1. Plot the graph of $f(x) = x^2 - 3x + 1$ along the interval $[-2, 5]$.

Solution:

In[46]:= **Plot$\left[x^2 - 3x + 1, \{x, -2, 5\}\right]$**

Out[46]=

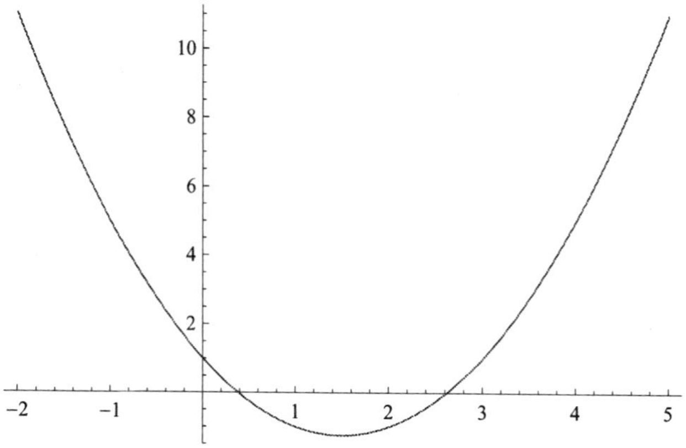

Example 2.2. Plot the graph of $y = \cos(3x)$ along the interval $[-4, 4]$.

Solution:

In[47]:= **Plot[Cos[3 x], {x, -4, 4}]**

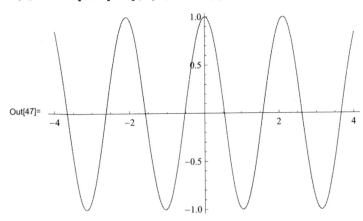

Out[47]=

Example 2.3. Plot the graphs of the two functions given in Examples 2.1 and 2.2 prior on the same set of axes to show their points of intersection.

Solution:

In[48]:= **Plot$\left[\left\{x^2 - 3x + 1, Cos[x]\right\}, \{x, -3, 6\}\right]$**

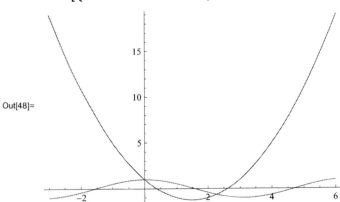

Out[48]=

Example 2.4. Plot the graphs of $f(x) = \frac{x^2 + x + 1}{x + 1}$ and $g(x) = \frac{\sin(4x)}{4}$ on the same set of axes.

Solution:

In[49]:= **Plot[{ (x^2 + x + 2) / (x + 1), Sin[4 x] / 4}, {x, -4, 4}]**

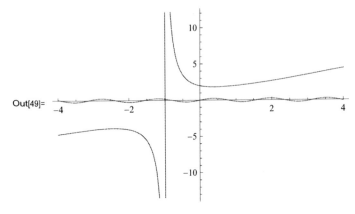

Out[49]=

Note that the graph of $y = (\sin 4 x)/4$ is displayed poorly in output above since its range (from -1 to 1) is too small compared to the range of $y = (x^2 + x + 2)/(x + 1)$. We can zoom in using the **PlotRange** option. The syntax for **PlotRange** is **PlotRange** → {**c, d**} (the arrow is generated by entering a minus sign (-) followed by greater than sign) where [c, d] is the interval on the y-axis to be displayed. More generally, **PlotRange** –> {{a, b}, {c, d}} specifies the interval [a, b] on the x-axis while [c, d] specifies the interval on the y-axis.

In[50]:= `Plot[{ (x^2 + x + 1) / (x + 1), Sin[4 x] / 4}, {x, -4, 4}, PlotRange → {-4, 4}]`

Out[50]=

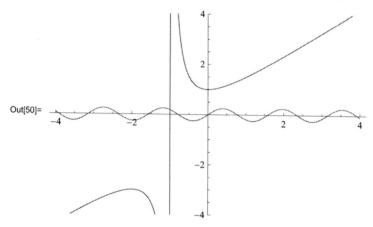

Example 2.5. Plot the graphs of the following functions.

a) $f(x) = \frac{x^2}{x^2-4}$ b) $f(x) = \sin x + \cos x$ c) $f(x) = x e^x + \ln x$ d) $f(x) = \frac{x^2}{x^2+4}$

Solution: We recall that the natural base e is entered as **E** or e (from the Basic Math Assistant Palette) and that $\ln x$ is **Log[x]**. Note also that $\sin x$ and $\cos x$ are to be entered as **Sin[x]** and **Cos[x]** (see Chapter 1 of this text for a discussion of *Mathematica's* notation). We leave it to the reader to experiment with different intervals for the domain of each graph so as to capture its salient features.

a)

In[51]:= `Plot[ x²/(4 - x²), {x, -5, 5}]`

Out[51]=

b)

In[52]:= **Plot[Sin[x] + Cos[x], {x, -2 Pi, 2 Pi}]**

Out[52]=

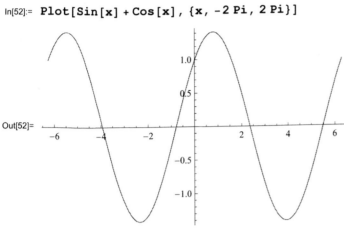

c)

In[53]:= **Plot[x E^x - Log[x], {x, -3, 3}]**

Out[53]=

NOTE: The above graph needs to be read carefully. First of all, it is clear from the graph above that $f(x) = x e^x - \ln x$ tends to ∞ as x tends to 0. It is also clear from the graph that $f(x)$ tends to ∞ as x tends to ∞. Note, however, that the graph suggests (incorrectly) that the domain is $[0, \infty)$. If we zoom in on the graph near $x = 0$, then we see that the domain does NOT include the point $x = 0$.

In[54]:= $\texttt{Plot}\left[\dfrac{x^2}{x^2+4}, \{x, -5, 5\}\right]$

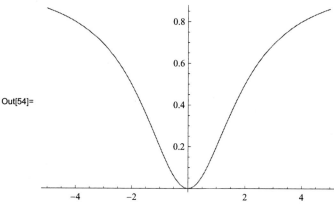

Out[54]=

2.1.2 Plot Options

Next, we will introduce various options that can be specified within the **Plot** command. To begin with, evaluating the command **Options[Plot]** displays the following options:

In[55]:= `Options[Plot]`

Out[55]= $\Big\{$ AlignmentPoint → Center, AspectRatio → $\dfrac{1}{\text{GoldenRatio}}$, Axes → True,
AxesLabel → None, AxesOrigin → Automatic, AxesStyle → {}, Background → None,
BaselinePosition → Automatic, BaseStyle → {}, ClippingStyle → None,
ColorFunction → Automatic, ColorFunctionScaling → True, ColorOutput → Automatic,
ContentSelectable → Automatic, CoordinatesToolOptions → Automatic,
DisplayFunction :→ $DisplayFunction, Epilog → {}, Evaluated → Automatic,
EvaluationMonitor → None, Exclusions → Automatic, ExclusionsStyle → None,
Filling → None, FillingStyle → Automatic, FormatType :→ TraditionalForm,
Frame → False, FrameLabel → None, FrameStyle → {}, FrameTicks → Automatic,
FrameTicksStyle → {}, GridLines → None, GridLinesStyle → {},
ImageMargins → 0., ImagePadding → All, ImageSize → Automatic,
ImageSizeRaw → Automatic, LabelStyle → {}, MaxRecursion → Automatic,
Mesh → None, MeshFunctions → {#1 &}, MeshShading → None, MeshStyle → Automatic,
Method → Automatic, PerformanceGoal :→ $PerformanceGoal,
PlotLabel → None, PlotPoints → Automatic, PlotRange → {Full, Automatic},
PlotRangeClipping → True, PlotRangePadding → Automatic, PlotRegion → Automatic,
PlotStyle → Automatic, PreserveImageOptions → Automatic, Prolog → {},
RegionFunction → (True &), RotateLabel → True, Ticks → Automatic,
TicksStyle → {}, WorkingPrecision → MachinePrecision $\Big\}$

■ PlotStyle

PlotStyle is an option for **Plot** that specifies the style of lines or points to be plotted. Among other things, one can use this option to specify a color of the graph and the thickness of the curve. **PlotStyle** should be followed by an arrow and then the option: **PlotStyle → {option}**. For example, if we want to plot a graph colored in red, we evaluate

In[56]:= `Plot[x², {x, -3, 3}, PlotStyle -> Red]`

Out[56]=

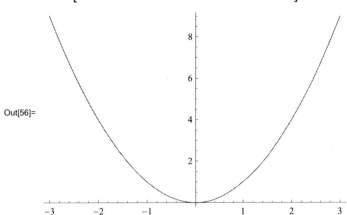

The next example shows how to use **PlotStyle** to specify two *styles:* a color and thickness.

In[57]:= `Plot[x², {x, -3, 3}, PlotStyle -> { Blue, Thickness[0.02]}]`

Out[57]=

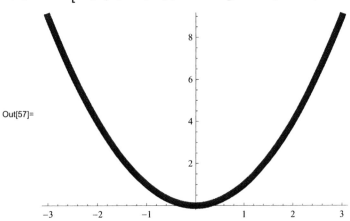

PlotStyle can also be used to specify options for two or more graphs. Here are two examples to demonstrate this:

In[58]:= `Plot[{x², x³ - x - 1}, {x, -3, 3}, PlotStyle -> {Green, Yellow }]`

Out[58]=

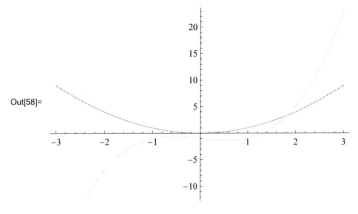

In[59]:= `Plot[{x`^{2}`, x`^{3}` - x - 1}, {x, -3, 3}, PlotStyle -> {{Magenta, Thickness[0.01]},`
`{Cyan, Thickness[0.001], Dashing[{0.01, 0.01, 0.01}]}}]`

Out[59]=

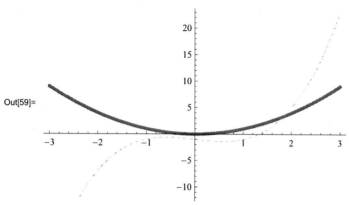

▪ PlotRange

We have already used the **PlotRange** option in Section 2.1 of this text (see Example 2.4 prior). This option specifies the range of
y-values on the graph that should be plotted. As observed in the same example in Section 2.1, some points of a graph may not be
plotted unless we specify the y-range of the plot. The option **PlotRange → All** includes all y-values corresponding to the
specified values of x. Here is an example.

In[60]:= `Plot[x`^{5}` - 2 x - 1, {x, -5, 5}]`

Out[60]=

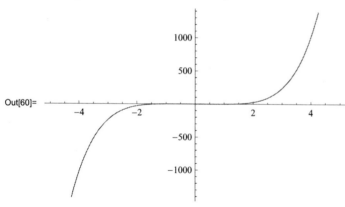

In[61]:= `Plot[x`^{5}` - 2 x - 1 , {x, -5, 5}, PlotRange -> All]`

Out[61]=

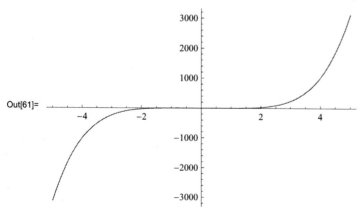

- **Axes**

There are several options regarding axes of plots. We consider four of them.

1. Axes: The specification **Axes → True** draws both axes, whereas **Axes → False** draws no axes and **Axes→{True,False}** draws the *x*-axis only. An example of the last case is given below.

In[62]:= **Plot[x Sin[3 x], {x, -10, 10}, Axes -> {True, False}]**

Out[62]=

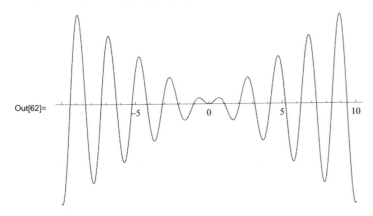

2. AxesLabel: The default specification **AxesLabel → None** leaves the axes unlabeled. On the other hand, **AxesLabel → expr** will only label the *y*-axis as **expr** and **AxesLabel → { "expr1", "expr2" }** labels both the *x*-axis and *y*-axis as **expr1** and **expr2**, respectively. Examples of both cases are given below.

In[63]:= **Plot[x Cos[x], { x, -10, 10}, AxesLabel -> y]**

Out[63]=

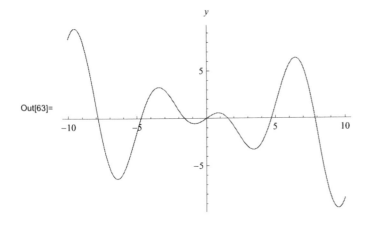

In[64]:= `Plot[x Cos[x], { x, -10, 10}, AxesLabel -> {"x", "y"}]`

Out[64]=

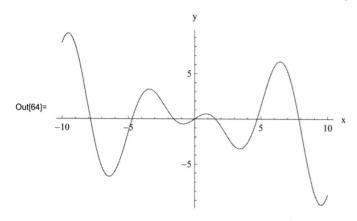

3. AxisOrigin: The option **AxesOrigin** specifies the location where the two axes should intersect. The default value given by **AxesOrigin → Automatic** chooses the intersection point of the axes based on an internal (*Mathematica*) algorithm. It usually chooses (0,0). The option **AxesOrigin → {a,b}** allows the user to specify the intersection point as **(a,b)**.

4. AxesStyle: This option specifies the style of the axes. Here is an example where we specify the thickness of the *x*-axis and color (blue) of the *y*-axis. We also use the **AxesOrigin** option.

In[65]:= `Plot[x Cos[x], { x, -10, 10}, AxesOrigin -> {-10, 10},`
            `AxesStyle -> { Blue, Thickness[0.01]},`
            `AxesLabel -> {"x", "y"}]`

Out[65]=

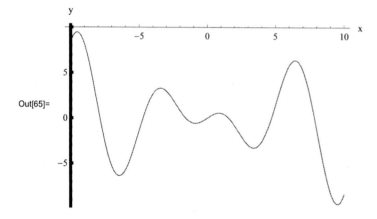

- **Frame**

There are several options regarding the frame (border) of a plot. We show these options in the following examples:

In[66]:= **Plot[x Cos[x], { x, -10, 10}, Frame -> True]**

Out[66]=

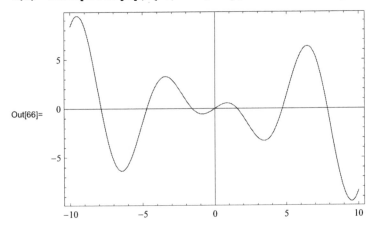

In[67]:= **Plot[x Cos[x], { x, -10, 10}, Frame -> True,**
     FrameLabel -> {"The graph of y = x cos x", "y-axis", None, None}]

Out[67]=

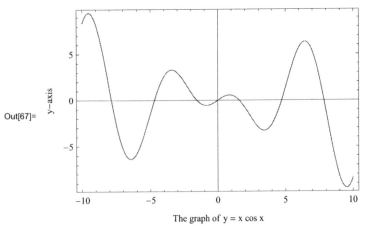

The graph of y = x cos x

In[68]:= **Plot[x Cos[x] , { x, -10, 10}, PlotStyle → Red, Frame -> True,**
     FrameLabel -> {"The graph of y = x cos x", "y-axis", None, None},
     FrameStyle -> {{Blue, Thickness[0.005]},
         {Yellow, Thickness[0.005]}, {Green, Thickness[0.013]}, {Orange} }]

Out[68]=

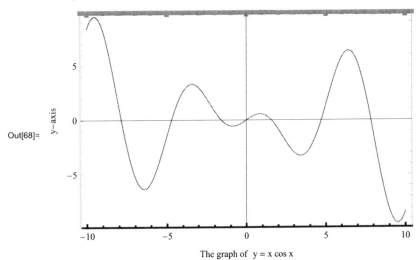

The graph of y = x cos x

We encourage the reader to experiment with this example by changing the color specifications to see which option controls which edge color of the frame.

▪ Show

The command **Show[graphics, options]** displays **graphics** (consisting of possibly many different graphics objects) using the options specified by **options**. Also **Show[plot1,plot2, ...]** displays the graphics **plot1, plot2, ...** on one coordinate system.

In[69]:= `plot1 = Plot[Sin[x], {x, -Pi, Pi} ];`

In[70]:= `plot2 = ListPlot[ {{0, 0}, {Pi / 2, 1}, {Pi, 0}}, PlotStyle → {Red, PointSize[.02]}];`

In[71]:= `Show[plot1, plot2]`

Out[71]=

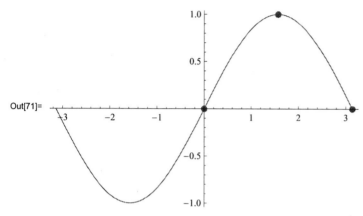

Here is an option we can use to identify the sine curve by inserting the expression $y = \sin x$ near its graph.

In[72]:= `Show[plot1, plot2,`
     `Epilog -> Text["y=sin x", {2.7, 1}, {0, 1}]]`

Out[72]=

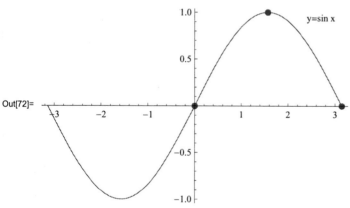

▪ Animation

Animate[expr, {t, a, b}] generates an animation of **expr** in which the parameter *t* varies from *a* to *b*.

Animate[expr, {t, a, b, dt}] generates an animation of **expr** in which *t* varies from *a* to *b* in steps of **dt**.

Animate[expr, {t, a_1, a_2, a_3, ..., a_n}] generates an animation of **expr** in which *t* takes on the discrete set of values a_1, a_2, a_3, ..., a_n.

Animate[expr, {t, a, b}, {s, c, d}, ...] generates an animation of **expr** in which *t* varies from *a* to *b*, *s* varies from *c* to *d*, and so on.

Important Note: If you are reading the printed version of this publication, then you will not be able to view any of the animations generated from the **Animate** command in this chapter. If you are reading the electronic version of this publication formatted as a *Mathematica* Notebook, then evaluate each **Animate** command to view the corresponding animation. Just click on the arrow button to start the animation. To control the animation just click at various points on the sliding bar or else manually drag the bar.

Example 2.6. Analyze the effect of the shift $f(x + a)$, $f(x) + a$, $f(b\,x)$, and $b\,f(x)$ for various values of a and b for the fucntion $f(x) = \cos x$.

Solution:

In[73]:= $\mathbf{f[x\_] := Cos[x]}$

In[74]:= $\mathbf{Animate[Plot[\{Cos[x], Cos[x + a]\}, \{x, -2\,Pi, 2\,Pi\},}$
$\qquad \mathbf{PlotStyle \rightarrow \{Black, Red\}, PlotRange \rightarrow \{-2, 2\}], \{a, 0, 8\}]}$

Out[74]=

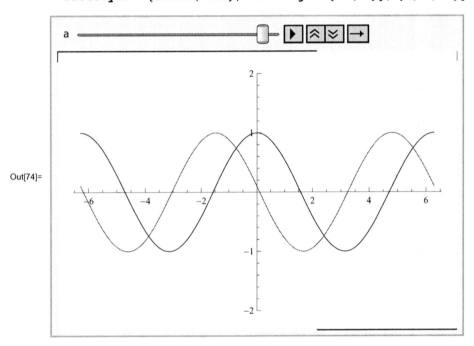

Next, we will animate the graphs of $f(x + a)$ (in red) and $f(x) + a$ (in blue) :

In[75]:= `Animate[Plot[{Cos[x], Cos[x + a], Cos[x] + a}, {x, -2 Pi, 2 Pi},`
       `PlotStyle → {Black, Red, Blue}, PlotRange → {-1, 5}], {a, 0, 6}]`

Out[75]=

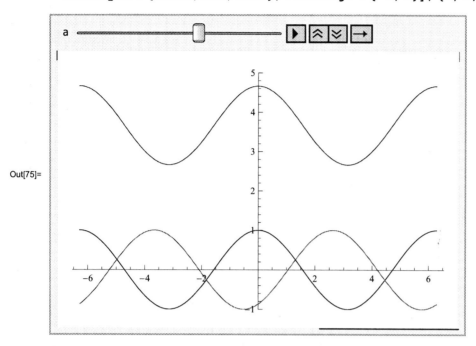

Here is the animation for the graphs of $f(b\,x)$ and $b\,f(x)$.

In[76]:= `Animate[Plot[{Cos[x], Cos[b * x], b * Cos[x]},`
       `{x, -2 Pi, 2 Pi}, PlotStyle → {Black, Red, Blue}], {b, 0, 8}]`

Out[76]=

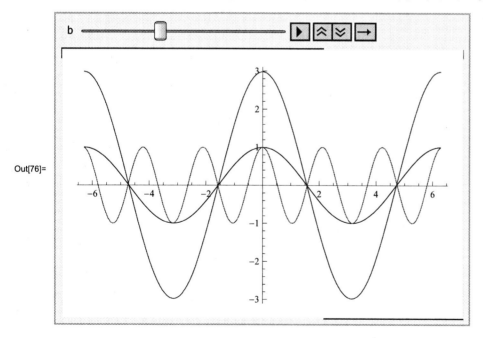

Here is an animation that shows all four shifts at once. We can fix as many parameters as we want (just click on their pause buttons) and analyze the behavior due to the remaining parameters.

In[77]:= `Animate[Plot[{Cos[ x] , Cos[x + a], Cos[x] + b, Cos[c x], d * Cos[x] }, {x, 0, 10},`
    `PlotStyle → {Black, Red, Blue, Green, Brown, Yellow}, PlotRange → {-5, 5}],`
    `{a, 0, 5}, {b, 0, 5}, {c, 0, 5}, {d, 0, 5}]`

Out[77]=

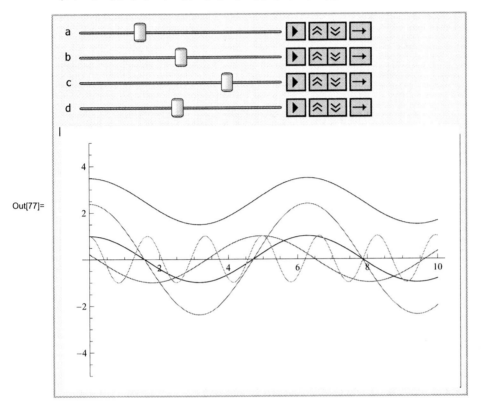

Example 2.7. Here is an animated example of a graph that shows the behavior of a general quadratic polynomial as we vary its coefficients.

Solution:

In[78]:= `Animate[Plot[a x^2 + b x + c, {x, -3, 3}, PlotRange → {-10, 10}],`
`{a, -3, 3}, {b, -3, 3}, {c, -3, 3}]`

Out[78]=

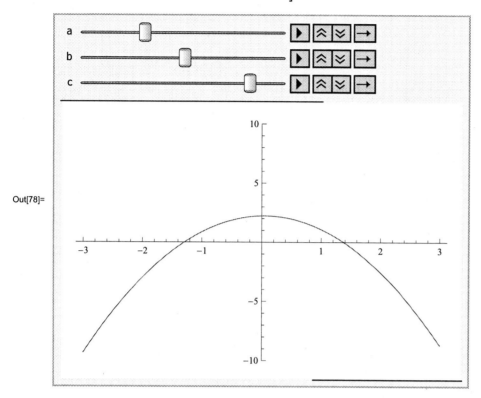

We suggest that you pause two of the parameters and vary the third one manually to see the change in the location of the zeros, the vertex, the regions of concavity, and the regions on which the graph increases and decreases. Then make the necessary changes to redo this problem for polynomials of higher degree.

■ Contour Plot

To end our discussion on graphics, we now consider plotting graphs of equations in two variables. Among such equations are the famous family of elliptic curves that arise in number theory: $y^2 = x^3 + a x + b$, where a and b are parameters. The command for graphing equations implicitly in two variables x and y is **ContourPlot[eqn, {x, a, b}, {y, c, d}]**, which displays the graph of **eqn** for which x varies from a to b and y varies from c to d.

Example 2.8. Plot the graphs of curves given by the equation $y^2 = x^3 + a x + b$ for various values of a and b.

Solution: First, we define a function $f[x, a, b]$ to represent the right-hand side of the equation $y^2 = x^3 + a x + b$ so that f is a function of x as well as a and b. We then plot the equation $y^2 = f[x, a, b]$, where we consider three different sets of values: $a = 1$, $b = 1$; $a = -4$, $b = 0$; and $a = -3$, $b = 3$.

In[79]:= `f[x_, a_, b_] := x^3 + a x + b`

In[80]:= **ContourPlot[y^2 == f[x, 1, 1], {x, -10, 10}, {y, -10, 10}, Axes → True, Frame -> False]**

Out[80]=

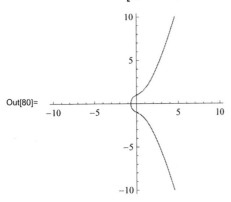

In[81]:= **ContourPlot[y^2 == f[x, -4, 0], {x, -10, 10}, {y, -10, 10}, Axes → True, Frame -> False]**

Out[81]=

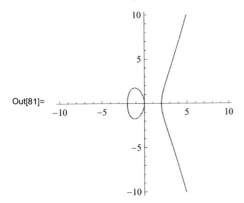

In[82]:= **ContourPlot[y^2 == f[x, -3, 3], {x, -10, 10}, {y, -10, 10}, Axes → True, Frame -> False]**

Out[82]=

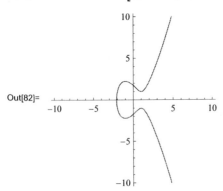

Discovery Exercise: Evaluate the following table and discuss which pararemeters produce curves that are familiar. Make sure to delete the semicolon at the end of the command.

In[83]:= **Table[ContourPlot[y^2 == f[x, a, b], {x, -10, 10},**
    {y, -10, 10}, Axes → True, Frame -> False] , {a, -4, 4}, {b, -3, 3}];

■ Exercises

In **Exercises** 1 through 8, plot the graphs of the given functions on the specified interval:

1. $f(x) = x^2 + 1$ on $[-5, 5]$

2. $g(x) = \frac{1}{x-2}$ on $[0, 4]$

3. $h(x) = \frac{\sin x}{x}$ on $[-\pi, \pi]$

4. $f(x) = x^3 - 5 x^2 + 10$ on $[-5, 5]$

5. $f(x) = \sqrt{32 - 2 x^2}$ on $[-4, 4]$

6. $f(x) = x + \frac{1}{x}$ for $[-10, 10]$

7. $f(x) = x^3 - x + 1$ on $[-3, 3]$

8. $g(x) = \frac{1 - \cos x}{x}$ on $[-\pi, \pi]$

9. Plot the graphs of $f(x) = x(x - 3)(x + 3)$ and $g(x) = \cos 2 x$ together on the same set of axes and over the interval $[-20, 20]$. Use the **PlotRange** option to adjust the range of the viewing window so that their points of intersection are visible.

In Exercises 10 through 13, plot the graphs of the given functions using at least one plot option discussed in this section.
NOTE: **ln** x is one of the built-in *Mathematica* functions and is entered as **Log[x]**. The logarithmic function $\log_a x$ is entered as **Log[a,x]**. For the natural base **e** you either type **E** or you can obtain *e* from the Basic Math Assistant Palette.

10. $f(x) = x^4 + 2 x^3 + 1$ for $-3 \le x \le 3$

11. $f(x) = x \ln x$ for $0 \le x \le 4$

12. $f(x) = 1 - \frac{1}{x^3} + \frac{1}{x}$ for $-20 \le x \le 20$

13. $f(x) = x e^x$ for $-4 \le x \le 4$

In Exercises 14 through 18, plot the graphs of the given pairs of functions on the same axes. Use the **PlotStyle** option to distinguish the graphs.

14. $f(x) = e^x$ and $g(x) = \ln x$

15. $f(x) = \frac{2 x}{x - 5}$ and $g(x) = \frac{x - 5}{2 x}$

16. $f(x) = x^2 - \sin x$ and $g(x) = \sqrt{x^4 + 1} - \sqrt{x^2 + 1}$

17. $f(x) = 3 x + 1$ and $g(x) = \frac{x - 1}{3}$

18. $f(x) = \sqrt[3]{x + 1}$ and $g(x) = (x - 1)^3$

19. Let $f(x) = (x^2 - 1)^{2/3}$.

a) Define f in *Mathematica* as it appears above and plot its graph.

b) Rewrite f as $f(x) = \sqrt[3]{(x^2 - 1)^2}$ plots its graph as it appears here.

c) Explain why the graphs are not identical. Generalize this remark to general functions with rational exponents.

20. Let $f(x) = \frac{2cx - x^2}{c^2}$, $c > 0$.

a) Graph f for various values of c. (You may use the **Animate** command.)

b) Use the graph in part a) to sketch the curve traced out by the vertices of the highest point as c varies. Can you guess what this curve is?

21. Use the **Animate** command to plot the graph of $f(x)$ by varying the parameters a, b, c, d, and e for each of the following functions. Discuss how each parameter affects the shape of the graph.

a) $f(x) = ax^3 + bx^2 + cx + d$

b) $f(x) = ax^4 + bx^3 + cx^2 + dx + e$

22. a) Use **ContourPlot** to plot the graph of the curve defined by the equation $y(y^2 - c)(y - d) = x(x - a)(x - b)$ for various values of a, b, c, d. (Hint: You may want to define **g[y,c,d]** as the left hand side and **f[x,a,b]** as the right hand side and then use the command **ContourPlot[f[x, a, b] == g[y, c, d], {x, -5, 5}, {y, -5, 5}, Frame → False, Axes → True]**.)

b) For the parameters you selected in part a, at how many points is the slope of this curve equal to zero? Estimate the x-coordinates of these points.

■ 2.2 Limits

Students should read Chapter 2 of Rogawski's *Calculus* [1] for a detailed discussion of the material presented in this section.

■ 2.2.1 Evaluating Limits

Limit[f, x −> a, Direction −> 1] computes the limit as x as approaches a from the left (i.e., x increases to a).

Limit[f, x −> a, Direction −> − 1] computes the limit as x approaches a from the right (i.e., x decreases to a).

Limit[f, x −> a] finds the limiting value of f as x approaches a.

NOTE: *Mathematica* will use the right-hand limit when evaluating **Limit.** If the limit does not exist, then *Mathematica* will attempt to explain why or else return the limit expression unevaluated if it has insufficient information about the function.

Example 2.9. Evaluate $\lim\limits_{x \to 1}\left(\dfrac{x^2+x+2}{x+1}\right)$.

Solution: Here is a table of values of the function $f(x) = \dfrac{x^2+x+2}{x+1}$ when x is sufficiently close to 1.

In[84]:= **f[x_] := $\dfrac{x^2 + x + 2}{x + 1}$**

In[85]:= **(*From the left*)**
Table[{x, f[x]}, {x, 0.8, 0.99, 0.01}] // TableForm

Out[85]//TableForm=

0.8	1.91111
0.81	1.91497
0.82	1.9189
0.83	1.9229
0.84	1.92696
0.85	1.93108
0.86	1.93527
0.87	1.93952
0.88	1.94383
0.89	1.9482
0.9	1.95263
0.91	1.95712
0.92	1.96167
0.93	1.96627
0.94	1.97093
0.95	1.97564
0.96	1.98041
0.97	1.98523
0.98	1.9901
0.99	1.99503

In[86]:= `(*From the right*)`
`  Table[{x, f[x]}, {x, 1.2, 1.01, -0.01}] // TableForm`

Out[86]//TableForm=

1.2	2.10909
1.19	2.10324
1.18	2.09743
1.17	2.09166
1.16	2.08593
1.15	2.08023
1.14	2.07458
1.13	2.06897
1.12	2.0634
1.11	2.05787
1.1	2.05238
1.09	2.04694
1.08	2.04154
1.07	2.03618
1.06	2.03087
1.05	2.02561
1.04	2.02039
1.03	2.01522
1.02	2.0101
1.01	2.00502

From the tables, it is reasonable to expect that the limit is 2. Here is the graph of the function together with the point (1, 2).

In[87]:= `plot1 = Plot[(x^2 + x + 2) / (x + 1), {x, -1, 2}, PlotRange → {0, 3}];`
`plot2 = Graphics[{Green, PointSize[Large], Point[{1, 2}] } ];`
`plot3 = Graphics[{Red, Line[{{1, 0}, {1, 2}, {0, 2}}]}];`
`Show[plot1, plot2, plot3]`

Out[90]=

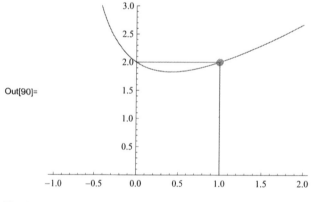

Evaluating the limit confirms this:

In[91]:= `Limit[ (x^2 + x + 2) / (x + 1), x -> 1]`

Out[91]= 2

Example 2.10. The height of a projectile, fired in the air with initial velocity 32 ft/s, is given by $y(t) = -16\,t^2 + 64\,t + 3$. Find the average velocity of the projectile over the interval $[1, t]$ for various values of t. Then find the instantaneous velocity at $t = 1$.

Solution: We define

In[92]:= $y[t\_] = -16 t^2 + 64 t + 3$

$v[t\_] = \dfrac{y[t] - y[1]}{t - 1}$

Out[92]= $3 + 64 t - 16 t^2$

Out[93]= $\dfrac{-48 + 64 t - 16 t^2}{-1 + t}$

In[94]:= $tt = \{2, 1.5, 1.01, 1.001, 1.0001, 1.00001\};$
Table[{tt[[k]], v[tt[[k]]]}, {k, 1, Length[tt]}] // TableForm

Out[95]//TableForm=

2	16
1.5	24.
1.01	31.84
1.001	31.984
1.0001	31.9984
1.00001	31.9998

Here **tt** is the list of values for *t* and **tt[[k]]** refers to the *k*th element in the list **tt** (see Chapter 1 of this text for an explanation of lists). Also, **Length[t]** gives the number of elements in the list **tt**, which is 6 for our example.

The above table clearly suggests that the instantaneous velocity at *t* = 1 is 32 ft/s. The graph below also verifies this.

In[96]:=

    plot1 = Plot[v[t], {t, 0, 2}, PlotRange → {0, 50}];
    y = Simplify[v[t]] /. t → 1;
    plot2 = Graphics[{ PointSize[Large], Point[{1, y}] }];
    plot3 = Graphics[{Red, Line[{{1, 0}, {1, y}, {0, y}}]}];

    Show[plot1, plot2, plot3]

Out[100]=

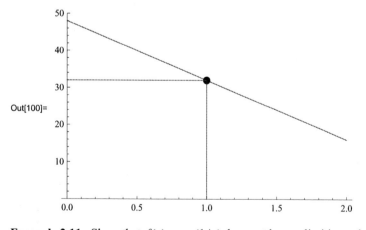

Example 2.11. Show that $f(x) = \cos(1/x)$ does not have a limiting value as *x* approaches 0.

Solution: We define

In[101]:= $f[x\_] := Cos[1 / x]$
$f[\{0.1, .05, 0.001, .0001, .000001\}]$

Out[102]= $\{-0.839072, 0.408082, 0.562379, -0.952155, 0.936752\}$

These values suggest that the limit does NOT exist. To make this clear, we consider the following two tables. The first table uses values of the form $x = 2/(2n + 1)\pi$, where n is a positive integer, while the second table uses $x = 1/(2n + 1)\pi$. Each of these sets of values for x approach 0 as $n \to \infty$.

In[103]:= **t1 = Table$\left[\dfrac{2.}{Pi\ (2\,n+1)},\ \{n,\ 1,\ 100,\ 10\}\right]$;**

f[t1]

Out[104]= $\{-1.83697 \times 10^{-16},\ -3.1847 \times 10^{-15},\ -4.40935 \times 10^{-15},\ 1.47143 \times 10^{-15},\ -2.10695 \times 10^{-14},$
$1.3233 \times 10^{-14},\ -9.30793 \times 10^{-15},\ -3.42715 \times 10^{-15},\ -2.59681 \times 10^{-14},\ -2.00873 \times 10^{-14}\}$

In[105]:= **t2 = Table$\left[\dfrac{1.}{Pi\ (2\,n+1)},\ \{n,\ 1,\ 100,\ 10\}\right]$;**

f[t2]

Out[106]= $\{-1.,\ -1.,\ -1.,\ -1.,\ -1.,\ -1.,\ -1.,\ -1.,\ -1.,\ -1.\}$

The first table indicates that the values of $f(x)$ approach 0, while the second table indicates the values approach -1. Recall that if the limit exists, then it must be unique. Thus, our limit does not exist because the values of f do not converge to a single value. Next, we analyze the graph of the function.

In[107]:= **Plot[f[x], {x, -1, 1}]**

Out[107]=

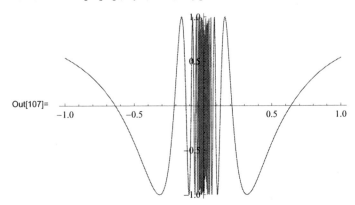

This indicates that there is too much oscillation around $x = 0$. Let us try zooming in around this point.

In[108]:= **Plot[Cos[1 / x], {x, -0.1, 0.1}]**

Out[108]=

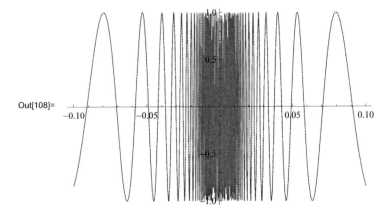

Note how zooming in on this graph does not help. This indicates that the limit does not exist.

Example 2.12. Consider the function $f(x) = \frac{2^{1/x} - 2^{-1/x}}{2^{1/x} + 2^{-1/x}}$. Find $\lim_{x \to 0} f(x)$.

Solution:

In[109]:= $\mathbf{Limit}\left[\dfrac{2^{1/x} - 2^{-1/x}}{2^{1/x} + 2^{1/x}}, \, x \to 0\right]$

Out[109]= $\dfrac{1}{2}$

It may appear that the limit is $\frac{1}{2}$, but the simplified form of $f(x)$ (using the **Simplify** command) shows this not to be the case. Instead we shall consider one-sided limits.

In[110]:= $\mathbf{Simplify}\left[\dfrac{2^{1/x} - 2^{-1/x}}{2^{1/x} + 2^{1/x}}\right]$

Out[110]= $\dfrac{1}{2}\left(1 - 4^{-1/x}\right)$

In[111]:= $\mathbf{Limit}\left[\dfrac{2^{1/x} - 2^{-1/x}}{2^{1/x} + 2^{1/x}}, \, x \to 0, \, \mathbf{Direction} \to 1\right]$

$\mathbf{Limit}\left[\dfrac{2^{1/x} - 2^{-1/x}}{2^{1/x} + 2^{1/x}}, \, x \to 0, \, \mathbf{Direction} \to -1\right]$

Out[111]= $-\infty$

Out[112]= $\dfrac{1}{2}$

Since the left- and right-hand limits are not the same, we conclude that the limit does not exist.

In[113]:= $\mathbf{Plot}\left[\dfrac{2^{1/x} - 2^{-1/x}}{2^{1/x} + 2^{1/x}}, \, \{x, -1, 1\}, \, \mathbf{PlotRange} \to \{-30, 1\}\right]$

Out[113]=

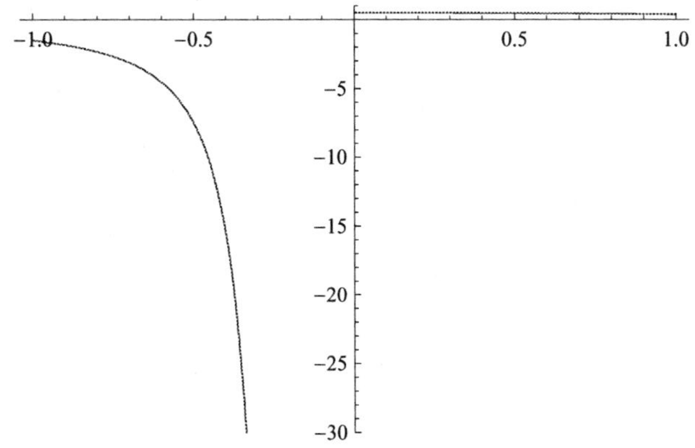

NOTE: One needs to be careful when using *Mathematica* to find limits. If you are not certain that the limit exists, use one-sided limits:

Example 2.13. Evaluate $\lim_{x \to 5^+} \frac{|x-5|}{x-5}$.

Solution:

In[114]:= **Limit[Abs[x - 5] / (x - 5), x -> 5, Direction -> -1]**

Out[114]= 1

Note that *Mathematica*'s convention for right-hand limits is "going in the negative direction." Thus, the standard notation $\lim\limits_{x\to5^+}$ should be evaluated as **Limit[f[x], $x \to 5$, Direction $\to -1$].** A similar remark applies to the left-hand limit.

Again, we can check the answer by plotting the graph of the function:

In[115]:= **Plot[Abs[x - 5] / (x - 5), {x, 3, 7}]**

Out[115]=

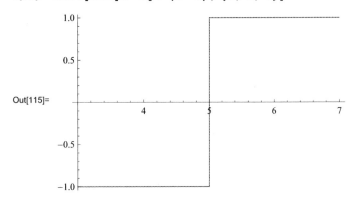

Warning: This plot does not show the true graph of $f(x)$ near $x = 5$. It may appear that f is continuous at $x = 5$ because of the vertical line there but this is not the case since f is undefined at $x = 5$ and its one-sided limits do not agree:

In[116]:= **Abs[x - 5] / (x - 5) /. x → 5**
Limit[Abs[x - 5] / (x - 5), x → 5, Direction → 1]
Limit[Abs[x - 5] / (x - 5), x → 5, Direction → -1]

Power::infy : Infinite expression $\dfrac{1}{0}$ encountered. ≫

Infinity::indet : Indeterminate expression 0 ComplexInfinity encountered. ≫

Out[116]= Indeterminate

Out[117]= -1

Out[118]= 1

Below is the true graph of f, which shows the (non-removable) discontinuity at $x = 5$.

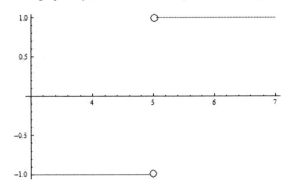

▪ 2.2.2 Limits Involving Trigonometric Functions

For trigonometric functions, *Mathematica* uses the same traditional notation in calculus except that the first letter of the trigonometric function must be capitalized. Thus, **Sin[x]** is *Mathematica*'s notation for $\sin x$ (see Appendix A of this text for a description of notational differences).

Example 2.14. Evaluate $\lim\limits_{x \to 0} \dfrac{\sin(4x)}{x}$.

Solution:

In[119]:= **Limit[Sin[4 x] / x, x -> 0]**

Out[119]= 4

Let us check the answer by graphing the function up close in the neighborhood of $x = 0$:

In[120]:= **Plot[Sin[4 x] / x, {x, -1, 1}]**

Out[120]=

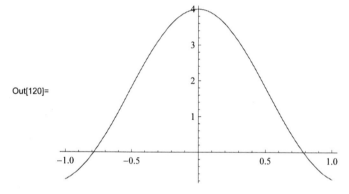

Example 2.15. Evaluate $\lim\limits_{t \to 0} \dfrac{\sin t}{|t|}$.

Solution: We will consider both the left- and right-hand limits.

In[121]:= **Limit$\left[\dfrac{\text{Sin[t]}}{\text{Abs[t]}}, \text{t} \to 0, \text{Direction} \to -1\right]$**

Out[121]= 1

In[122]:= **Limit$\left[\dfrac{\text{Sin[t]}}{\text{Abs[t]}}, \text{t} \to 0, \text{Direction} \to 1\right]$**

Out[122]= -1

Thus, the limit does not exist. This can be clearly seen from the graph of the function below.

In[123]:= `Plot[ Sin[x]/Abs[x] , {x, -2 Pi, 2 Pi}]`

Out[123]=

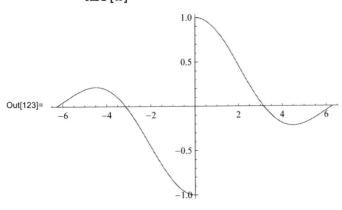

Example 2.16. Find

a) $\lim_{x \to 0} \frac{\cos x - 1}{\sin x}$ b) $\lim_{x \to 0} \tan x \cos(\sin 1/x)$

Solution:

In[124]:= `a = Limit[ (Cos[x] - 1) / Sin[x], x → 0]`

Out[124]= 0

In[125]:= `b = Limit[Tan[x] Cos[Sin[1 / x]], x → 0]`

Out[125]= 0

NOTE: In your textbook, it is proven that $\lim_{x \to 0} \frac{\cos x - 1}{x} = 0$ and $\lim_{x \to 0} \frac{\sin x}{x} = 1$. Writing $\frac{\cos x - 1}{\sin x} = \left(\frac{\cos x - 1}{x}\right) / \left(\frac{\sin x}{x}\right)$, we see that the answer for part a) is valid by applying the quotient rule for limits. For the second limit in part b), we note that $-1 \le \cos(\sin(1/x)) \le 1$ and hence $-|\tan x| \le \tan x \cos(\sin(1/x)) \le |\tan x|$. Since $\lim_{x \to 0} \tan x = \lim_{x \to 0}(-\tan x) = 0$ we call upon the Squeeze Theorem to conclude that $\lim_{x \to 0} \tan x \cos(\sin(1/x)) = 0$.

The following graphs verify both answers.

In[126]:= `Plot[ Cos[x] - 1/Sin[x] , {x, -2 Pi, 2 Pi}]`

Out[126]=

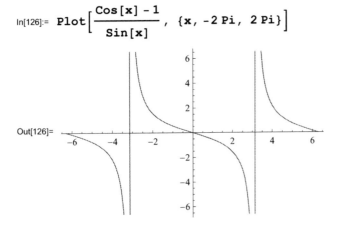

In[127]:= **Plot[Tan[x] * Cos[Sin[1 / x]], {x, -2 Pi, 2 Pi}]**

Out[127]=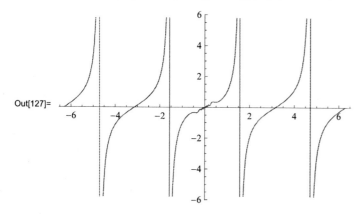

Example 2.17. Find $\lim_{x \to c} \frac{\cos x - \cos c}{x - c}$ for values of $c = 0$, $\pi/6$, $\pi/4$, $\pi/3$, $\pi/2$.

Solution: We will use the substitution command /. to evaluate the limit for different values of c.

In[128]:= **Limit$\left[\dfrac{\text{Cos[x] - Cos[c]}}{\text{x - c}}, \text{x} \to \text{c}\right]$ /. c -> {0, Pi / 6, Pi / 4, Pi / 3, Pi / 2}**

Out[128]= $\left\{0, -\dfrac{1}{2}, -\dfrac{1}{\sqrt{2}}, -\dfrac{\sqrt{3}}{2}, -1\right\}$

Can you guess a general formula for the answer in terms of c? (Hint: What trigonometric function takes on these values?)

Example 2.18. Find $\lim_{x \to 0} \frac{\cos(m x) - 1}{x^2}$ for various values of m. Then make a general statement about this limit and prove your assertion.

Solution: Here is a table of limits for integer values of m ranging from 1 to 10.

In[129]:= **Table$\left[\text{Limit}\left[\dfrac{\text{Cos[m x] - 1}}{\text{x}^2}, \text{x} \to 0\right], \{\text{m, 1, 10}\}\right]$**

Out[129]= $\left\{-\dfrac{1}{2}, -2, -\dfrac{9}{2}, -8, -\dfrac{25}{2}, -18, -\dfrac{49}{2}, -32, -\dfrac{81}{2}, -50\right\}$

A reasonable guess at a general formula for the answer would be $\lim_{x \to 0}(\cos m x - 1)/x^2 = -m^2/2$. We can check this with values of m ranging from 10 to 20.

In[130]:= **Table$\left[\left\{\text{Limit}\left[\dfrac{\text{Cos[m x] - 1}}{\text{x}^2}, \text{x} \to 0\right], -\text{m}^2 / 2\right\}, \{\text{m, 10, 20}\}\right]$**

Out[130]= $\left\{\{-50, -50\}, \left\{-\dfrac{121}{2}, -\dfrac{121}{2}\right\}, \{-72, -72\}, \left\{-\dfrac{169}{2}, -\dfrac{169}{2}\right\}, \{-98, -98\}, \left\{-\dfrac{225}{2}, -\dfrac{225}{2}\right\},\right.$

$\left.\{-128, -128\}, \left\{-\dfrac{289}{2}, -\dfrac{289}{2}\right\}, \{-162, -162\}, \left\{-\dfrac{361}{2}, -\dfrac{361}{2}\right\}, \{-200, -200\}\right\}$

For a mathematical proof, first take $m = 1$ and plot the graph

In[131]:= `Plot[` $\dfrac{\text{Cos[x]} - 1}{\text{x}^2}$ `, {x, -Pi, Pi}, AxesOrigin -> {0, 0}]`

Out[131]=

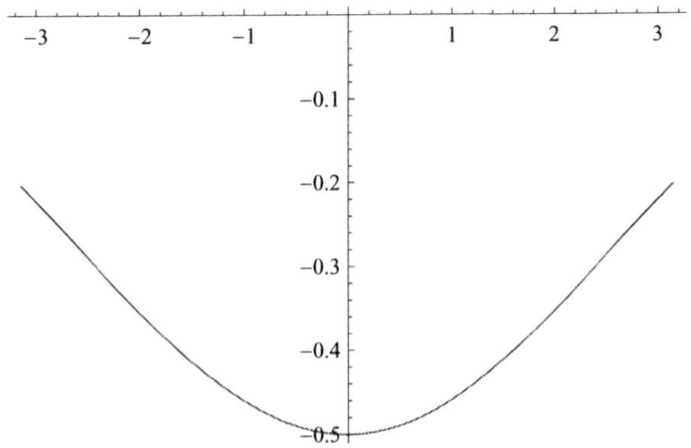

The graph above confirms that the limit is $-1/2$.

For the general case, let $t = m\,x$ so that $x^2 = \frac{t^2}{m^2}$. Then note that $x \to 0$ if and only if $t \to 0$. Thus, the limit can be evaluated in terms of t as

$$\lim_{x \to 0} \frac{\cos m\,x - 1}{x^2} = \lim_{t \to 0} \frac{\cos t - 1}{t^2/m^2} = m^2 \lim_{t \to 0} \frac{\cos t - 1}{t^2} = -\frac{m^2}{2}.$$

▪ 2.2.3 Limits Involving Infinity

Example 2.19. Evaluate $\lim\limits_{x \to \infty} (3\,x - 2) \Big/ \sqrt{2\,x^2 + 1}$ and $\lim\limits_{x \to -\infty} (3\,x - 2) \Big/ \sqrt{2\,x^2 + 1}$.

Solution:

In[132]:= `Limit[(3 x - 2) / Sqrt[2 x^2 + 1], x -> Infinity]`

Out[132]= $\dfrac{3}{\sqrt{2}}$

In[133]:= `N[%]`

Out[133]= `2.12132`

In[134]:= `Limit[(3 x - 2) / Sqrt[2 x^2 + 1], x → -Infinity]`

Out[134]= $-\dfrac{3}{\sqrt{2}}$

Observe how the two limits differ. The following graph confirms this.

In[135]:= **Plot[(3 x - 2) / Sqrt[2 x^2 + 1], {x, -30, 30}]**

Out[135]=

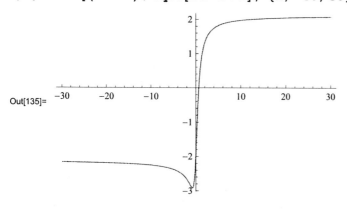

NOTE: Can you explain the cusp on the graph near $x = 0$?

Example 2.20. Evaluate $\lim\limits_{x \to 2^-} \dfrac{\sqrt{4-x^2}}{x-2}$.

Solution:

In[136]:= **Limit[Sqrt[4 - x^2] / (x - 2), x -> 2, Direction -> 1]**

Out[136]= $-\infty$

We plot the function over two different ranges to visually understand why the answer is $-\infty$. Notice how the first range fails to show this.

In[137]:= **Plot$\left[\dfrac{\text{Sqrt[4 - x^2]}}{\text{x - 2}}, \{x, 1, 3\}\right]$**

Out[137]=

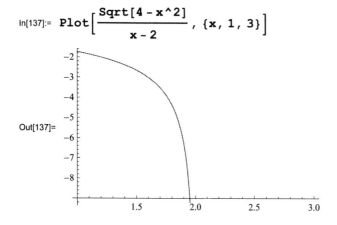

In[138]:= $\text{Plot}\left[\dfrac{\text{Sqrt}[4-x^2]}{x-2}, \{x, 1, 3\}, \text{PlotRange} \rightarrow \{-100, 10\}\right]$

Out[138]=

NOTE: The plot domain is specified to be [1, 3], but observe that this function is undefined for values of *x* greater than 2 because this results in taking the square root of a negative number.

Example 2.21. Evaluate $\lim\limits_{x \to \infty} \sin x$.

Solution:

In[139]:= $\text{Limit}[\text{Sin}[x], x \rightarrow \text{Infinity}]$

Out[139]= $\text{Interval}[\{-1, 1\}]$

Here, *Mathematica* is telling us that the limit does not exist by returning the range of values for $\sin x$ as *x* approaches infinity.

Example 2.22. Find $\lim_{x\to\infty} \frac{\sin x}{x}$.

Solution:

In[140]:= $\text{Limit}\left[\dfrac{\text{Sin}[x]}{x}, x \rightarrow \text{Infinity}\right]$

Out[140]= 0

We can verify this limit by using the Squeeze Theorem. In our case, we take $f(x) = -1/|x|$, $g(x) = \frac{\sin x}{x}$ and $h(x) = 1/|x|$. Then $f(x) \le g(x) \le h(x)$ (recall that $-1 \le \sin x \le 1$ for all *x*).

In[141]:= $\text{Plot}[\{-1 \,/\, \text{Abs}[x], \text{Sin}[x] \,/\, x, 1 \,/\, \text{Abs}[x]\},$
        $\{x, 0, 30\}, \text{PlotStyle} \rightarrow \{\text{Red, Green, Blue}\}]$

Out[141]=

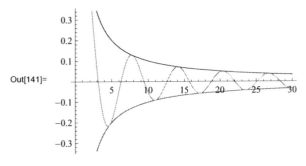

Since $1/|x|$ and $-1/|x|$ both approach 0 as $x \to \infty$, we conclude that $(\sin x)/x$ approaches zero as well.

Example 2.23. Evaluate $\lim_{x\to\infty}\left(\frac{e^x}{x^n}\right)$, where n is any integer.

Solution:

In[142]:= **Table[Limit[e^x / x^n, x $\to$ Infinity], {n, 1, 200, 10}]**

Out[142]= $\{\infty, \infty, \infty, \infty, \infty, \infty, \infty, \infty, \infty, \infty, \infty, \infty, \infty, \infty, \infty, \infty, \infty, \infty, \infty, \infty\}$

This table suggests that the limit is infinity. We confirm this with *Mathematica*:

In[143]:= **Limit$\left[\dfrac{e^x}{x^n}, x \to \infty\right]$**

Out[143]= ComplexInfinity

NOTE: This example reveals that exponential functions grow more *quickly* than polynomial functions.

Example 2.24. Evaluate $\lim_{x\to 1^+}\left(\frac{1}{\ln x} - \frac{1}{x-1}\right)$.

Solution:

In[144]:= **Limit[(1/Log[x])-(1/(x-1)),x->1,Direction->1]**

Out[144]= $\dfrac{1}{2}$

Again, we can graph the function near $x = 1$ to visually understand why the answer is $1/2$ (we leave this to the student). Note, however, that this example shows that $1/\ln x$ and $1/(x-1)$ both grow to ∞ at the same rate as $x \to 1^+$.

Example 2.25. Let $f(x) = \frac{x^n-1}{x^m-1}$. Evaluate $\lim_{x\to 1} f(x)$ by substituting in various values of m and n.

Solution:

In[145]:= **Table[Limit[(x^n - 1) / (x^m - 1), x $\to$ 1], {m, 1, 10}, {n, 1, 10}] // TableForm**

Out[145]//TableForm=

1	2	3	4	5	6	7	8	9	10
$\frac{1}{2}$	1	$\frac{3}{2}$	2	$\frac{5}{2}$	3	$\frac{7}{2}$	4	$\frac{9}{2}$	5
$\frac{1}{3}$	$\frac{2}{3}$	1	$\frac{4}{3}$	$\frac{5}{3}$	2	$\frac{7}{3}$	$\frac{8}{3}$	3	$\frac{10}{3}$
$\frac{1}{4}$	$\frac{1}{2}$	$\frac{3}{4}$	1	$\frac{5}{4}$	$\frac{3}{2}$	$\frac{7}{4}$	2	$\frac{9}{4}$	$\frac{5}{2}$
$\frac{1}{5}$	$\frac{2}{5}$	$\frac{3}{5}$	$\frac{4}{5}$	1	$\frac{6}{5}$	$\frac{7}{5}$	$\frac{8}{5}$	$\frac{9}{5}$	2
$\frac{1}{6}$	$\frac{1}{3}$	$\frac{1}{2}$	$\frac{2}{3}$	$\frac{5}{6}$	1	$\frac{7}{6}$	$\frac{4}{3}$	$\frac{3}{2}$	$\frac{5}{3}$
$\frac{1}{7}$	$\frac{2}{7}$	$\frac{3}{7}$	$\frac{4}{7}$	$\frac{5}{7}$	$\frac{6}{7}$	1	$\frac{8}{7}$	$\frac{9}{7}$	$\frac{10}{7}$
$\frac{1}{8}$	$\frac{1}{4}$	$\frac{3}{8}$	$\frac{1}{2}$	$\frac{5}{8}$	$\frac{3}{4}$	$\frac{7}{8}$	1	$\frac{9}{8}$	$\frac{5}{4}$
$\frac{1}{9}$	$\frac{2}{9}$	$\frac{1}{3}$	$\frac{4}{9}$	$\frac{5}{9}$	$\frac{2}{3}$	$\frac{7}{9}$	$\frac{8}{9}$	1	$\frac{10}{9}$
$\frac{1}{10}$	$\frac{1}{5}$	$\frac{3}{10}$	$\frac{2}{5}$	$\frac{1}{2}$	$\frac{3}{5}$	$\frac{7}{10}$	$\frac{4}{5}$	$\frac{9}{10}$	1

Can you guess a formula for $\lim_{x\to 1} f(x)$ in terms of m and n? Enter the command **Limit[(x^n − 1) / (x^m − 1), $x \to$ 1]** into an input box and evaluate it to verify your conjecture.

Let us end this section with an example where the **Limit** command is used to evaluate the *derivative* of a function (in anticipation of commands introduced in the next chapter for computing derivatives).

By definition, the derivative of a function f at x (i.e., the slope of its tangent line at x) is

$$f'(x) = \lim_{\Delta x \to 0} \frac{f(x + \Delta x) - f(x)}{\Delta x}.$$

Example 2.26. Find the derivative of $f(x) = \dfrac{1}{x}$ according to the limit definition.

Solution: We first examine the derivative by tabulating values of the difference quotient, $\frac{f(x + \Delta x) - f(x)}{\Delta x}$, for some arbitrarily chosen values of Δx:

```
In[146]:= f[x_] := 1 / x
         delta = {0.1, 0.01, .0001, .00001, .000001, .00000001};
         Table[{delta[[k]], Simplify[(f[x + delta[[k]]] - f[x])/delta[[k]]]},
           {k, 1, Length[delta]}] // TableForm
```

Out[148]//TableForm=

0.1	$-\dfrac{1.}{0.1\,x + x^2}$
0.01	$-\dfrac{1.}{0.01\,x + x^2}$
0.0001	$-\dfrac{1.}{0.0001\,x + x^2}$
0.00001	$-\dfrac{1.}{0.00001\,x + x^2}$
$1.\times 10^{-6}$	$-\dfrac{1.}{1.\times 10^{-6}\,x + x^2}$
$1.\times 10^{-8}$	$-\dfrac{1.}{1.\times 10^{-8}\,x + x^2}$

This table suggests that $f'(x) = -1/x^2$ in the limit as $\Delta x \to 0$. We confirm this with *Mathematica*:

```
In[149]:= Limit[(f[x + Deltax] - f[x]) / Deltax, Deltax -> 0]
```

Out[149]= $-\dfrac{1}{x^2}$

- **Exercises**

In Exercises 1 through 8, compute the limits:

1. $\lim\limits_{x \to 1} \dfrac{x^2 - 1}{x - 1}$ 2. $\lim\limits_{x \to -5} \dfrac{100}{x + 5}$ 3. $\lim\limits_{x \to \infty} \dfrac{1 + x + x^2}{\sqrt[3]{x^{10} - x}}$ 4. $\lim\limits_{x \to 0} \dfrac{\sin x}{x}$

5. $\lim\limits_{x \to 0} \dfrac{\sin 5x}{3x}$ 6. $\lim\limits_{x \to 0} \dfrac{1 - \cos x}{4x}$ 7. $\lim\limits_{x \to 3} \dfrac{x^3 - 27}{x^2 - 9}$ 8. $\lim\limits_{x \to -\infty} \dfrac{x^3 - 27}{x^2 - 6}$

In Exercises 9 through 13, evaluate each of the limits. Verify your answers by plotting the graph of each function in the neighborhood of the limit point.

9. $\lim\limits_{x \to 2}\left(\dfrac{2x - 1}{4 - 3x}\right)$ 10. $\lim\limits_{x \to 0^+}\left(\dfrac{1 - \ln x}{e^{1/x}}\right)$ 11. $\lim\limits_{x \to 0^+}\left(\dfrac{1}{x} - \ln x\right)$

12. $\lim\limits_{x \to \left(\frac{\pi}{2}\right)^-}(\sec 3x \cos 5x)$ 13. $\lim\limits_{x \to 0}(\sin x)\cos\left(\dfrac{1}{x}\right)$

14. Use various values of a to find the following limits. Confirm your answers by plotting the graph of each function corresponding to your chosen values for a. Make a conjecture for a general formula. Then verify your conjecture by using *Mathematica* to

evaluate the limits but keeping the constant a unassigned.

a) $\lim\limits_{x \to a} \dfrac{x^3 - a^3}{x - a}$ b) $\lim\limits_{x \to 1} \dfrac{x^3 - a x^2 + a x - 1}{x - 1}$

15. Consider the quadratic function $f(x) = a x^2 - x + 1$. Plot the graph of f using small values of a. What do you observe about the roots of f? What is the limit of the roots of f as $a \to 0$?   Hint: Use the command **Animate**$\left[\text{Plot}\left[a x^2 - x + 1, \{x, 0, 50\}, \text{PlotRange} \to \{-50, 50\}\right], \{a, 0, .1, .01\}\right]$ to help you analyze the root and then change the values of a as well as the plot domain. Then use the quadratic formula to prove your assertion. NOTE: One can also use the **Solve** or **Roots** commands to determine the roots of f.

■ 2.3 Continuity

Students should read Section 2.4 of Rogawski's *Calculus* [1] for a detailed discussion of the material presented in this section.

Recall that a function is continuous at $x = a$ if and only if $\lim_{x \to a} f(x) = f(a)$. Graphically, this means that there is no break (or jump) in the graph of f at the point $(a, f(a))$. It is not possible to indicate this discontinuity using computer graphics for the situation where the limit exists and the function is defined at a but the limit is not equal to $f(a)$. For other cases of discontinuity, computer graphics are very helpful.

To verify if a given function is continuous at a point, we evaluate its limit there and check if this limit is equal to the value of the function.

Example 2.27. Show that the function $f(x) = x^3 - 1$ is continuous everywhere.

Solution: We could draw the graph and observe this fact. On the other hand, we can get *Mathematica* to check continuity:

In[150]:= **f[x_] := x^3 - 1**
       Limit[f[x], x → c] == f[c]

Out[151]= True

This means that $\lim_{x \to c} f(x) = f(c)$ and hence f is continuous everywhere.

Example 2.28. Find points of discontinuity for each of the following functions:

a) Let $f(x) = \begin{cases} \frac{x^2-1}{x-1}, & \text{if } x \neq 1 \\ 2, & \text{if } x = 1. \end{cases}$

b) Let $g(x) = \begin{cases} \frac{x^2-1}{x-1}, & \text{if } x \neq 1 \\ 6, & \text{if } x = 1. \end{cases}$

Solution: The command **If[cond, true, false]** evaluates **true** if **cond** is satisfied and gives **false** if **cond** is not satisfied. This command can be used to define piece-wise functions such as those in this example.

a) We first check continuity of f at $x = 1$.

In[152]:= **f[x_] := If$\left[$x ≠ 1, $\dfrac{x^2 - 1}{x - 1}$, 2$\right]$**

In[153]:= **Limit[f[x], x → 1] == f[1]**

Out[153]= True

Hence, the function is continuous at $x = 1$. For continuity at other points, we observe that the rational function $\frac{x^2-1}{x-1}$ simplifies to $x + 1$ in this case (factor the numerator!) and thus is continuous at any point except $x = 1$. Thus, f is continuous everywhere. We can also confirm this by examining the graph of f below.

In[154]:= **Plot[f[x], {x, -6, 6}]**

Out[154]=

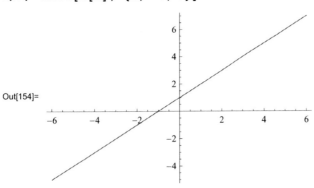

b) As in part a, we first consider continuity of g at $x = 1$.

In[155]:= $g[x\_] := If\left[x \neq 1, \frac{x^2-1}{x-1}, 6\right]$

In[156]:= **Limit[g[x], x → 1] == g[1]**

Out[156]= False

Thus, g is NOT continuous at $x = 1$. For continuity at other points, we again observe that the rational function $\frac{x^2-1}{x-1} = x + 1$ and thus is continuous for $x \neq 1$.

Caution: The plot of the graph of g given below indicates (incorrectly) that g is continuous everywhere! Care must be taken when examining *Mathematica* plots to draw conclusions about continuity.

In[157]:= **Plot[g[x], {x, -6, 6}]**

Out[157]=

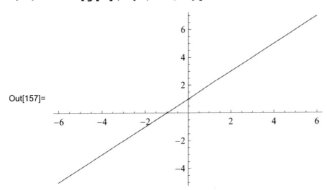

Example 2.29.   Let $f(x) = \begin{cases} 2x + c, & \text{if } x \geq 2 \\ x^2 + cx - 1, & \text{if } x < 2. \end{cases}$

For what values of c is f continuous over its entire domain?

Solution: For $x > 2$, we have $f(x) = 2x + c$. Hence, f is continuous on the interval $(2, \infty)$ since the interval is open. For $x < 2$, $f(x) = x^2 + cx - 1$. Thus, f is continuous on $(-\infty, 2)$ for the same reason. For f to be continuous at $x = 2$, we must have $\lim_{x \to 2} f(x) = f(2)$. But the limit exists if and only if

$$\lim_{x \to 2^-} f(x) = \lim_{x \to 2^+} f(x)$$

Note that $\lim_{x \to 2^+} f(x) = 4 + c = f(2)$. Thus, it suffices to find all values of c for which the left-hand limit and the right-hand limit are equal. This can be done using *Mathematica*'s **Solve** command.

In[158]:= **Clear[c, f]**
f[x_] := If[x < 2, x^2 + c x - 1, 2 x + c]

In[160]:= **lhs = Limit[f[x], x → 2, Direction → 1]**
rhs = Limit[f[x], x → 2, Direction → -1]

Out[160]= $3 + 2 c$

Out[161]= $4 + c$

In[162]:= **Solve[lhs == rhs , c]**

Out[162]= $\{\{c \to 1\}\}$

Thus, f is continuous if $c = 1$. We confirm this by plotting the graph of f corresponding to this c value.

In[163]:= **Plot[f[x] /. c → 1, {x, -5, 7}]**

Out[163]=

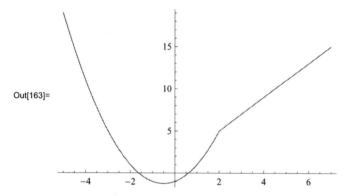

Example 2.30. Let $f(x) = \begin{cases} \sin(\frac{1}{x}), & \text{if } x \neq 0 \\ 0, & \text{if } x = 0 \end{cases}$. Prove that for any number k between -1 and 1 there exists a value for c such that $f(c) = k$.

NOTE: Observe that f is not continuous at $x = 0$ so the converse of the Intermediate Value Theorem does not hold.

Solution: For $k = 0$, we choose $c = 0$ so that $f(0) = 0$. For any nonzero k between -1 and 1, define $y = \sin^{-1} k$ (using the principal domain of the sine function) and let $c = 1/y$. Then $f(c) = \sin(1/c) = \sin y = k$. The graph of f following shows that there are in fact infinitely many choices for c.

In[164]:= **f[x_] := Sin[1 / x]**
         Plot[f[x], {x, -Pi, Pi}]

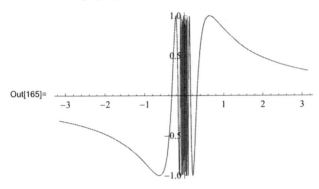

Out[165]=

■ Exercises

1. Let $f(x) = \begin{cases} e^x, & \text{if } x \le 0 \\ \ln x, & \text{if } x > 0 \end{cases}$.

a) Graph the above function and discuss the type of discontiniuty at $x = 0$.

b) Repeat part a. for the function

$$f(x) = \begin{cases} \cos\left(\frac{\pi x}{2}\right), & \text{if } |x| \le 1 \\ |x - 1|, & \text{if } |x| > 1 \end{cases}.$$

2. Find values for c in which f (defined below) is continuous over its entire domain:

$$f(x) = \begin{cases} x^2 + c, & x < 1, \\ c\,e^x, & x \ge 1 \end{cases}$$

Plot the graph of f corresponding to these c values.

3. Let

$$f(x) = \begin{cases} x + 1, & \text{if } |x| \le 2 \\ x^2 - c, & \text{if } |x| > 2 \end{cases}.$$

a) For what value(s) of c is the function continuous at $x = 2$? With this choice of c does f have a discontinuity at any other point? Plot the graph of the function.

b) For what value(s) of c is the function continuous at $x = -2$? With this choice of c does f have a discontinuity at any other point? Plot the graph of the function.

4. Find values of a and b such that the function f is continuous everywhere where $f(x) = \begin{cases} 2ax + b, & x < -5 \\ 6b, & -5 \le x < 1 \\ 3, & x \ge 1 \end{cases}$. HINT: Solve

first for b by equating the second and third expressions for f.

Chapter 3 Differentiation

■ 3.1 The Derivative

Students should read Sections 3.1-3.5 of Rogawski's *Calculus* [1] for a detailed discussion of the material presented in this section.

■ 3.1.1 Slope of Tangent

The derivative is one of the most fundamental concepts in calculus. Its pointwise definition is given by

$$f'(a) = \lim_{h \to 0} \frac{f(h + a) - f(a)}{h}$$

where geometrically $f'(a)$ is the slope of the line tangent to the graph of $f(x)$ at $x = a$ (provided the limit exists). We can view this graphically in the illustration below, where the tangent line (shown in blue) is viewed as a limit of secant lines (one shown in red) as $h \to 0$.

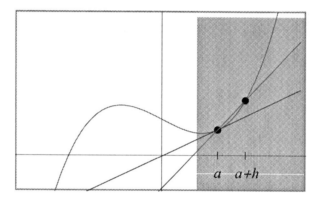

Example 3.1. Calculate the derivative of $f(x) = \frac{x^2}{3}$ at $x = 1$ using the pointwise definition of a derivative.

Solution: We first use the **Table** command to tabulate slopes of secant lines passing through the points at $a = 1$ and $a + h = 1 + h$ by choosing arbitrarily small values for h (taken as reciprocal powers of 10):

```
In[166]:= f[x_] = x^2 / 3;
        a = 1;
        h = 10^(-n);
        TableForm[N[Table[{h, (f[a + h] - f[a])/h}, {n, 1, 5}]]]
```

```
Out[169]//TableForm=
        0.1        0.7
        0.01       0.67
        0.001      0.667
        0.0001     0.6667
        0.00001    0.66667
```

Note our use of the **TableForm** command, which displays a list as an array of rectangular cells. From the table output, we infer that $f'(1) = 2/3$. A more rigorous approach is to algebraically simplify the difference quotient, $\frac{f(a+h)-f(a)}{h}$:

In[170]:= **Clear[h]**

$$\textbf{Simplify}\left[\frac{\textbf{f[a + h] - f[a]}}{\textbf{h}}\right]$$

Out[171]= $\dfrac{2 + h}{3}$

It is now clear that $\frac{f(a+h)-f(a)}{h} \to \frac{2}{3}$ as $h \to 0$. This can be checked using *Mathematica*'s **Limit** command:

In[172]:= $\textbf{Limit}\left[\dfrac{\textbf{f[a + h] - f[a]}}{\textbf{h}}, \textbf{h} \to \textbf{0}\right]$

Out[172]= $\dfrac{2}{3}$

Below is a plot of the graph of $f(x)$ (in black) and its corresponding tangent line (in blue), which also confirms our answer:

In[173]:= **Plot[{f[x], f'[a] (x - a) + f[a]}, {x, -2, 2}, PlotStyle → {Black, Blue}]**

Out[173]=

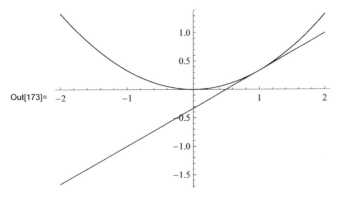

NOTE: Recall that the tangent line of $f(x)$ at $x = a$ is given by the equation $y = f'(a)(x - a) + f(a)$.

ANIMATION: Evaluate the following inputs to see animations of the secant lines approach the tangent line (from the right and left).

Important Note: If you are reading the printed version of this publication, then you will not be able to view any of the animations generated from the **Animate** command in this chapter. If you are reading the electronic version of this publication formatted as a *Mathematica* Notebook, then evaluate each **Animate** command to view the corresponding animation. Just click on the arrow button to start the animation. To control the animation just click at various points on the sliding bar or else manually drag the bar.

In[174]:= `(* From the right *)`
`fa1[x_] := x^2 / 3;`
`a1 = 1;`
`Animate[Plot[`
`    {fa1[x], fa1'[a1] (x - a1) + fa1[a1], (fa1[a1 + h] - fa1[a1]) / h * (x - a1) + fa1[a1]},`
`    {x, 0, 2}, PlotStyle → {Black, Blue, Red}], {h, 1.5, 0.1, -0.05}]`

Out[176]=

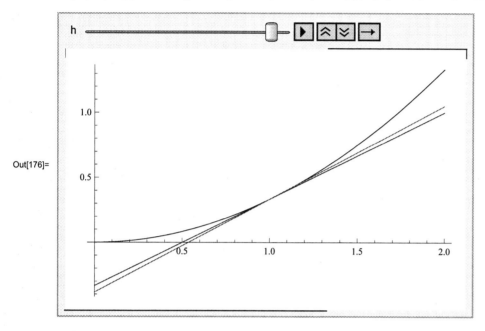

In[177]:= `(* From the left *)`
`fa1[x_] := x^2 / 3; a1 = 1;`
`Animate[Plot[`
`    {fa1[x], fa1'[a1] (x - a1) + fa1[a1], (fa1[a1 + h] - fa1[a1]) / h * (x - a1) + fa1[a1]},`
`    {x, 0, 2}, PlotStyle → {Black, Blue, Red}], {h, -1.0, -0.1, 0.05}]`

Out[178]=

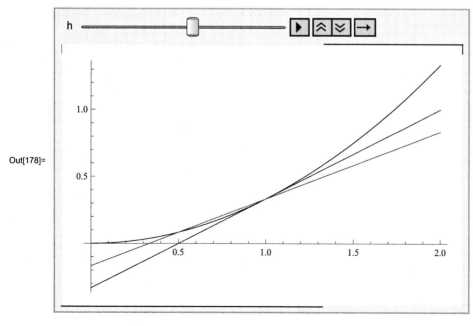

■ 3.1.2 Derivative as a Function

The derivative is best thought of as a slope function, one that gives the slope of the tangent line at any point on the graph of $f(x)$ where this slope exists:

$$f'(x) = \lim_{h \to 0} \frac{f(x+h) - f(x)}{h} .$$

Example 3.2. Compute the derivative of $f(x) = \sin x$ using the limit definition.

Solution: We first simplify the corresponding difference quotient to obtain

In[179]:= **Clear[h]**
   f[x_] = Sin[x];
   Simplify[(f[x + h] - f[x]) / h]

Out[181]= $\dfrac{-\text{Sin}[x] + \text{Sin}[h + x]}{h}$

Here, it is not clear what the limit of the difference quotient is as $h \to 0$. To anticipate the answer for the derivative without algebraic manipulation, we first note that since $\sin x$ is periodic, so should its derivative be. A plot of the difference quotient (as a function of x) for several arbitrarily small values of h reveals the derivative to be $\cos x$. Students should recognize from trigonometry that the graph of $\cos x$ is merely a left horizontal translation of $\sin x$ by $\frac{\pi}{2}$.

In[182]:= **plot1 = Plot[{f[x], Cos[x]}, {x, -Pi, Pi}, PlotStyle → {Black, Blue}]**

Out[182]=

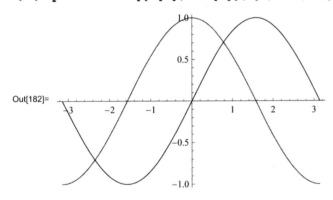

In[183]:= **Clear[h]**
   plot2 = Plot[Evaluate[Table[(f[x + h] - f[x]) / h, {h, 0.1, 0.7, 0.3}]],
   {x, -Pi, Pi}, PlotStyle → Red]

Out[184]=

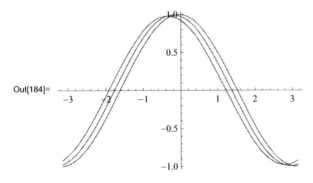

In[185]:= **Show[plot1, plot2]**

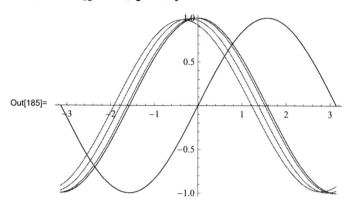

Out[185]=

Of course, there are a number of methods to compute the derivative directly in *Mathematica*. One method is to evaluate the command **D[*f*, *x*]** for a function *f* defined with respect to the variable *x*. A second method is to merely evaluate the expression **f'[x]** using the traditional prime (apostrophe symbol) notation. A third method is to use the command $\partial_\square \square$. We shall only discuss the first two methods since the third method is usually reserved for derivatives of functions depending on more than one variable, a topic that is treated in the third volume of this publication.

Example 3.3. Compute the derivative of $\sin\left(x^2\right)$ and evaluate it at $x = \sqrt{\dfrac{\pi}{4}}$.

Solution:

Method 1:

In[186]:= **D[Sin[x^2], x]**
   D[Sin[x^2], x] /. x → Sqrt[Pi / 4]

Out[186]= $2 \, x \, \text{Cos}\left[x^2\right]$

Out[187]= $\sqrt{\dfrac{\pi}{2}}$

NOTE: Recall the substitution command **/. *x* −> *a*** was discussed in an earlier section.

Method 2:

In[188]:= **f[x_] = Sin[x^2]**
   f'[x]
   f'[Sqrt[Pi / 4]]

Out[188]= $\text{Sin}\left[x^2\right]$

Out[189]= $2 \, x \, \text{Cos}\left[x^2\right]$

Out[190]= $\sqrt{\dfrac{\pi}{2}}$

Warning: Observe that the derivative of $\sin\left(x^2\right)$ is NOT $\cos\left(x^2\right)$ but $2\,x\cos\left(x^2\right)$. This is because $\sin\left(x^2\right)$ is a composite function. A rule for differentiating composite functions, known as as the Chain Rule, is discussed in ection 3.7 of Rogawski's *Calculus*.

Example 3.4. Compute the derivative of $f(x) = \begin{cases} \frac{\sin x}{x} & \text{if } x \neq 0 \\ 0 & \text{if } x = 0 \end{cases}$.

Solution: To define functions described by two different formulas over separate domains, we employ *Mathematica*'s **If[expr, p, q]** command:

In[191]:= **f[x_] = If[x ≠ 0, Sin[x] / x, 0]**

Out[191]= $\text{If}\left[x \neq 0, \dfrac{\text{Sin}[x]}{x}, 0\right]$

In[192]:= **f'[x]**

Out[192]= $\text{If}\left[x \neq 0, -\dfrac{\text{Sin}[x]}{x^2} + \dfrac{\text{Cos}[x]}{x}, 0\right]$

NOTE: It is clear for $x \neq 0$ that the derivative is $-\frac{\sin x}{x^2} + \frac{\cos x}{x}$ as a result of the Quotient Rule. For $x = 0$, *Mathematica*'s answer that $f'(0) = 0$ is actually incorrect! Note that the fact that $f(0) = 0$ does not mean that f is a constant. One cannot differentiate a formula that is valid at only a single point; it is also necessary to understand how the function behaves in a neighborhood of this point.

A plot of the graph of $f(x)$ reveals that it is discontinuous at $x = 0$, that is, $\lim_{x \to 0} f(x) \neq f(0)$, and thus not differentiable there.

In[193]:= **Plot[f[x], {x, -3 Pi, 3 Pi}]**

Out[193]=

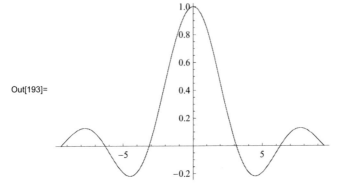

Observe that the point $f(0) = 0$ is not distinguished in the *Mathematica* plot above so that the (removable) discontinuity is detected only by examining the behavior of f around $x = 0$ (the true graph of f is shown following).

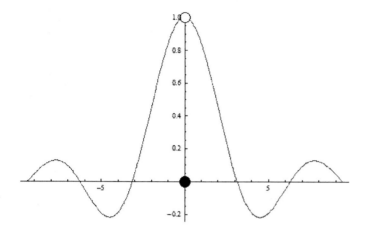

In particular, $f(x) \to 1$ as $x \to 0$. We confirm this with *Mathematica*.

In[194]:= **Limit[f[x], x → 0]**

Out[194]= 1

Of course, it is also possible to compute $f'(0)$ directly from the limit definition. Here, the difference quotient behaves as $\frac{\sin h}{h^2}$ as the output below shows. Since its limit does not exist as $h \to 0$, we conclude that $f'(0)$ is undefined.

In[195]:= **Simplify[(f[0 + h] - f[0]) / h]**
Limit[(f[0 + h] - f[0]) / h, h → 0]

Out[195]= $\begin{cases} \frac{\text{Sin[h]}}{h^2} & h \neq 0 \\ 0 & \text{True} \end{cases}$

Out[196]= ∞

NOTE: The discontinuity of f at $x = 0$ can be removed by redefining it there to be $f(0) = 1$. What is $f'(0)$ in this case?

Example 3.5 Find the equation of the tangent line to the graph of $f(x) = \sqrt{x+1}$ at $x = 2$.

Solution: Remember that the tangent line to a function f(x) at x = a is L(x) = f(a) + f '(a) (x-- a). Hear a = 2:

In[197]:=

Clear[f, L]

f[x_] = $\sqrt{x + 1}$

L[x_] = f[2] + f'[2] (x - 2)

Out[198]= $\sqrt{1 + x}$

Out[199]= $\sqrt{3} + \dfrac{-2 + x}{2\sqrt{3}}$

To see that L(x) is indeed the desired tangent line, we will plot f and L together.

In[200]:= `Plot[{f[x], L[x]}, {x, 0, 4}]`

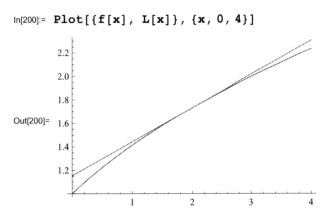

Out[200]=

Example 3.6. Find an equation of the line passing through the point $P(2, -3)$ and tangent to the graph of $f(x) = x^2 + 1$.

Solution: Let us refer to $Q(a, f(a))$ as the point of tangency for our desired tangent line. To determine Q, we compute the slope of our desired tangent line from two different perspectives:

1. Slope of line segment PQ:

In[201]:= `Clear[a]`
`f[x_] = x^2 + 1`
`m = (f[a] - (-3)) / (a - 2)`

Out[202]= $1 + x^2$

Out[203]= $\dfrac{4 + a^2}{-2 + a}$

2. Derivative of $f(x)$ at $x = a$:

In[204]:= `f[x_] = x^2 + 1`
`f'[a]`

Out[204]= $1 + x^2$

Out[205]= $2\,a$

Equating the two formulas for slope above and solving for a yields

In[206]:= `Solve[m == f'[a], a]`
`N[%]`

Out[206]= $\left\{\left\{a \to 2\left(1 - \sqrt{2}\right)\right\}, \left\{a \to 2\left(1 + \sqrt{2}\right)\right\}\right\}$

Out[207]= $\{\{a \to -0.828427\}, \{a \to 4.82843\}\}$

Since there are two valid solutions for a, we have in fact found two such tangent lines. Their equations are given by

In[208]:= **Clear[y1, y2]**

$$y1[x\_] = Simplify\left[f'[a] \ (x - a) + f[a] \ /. \ a \to 2 \left(1 - \sqrt{2}\right)\right]$$

$$y2[x\_] = Simplify\left[f'[a] \ (x - a) + f[a] \ /. \ a \to 2 \left(1 + \sqrt{2}\right)\right]$$

Out[209]= $-11 + 8\sqrt{2} - 4\left(-1 + \sqrt{2}\right) x$

Out[210]= $-11 - 8\sqrt{2} + 4\left(1 + \sqrt{2}\right) x$

Plotting these tangent lines together with the graph of $f(x)$ confirms that our solution is correct:

In[211]:= **Plot[{f[x], y1[x], y2[x]}, {x, -6, 6},**
   PlotRange → {-10, 40}, PlotStyle → {Black, Blue, Blue}]

Out[211]=

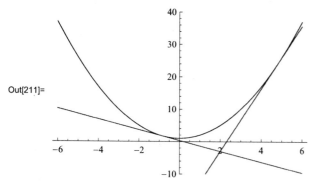

NOTE: How would the solution change if we move the given point in the problem to $P(2, 5)$? Or $P(2, 10)$?

■ Exercises

In Exercises 1 through 3, compute the derivatives of the given functions:

1. $f(x) = 3x^2 + 1$ 2. $g(x) = \frac{1}{x^3}$ 3. $h(x) = \frac{\sin x}{\cos x}$

In Exercises 4 and 5, evaluate the derivatives of the given functions at the specified values of x:

4. $f(x) = (x - 1)(x + 1)$ at $x = 1$ 5. $g(x) = \frac{\sqrt{x} + 1}{\sqrt{x} - 1}$ at $x = 9$

In Exercises 6 and 7, compute the derivatives of the given functions:

6. $f(x) = |x + 3|$ 7. $g(x) = |x^2 - 4|$

Hint: Recall the absolute value function: $|x| = \begin{cases} x & \text{if } x \geq 0 \\ -x & \text{if } x < 0 \end{cases}$. Use the **If** command to define these absolute functions (see

Example 3.4). Note that *Mathematica* does have a built-in Abs[x] command for defining the absolute value of x, but *Mathematica* treats Abs[x] as a complex function; thus its derivative Abs'[x] is NOT defined. The real derivative of Abs[x] for real values of x can still be found using the numerical derivative **ND** command but we shall not discuss it here.

8. Find an equation of the line tangent to the graph of $x - y^2 = 0$ at the point $P(9, -3)$.

9. Find an equation of the line passing through the point $P(2, -3)$ and tangent to the graph of $y = x^2$.

■ 3.2.   Higher-Order Derivatives

Students should read Section 3.5 of Rogawski's *Calculus* [1] for a detailed discussion of the material presented in this section.

Suppose one is interested in securing higher order derivatives of a function. Reasons for doing so include applications to maximum and minimum values, points of inflection, and physical applications such as velocity and acceleration and jerk, which all fit into such a context.

Example 3.6. Compute the first eight derivatives of $f(x) = \sin x$. What is the 255th derivative of f?

Solution: Here are the first eight derivative of f:

```
In[212]:= f[x_] = Sin[x];
         TableForm[Table[{n, D[f[x], {x, n}]}, {n, 1, 8}]]
```

Out[213]//TableForm=

```
    1    Cos[x]
    2    -Sin[x]
    3    -Cos[x]
    4    Sin[x]
    5    Cos[x]
    6    -Sin[x]
    7    -Cos[x]
    8    Sin[x]
```

We observe from the output that the higher-order derivatives of f are periodic modulo 4, which means they repeat every four derivatives. Since 255 has remainder 3 when divided by 4, it follows that $f^{(255)}(x) = f^{(3)}(x) = -\cos x$. Of course, *Mathematica* can compute this derivative directly (see output below), but the pattern above gives us a more in-depth understanding of the higher-order derivatives of $\sin x$.

```
In[214]:= D[f[x], {x, 255}]
```

Out[214]= $-\text{Cos}[x]$

Example 3.7. Compute the first three derivatives of $f(x) = x \cos x$.

Solution: We use the command **D[f, {x, n}]** to compute the nth derivative of f. Here, we set $n = 1, 2, 3$.

```
In[215]:= f[x_] = x * Cos[x]
```

Out[215]= $x \, \text{Cos}[x]$

```
In[216]:= D[f[x], x]
```

Out[216]= $\text{Cos}[x] - x \, \text{Sin}[x]$

```
In[217]:= D[f[x], {x, 2}]
```

Out[217]= $-x \, \text{Cos}[x] - 2 \, \text{Sin}[x]$

```
In[218]:= D[f[x], {x, 3}]
```

Out[218]= $-3 \, \text{Cos}[x] + x \, \text{Sin}[x]$

A quicker way to generate a list of higher-order derivatives is to use the **Table** command. For example, here is a list of the first five derivatives of f:

In[219]:= **Table[D[f[x], {x, n}], {n, 1, 5}]**

Out[219]= {Cos[x] - x Sin[x], -x Cos[x] - 2 Sin[x],

   -3 Cos[x] + x Sin[x], x Cos[x] + 4 Sin[x], 5 Cos[x] - x Sin[x]}

Discovery Exercise: Find a formula for the *n*th derivative of *f* based on the pattern above. Can you prove your claim using mathematical induction? What is the 100th derivative of *f* in this case? Check your answer using *Mathematica*.

■ Exercises

1. Let $f(x) = 1/x$.

a) Compute the first five higher-order derivatives of *f*.

b) What is the 10th derivative of *f*?

c) Obtain a general formula for the *n*th derivative based on the pattern. Then use the principle of mathematical induction to justify your claim.

2. Consider $f(x) = x \sin x$. Determine the first eight derivatives of *f* and obtain a pattern. Justify your contention.

In Exercises 3 and 4, compute $f^{(k)}(x)$ for k = 1,2,3,4.

3. $f(x) = \left(1 + x^2\right)^{\frac{6}{5}}$

4. $f(x) = \frac{1-x^2}{1-3x+2x^3}$

■ 3.3   Chain Rule and Implicit Differentiation

Students should read Sections 3.7 and 3.10 of Rogawski's *Calculus* [1] for a detailed discussion of the material presented in this section.

In this section, we demonstrate not only how *Mathematica* uses the Chain Rule to differentiate composite functions but also to compute derivatives of functions defined implicitly by equations where solving for the dependent variable is not feasible.

Example 3.8. Find all horizontal tangents of $f(x) = \sqrt{\frac{x^4-x+1}{x^4+x+1}}$.

Solution: We first compute the derivative of *f*, which requires the Chain Rule.

In[220]:= **f[x_] := $\sqrt{\dfrac{x^4 - x + 1}{x^4 + x + 1}}$;**

   Simplify[f'[x]]

Out[221]= $\dfrac{-1 + 3 x^4}{\sqrt{\dfrac{1-x+x^4}{1+x+x^4}}\ \left(1 + x + x^4\right)^2}$

Horizontal tangents have zero slope and so it suffices to solve $f'(x) = 0$ for *x*.

In[222]:= **Solve[f'[x] == 0, x]**

Out[222]= $\left\{\left\{x \to -\dfrac{1}{3^{1/4}}\right\}, \left\{x \to -\dfrac{i}{3^{1/4}}\right\}, \left\{x \to \dfrac{i}{3^{1/4}}\right\}, \left\{x \to \dfrac{1}{3^{1/4}}\right\}\right\}$

Observe that the solutions above are nothing more than the zeros of the numerator of $f'(x)$. We ignore the second and third solutions listed above, which are imaginary. Hence, $x = \sqrt[4]{1/3} \approx 0.76$ and $x = -\sqrt[4]{1/3}$. A plot of the graph of f below confirms our solution.

In[223]:= **Plot[f[x], {x, -2, 2}]**

Out[223]=

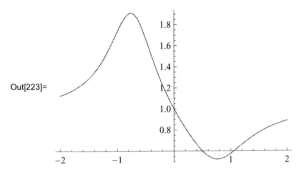

Example 3.9. Find all horizontal tangents of the lemniscate described by $2\left(x^2 + y^2\right)^2 = 25\left(x^2 - y^2\right)$.

Solution: Implicit differentiation is required here to compute $\frac{dy}{dx}$, which involves first differentiating the lemniscate equation and then solving for our derivative. Observe that we make the substitution $y \to y(x)$, which makes explicit our assumption that y depends on x.

In[224]:= **Clear[x, y]**
eq = 2 (x^2 + y^2)^2 == 25 (x^2 - y^2)

Out[225]= $2\left(x^2 + y^2\right)^2 == 25\left(x^2 - y^2\right)$

In[226]:= $2\left(x^2 + y^2\right)^2 == 25\left(x^2 - y^2\right)$

Out[226]= $2\left(x^2 + y^2\right)^2 == 25\left(x^2 - y^2\right)$

In[227]:= **deq = D[eq /. y → y[x], x]**

Out[227]= $4\left(x^2 + y[x]^2\right)(2x + 2y[x]y'[x]) == 25(2x - 2y[x]y'[x])$

In[228]:= **Solve[deq, y'[x]]**

Out[228]= $\left\{\left\{y'[x] \to \dfrac{25x - 4x^3 - 4xy[x]^2}{y[x]\left(25 + 4x^2 + 4y[x]^2\right)}\right\}\right\}$

To find horizontal tangents, it suffices to find where the numerator of $y'(x)$ vanishes (since the denominator never vanishes except when $y = 0$). Thus, we solve the system of equations $25x - 4x^3 - 4xy^2 = 0$ and $2\left(x^2 + y^2\right)^2 = 25\left(x^2 - y^2\right)$ since the solutions must also lie on the lemniscate.

In[229]:= **Solve[{eq, 25 x - 4 x^3 - 4 x * y^2 == 0}, {x, y}]**

Out[229]= $\left\{\{x \to 0, y \to 0\}, \left\{x \to 0, y \to -\dfrac{5i}{\sqrt{2}}\right\}, \left\{x \to 0, y \to \dfrac{5i}{\sqrt{2}}\right\}, \left\{x \to -\dfrac{5\sqrt{3}}{4}, y \to -\dfrac{5}{4}\right\},\right.$

$\left.\left\{x \to -\dfrac{5\sqrt{3}}{4}, y \to \dfrac{5}{4}\right\}, \left\{x \to \dfrac{5\sqrt{3}}{4}, y \to -\dfrac{5}{4}\right\}, \left\{x \to \dfrac{5\sqrt{3}}{4}, y \to \dfrac{5}{4}\right\}\right\}$

From the output, we see that there are four valid solutions at $\left(5\sqrt{3}\,/4,\ 5/4\right) \approx (2.17,\ 1.25)$, $\left(-5\sqrt{3}\,/4,\ 5/4\right)$, $\left(5\sqrt{3}\,/4,\ -5/4\right)$, and $\left(-5\sqrt{3}\,/4,\ -5/4\right)$, which can be confirmed by inspecting the graph of the lemniscate below. Observe the symmetry in the solutions.

In[230]:= **N[5 * Sqrt[3] / 4]**

Out[230]= 2.16506

In[231]:= **ContourPlot[2 (x^2 + y^2)^2 == 25 (x^2 - y^2), {x, -4, 4}, {y, -2, 2}]**

Out[231]=

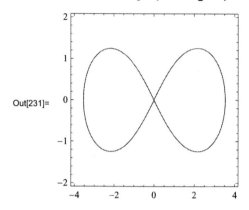

■ Exercises

1. Find all horizontal tangents of $g(x) = \left(\frac{x^2}{x+1}\right)^7$.

2. Find all tangents along the curve $h(x) = \sqrt{x + \sqrt{x}}$ whose slope equals 1/2.

3. Find all vertical tangents of the cardioid described by $x^2 + y^2 = \left(2\,x^2 + 2\,y^2 - x\right)^2$.

4. Compute the first and second derivatives of

$$f(x) = \begin{cases} x\cos\frac{1}{x} & \text{if } x \neq 0 \\ 0 & \text{if } x = 0 \end{cases}.$$

5. Compute the first and second derivatives of

$$g(x) = \begin{cases} x^2\cos\frac{1}{x} & \text{if } x \neq 0 \\ 0 & \text{if } x = 0 \end{cases}.$$

How do these derivatives at the origin compare with those in the previous exercise?

6. Based on your investigations of the previous two exercises, explain the behavior of higher-order derivatives of

$$h(x) = \begin{cases} x^n\cos\frac{1}{x} & \text{if } x \neq 0 \\ 0 & \text{if } x = 0 \end{cases}$$

at the origin for positive integer values of *n*.

7. Calculate the implicit derivative of y with respect to x of: $xy^2 + x^2 y^4 -- x^3 = 5$.

8. Plot $\left(x^2 + y^2\right)^2 = \left(x^2 - y^2\right) + 2$ for $-4 \le x \le 4$ and $-4 \le y \le 4$. Then determine how many horizontal tangent lines the curve appears to have and find the points where these occur.

■ 3.4   Derivatives of Inverse, Exponential, and Logarithmic Functions

Students should read Sections 3.8-3.9 of Rogawski's *Calculus* [1] for a detailed discussion of the material presented in this section.

Exponential functions arise naturally. For example, mathematical models for the growth of a population or the decay of a radioactive substance involve exponential functions. In this section, we will explore exponential functions and their inverses, called logarithmic functions, using *Mathematica*. We begin with a review of inverse functions in general.

■ 3.4.1. Inverse of a Function

Recall that a function $g(x)$ is the inverse of a given function $f(x)$ if $f(g(x)) = g(f(x)) = x$. The inverse of $f(x)$ is denoted by $f^{-1}(x)$. We note that a necessary and sufficient condition for a function to have an inverse is that it must be one-to-one. On the other hand, a function is one-to-one if it is strictly increasing or strictly decreasing throughout its domain.

Example 3.13. Determine if the function $f(x) = x^2 - x + 1$ has an inverse on the domain $(-\infty, \infty)$. If it exists, then find the inverse.

Solution: We note that $f(0) = f(1) = 1$. Thus, f is not one-to-one. We can also plot the graph of f and note that it fails the Horizontal Line Test since it is not increasing on its domain.

In[232]:= `Clear[f, g]`

In[233]:= `f[x_] = x^2 - x + 1;`
`Plot[f[x], {x, -1, 2}]`

Out[234]=

However, observe that if we restrict the domain of f to an interval where f is either increasing or decreasing, say $[0.5, \infty)$, then its inverse exists (see plot below).

In[235]:= **plotf = Plot[f[x], {x, 0.5, 5}]**

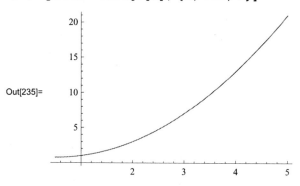

Out[235]=

To find the inverse on this restricted domain, we set $y = f^{-1}(x)$. Then $f(y) = x$. Thus, we solve for y from the equation $f(y) = x$.

In[236]:= **sol = Solve[f[y] == x, y]**

Out[236]= $\left\{\left\{y \to \frac{1}{2}\left(1 - \sqrt{-3 + 4x}\right)\right\}, \left\{y \to \frac{1}{2}\left(1 + \sqrt{-3 + 4x}\right)\right\}\right\}$

Note that *Mathematica* gives two solutions. Only the second one is valid, having range $[0.5, \infty)$, which agrees with the domain of f. Thus,

$$f^{-1}(x) = \frac{1}{2}\left(1 + \sqrt{-3 + 4x}\right).$$

To extract this solution from the above output, we use the syntax below and denote the inverse function in *Mathematica* by $g(x)$ (*Mathematica* interprets the notation $f^{-1}(x)$ as $\frac{1}{f(x)}$, the reciprocal of f).

In[237]:= **g[x_] = sol[[2, 1, 2]]**

Out[237]= $\frac{1}{2}\left(1 + \sqrt{-3 + 4x}\right)$

To verify that $f(g(x)) = x$, we use the **Simplify** command.

In[238]:= **Simplify[f[g[x]] == x]**

Out[238]= True

NOTE: One can also attempt to verify $g(f(x)) = x$. However, *Mathematica* cannot confirm this identity (see output below) because it is unable to simplify the radical, which it treats as a complex square root. Students are encouraged to algebraically check this identity on their own.

In[239]:= **Simplify[g[f[x]] == x]**

Out[239]= $1 + \sqrt{(-1 + 2x)^2} == 2x$

Lastly, a plot of the graphs of $f(x)$ and $g(x)$ (in black and blue, respectively) shows their expected symmetry about the diagonal line $y = x$ (in red). Observe that the domain of g is $[3/4, \infty)$, which is the range of f.

In[240]:= `plotg = Plot[g[x], {x, 3 / 4, 5}, PlotStyle → Red, AspectRatio → Automatic]`

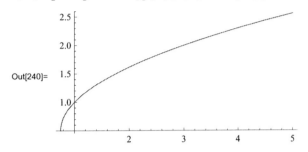

Out[240]=

In[241]:= `Show[plotf, plotg, Graphics[{Dashing[{0.05, 0.05}], Line[{{0, 0}, {5, 5}}]}],`
`PlotRange → {0, 5}, AspectRatio → Automatic]`

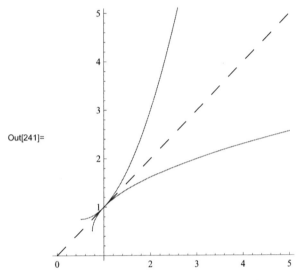

Out[241]=

Example 3.14. Determine if the function $f(x) = x^3 + x$ has an inverse. If it exists, then compute $\left(f^{-1}\right)'(2)$.

Solution: Since $f'(x) = 3x^2 + 1 > 0$ for all x, we see that f is increasing on its domain. Thus, it has an inverse. Again, we can solve for this inverse as in the previous example:

In[242]:= `Clear[f, g, x, sol]`
`f[x_] := x^3 + x`
`sol = Solve[f[y] == x, y]`

Out[244]= $\left\{\left\{y \to -\dfrac{\left(\frac{2}{3}\right)^{1/3}}{\left(9\,x + \sqrt{3}\,\sqrt{4 + 27\,x^2}\right)^{1/3}} + \dfrac{\left(9\,x + \sqrt{3}\,\sqrt{4 + 27\,x^2}\right)^{1/3}}{2^{1/3}\,3^{2/3}}\right\},\right.$

$\left\{y \to \dfrac{1 + i\,\sqrt{3}}{2^{2/3}\,3^{1/3}\left(9\,x + \sqrt{3}\,\sqrt{4 + 27\,x^2}\right)^{1/3}} - \right.$

$\left.\left(\left(1 - i\,\sqrt{3}\right)\left(9\,x + \sqrt{3}\,\sqrt{4 + 27\,x^2}\right)^{1/3}\right)\Big/\left(2 \times 2^{1/3}\,3^{2/3}\right)\right\},$

$\left\{y \to \dfrac{1 - i\,\sqrt{3}}{2^{2/3}\,3^{1/3}\left(9\,x + \sqrt{3}\,\sqrt{4 + 27\,x^2}\right)^{1/3}} - \right.$

$\left.\left.\left(\left(1 + i\,\sqrt{3}\right)\left(9\,x + \sqrt{3}\,\sqrt{4 + 27\,x^2}\right)^{1/3}\right)\Big/\left(2 \times 2^{1/3}\,3^{2/3}\right)\right\}\right\}$

Only the first solution listed above is valid, being real valued. Thus,

$$f^{-1}(x) = -\dfrac{\left(\frac{2}{3}\right)^{1/3}}{\left(9x + \sqrt{3}\,\sqrt{4 + 27x^2}\right)^{1/3}} + \dfrac{\left(9x + \sqrt{3}\,\sqrt{4 + 27x^2}\right)^{1/3}}{2^{1/3}\,3^{2/3}}.$$

Again we denote our inverse by $g(x)$:

In[245]:= `g[x_] = sol[[1, 1, 2]]`

Out[245]= $-\dfrac{\left(\frac{2}{3}\right)^{1/3}}{\left(9\,x + \sqrt{3}\,\sqrt{4 + 27\,x^2}\right)^{1/3}} + \dfrac{\left(9\,x + \sqrt{3}\,\sqrt{4 + 27\,x^2}\right)^{1/3}}{2^{1/3}\,3^{2/3}}$

Lastly, we compute $g'(2)$.

In[246]:= `Simplify[g'[2]]`
`N[%]`

Out[246]= $\left(3^{1/3}\left(14 + 3\sqrt{21}\right)\left(3^{1/3} + \left(9 + 2\sqrt{21}\right)^{2/3}\right)\right)\Big/\left(28\left(9 + 2\sqrt{21}\right)^{4/3}\right)$

Out[247]= 0.25

NOTE: The easier approach in computing $g'(2)$ without having to explicitly differentiate $g(x)$ is to instead use the relation $\left(f^{-1}\right)'(x) = 1/f'\left(f^{-1}(x)\right)$, which shows that the derivative of f at a point (a, b) on its graph and the derivative of f^{-1} (or g in our case) at the corresponding inverse point (b, a) on its graph are reciprocal. In particular, since $f(1) = 2$ and $f^{-1}(2) = 1$, we have $\left(f^{-1}\right)'(2) = 1/f'\left(f^{-1}(2)\right) = 1/f'(1) = 1/4$.

In[248]:= `1 / f'[g[2]]`
`N[%]`

$$
\text{Out[248]= } 1 \Bigg/ \left(1 + 3 \left(-\left(\frac{2}{3\left(18 + 4\sqrt{21}\right)} \right)^{1/3} + \frac{\left(\frac{1}{2}\left(18 + 4\sqrt{21}\right) \right)^{1/3}}{3^{2/3}} \right)^{2} \right)
$$

Out[249]= `0.25`

NOTE: The plot below illustrates how the slopes of the two tangent lines, that of f at (1, 2) and that of g at (2, 1) (both in blue), are reciprocal.

In[250]:= `Plot[{f[x], g[x], f'[1] (x-1) + f[1], g'[2] (x-2) + g[2]}, {x, -1, 5},`
`    PlotRange → {-1, 5}, PlotStyle → {Black, Red, Blue, Blue}, AspectRatio → Automatic]`

Out[250]=

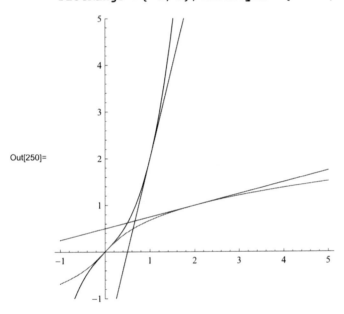

■ 3.4.2. Exponential and Logarithmic Functions

One of the most important functions in mathematics and its applications is the *exponential* function. In particular, the *natural exponential* function $f(x) = e^x$, where

$$ e = \lim_{x \to 0}(1 + x)^{1/x} \approx 2.718. $$

In *Mathematica,* we use the capital letter **E** or blackboard bold letter e from the Basic Math Input submenu of the Palettes menu to denote the Euler number.

In[251]:= `Limit[ (1 + x) ^ (1 / x), x → 0]`

Out[251]= e

Every exponential function $f(x) = a^x$, $a \neq 1$, $a > 0$, where $a \neq 1$ and $a > 0$, has domain $(-\infty, \infty)$ and range $(0, \infty)$. It is also one-to-one on its domain. Hence, it has an inverse. The inverse of an exponential function $f(x) = a^x$ is called the *logarithm* function and is denoted by $g(x) = \log_a x$. The inverse of the natural exponential function is denoted by $g(x) = \ln x$ and is called the *natural logarithm*. In *Mathematica,* we use **Log[a,x]** for $\log_a x$ and **Log[x]** for $\ln x$. Below is a plot of the graphs of e^x and $\ln x$ in black and red, respectively. Observe their symmetry about the dashed line $y = x$.

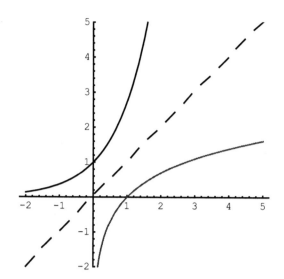

Please refer to Section 3.9 of Rogawski's *Calculus* textbook for derivative formulas of general exponential and logarithmic functions.

Example 3.15. Compute derivatives of the following functions.

a) $f(x) = 2^x$ b) $f(x) = 6\,x^2 + 4\,e^x$ c) $f(x) = \log_{10} x^2$ d) $f(x) = \ln\!\left(\cos\!\left(e^{3\,x}\right)\right)$

Solution: We will input the functions directly and use the command **D** to find each derivative. Thus, for a) we will evaluate $D[2^x, x]$. Again, note that Log[2] should be read as ln 2.

a)

In[252]:= **D[2^x, x]**

Out[252]= $2^x \, \text{Log}[2]$

b)

In[253]:= $\mathbf{D\left[6\ x^2 + 4\ E^x,\ x\right]}$

Out[253]= $4\ e^x + 12\ x$

c)

In[254]:= **D[Log[10, x^2], x]**

Out[254]= $\dfrac{2}{x\ \text{Log}[10]}$

d)

In[255]:= $\mathbf{f = D\left[Log\left[Cos\left[E^{3\,x}\right]\right],\ x\right]}$

Out[255]= $-3\ e^{3\,x}\ \text{Tan}\!\left[e^{3\,x}\right]$

Example 3.16. Find points on the graph of $f(x) = x^2\,e^{3\,x+5} + 3\,x$ where the tangent lines are parallel to the line $y = 3\,x - 1$.

Solution: Since the slope of the given line equals 3 it suffices to solve $f'(x) = 3$ for x to locate these point(s).

In[256]:= **Clear[f, sol]**
 f[x_] = x² E³ˣ⁺⁵ + 3 x
 sol = Solve[f'[x] == 3, x]

Out[257]= $3 x + e^{5+3 x} x^2$

Out[258]= $\left\{\left\{x \to -\frac{2}{3}\right\}, \{x \to 0\}\right\}$

Thus there are two solutions: $\left(-2/3, -2 + 4 e^3/9\right)$ and $(0, 0)$.

In[259]:= **x0 = sol[[1, 1, 2]]**
 x1 = sol[[2, 1, 2]]
 f[x0]
 f[x1]

Out[259]= $-\frac{2}{3}$

Out[260]= 0

Out[261]= $-2 + \frac{4 e^3}{9}$

Out[262]= 0

The plot that follows on the next page confirms that the two corresponding tangent lines (in blue) are indeed parallel to the given line (in red).

In[263]:= **y1 = f[x0] + f'[x0] (x - x0)**
 y2 = f[x1] + f'[x1] (x - x1)
 Plot[{f[x], y1, y2, 3 x - 2}, {x, -1, 1},
  PlotRange → {-5, 15}, PlotStyle → {Black, Blue, Blue, Red}]

Out[263]= $-2 + \frac{4 e^3}{9} + 3 \left(\frac{2}{3} + x\right)$

Out[264]= $3 x$

Out[265]=

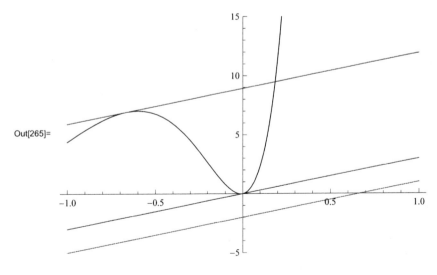

NOTE: One would expect the tangent line at the origin to be horizontal based on a visual inspection of the graph of f, but this demonstrates the pitfall of using a graphing approach.

■ Exercises

In Exercises 1 through 4, compute derivatives of the given functions.

1. $f(x) = x^2 \, e^{x^3 - 4x}$

2. $f(x) = x^a + a^x$

3. $f(x) = \ln(x - 1) + \ln(x + 1)$ 4. $f(x) = \log_{10}\left(x\left(\frac{x^3 - 3x + 1}{x^2 - 2x - 3}\right)^{3/2}\right)$

5. Find the second and third derivatives of $f(x) = e^x \ln x$.

6. Let $f(x) = \cos x + \ln x$. Plot the graphs of f and f' on the same set of axes.

7. Find an equation of the line tangent to the graph of $f(x) = \frac{\ln x}{x^2}$ that is parallel to the x-axis.

8. **Discovery Exercise**: Define $\sinh x = (e^x - e^{-x})/2$ and $\cosh x = (e^x + e^{-x})/2$. These functions are called the *hyperbolic sine* and *hyperbolic cosine* of x, respectively.

a) Determine the initial eight derivatives of each of these two hyperbolic functions.

b) Determine general formulas for the nth derivatives of these functions based on the pattern and verify your contentions via mathematical induction.

c) How do the higher-order derivatives of $\sinh x$ and $\cosh x$ compare with those of the trigonometric functions $\sin x$ and $\cos x$?

Chapter 4   Applications of the Derivative

We have seen how the derivative of a function is itself a function. This idea leads to many possible applications, some of which we will now explore with *Mathematica* to demonstrate its ability to manipulate and calculate complicated or tedious expressions.

■ 4.1 Related Rates

Students should read Section 3.11 of Rogawski's *Calculus* [1] for a detailed discussion of the material presented in this section.

Example 4.1. Let us assume a rubber ball is sitting out in the sun and that the heat causes its surface area to increase at the rate of 1.5 square centimeters per hour. How fast is the radius increasing when the radius is 2 centimeters?

Solution: To solve this problem, we will need the formula for the surface area of a sphere: $S = 4\pi r^2$. Here, the surface area S and the radius r are expressed as functions of t (time).

In[266]:= `Clear[S]`
       `sa = S[t] == 4 π r[t]^2`

Out[267]= $S[t] == 4 \pi r[t]^2$

In[268]:= `dsa = D[sa, t]`

Out[268]= $S'[t] == 8 \pi r[t] r'[t]$

Now differentiate this formula and solve for $r'(t)$:

In[269]:= `sol = Solve[dsa, r'[t]]`

Out[269]= $\left\{\left\{r'[t] \rightarrow \dfrac{S'[t]}{8 \pi r[t]}\right\}\right\}$

Since the output above is a nested list (each set of curly braces denotes a list; see Chapter 1 of this manual for a description of nested lists) and our solution, $\frac{S'(t)}{8\pi r(t)}$, represents the second element of the first (inner) list, we can extract it in order to define $r'(t)$ as follows:

In[270]:= `r'[t] = sol[[1, 1, 2]]`

Out[270]= $\dfrac{S'[t]}{8 \pi r[t]}$

Since we are given that $S'(t) = 1.5$ and $r(t) = 2$, we substitute these into the formula for $r'(t)$:

In[271]:= `r'[t] /. {S'[t] → 1.5, r[t] → 2}`

Out[271]= 0.0298416

Therefore, when the radius is 2 cm, it is increasing at the rate of about .0298 cm per hour.

■ Exercises

1. If the volume of a cube is increasing at the rate of 2 cubic inches per minute, how fast is the length of one of its sides increasing when that side is 8 inches?

2. A particle is moving along a parabola $y = 2x^2 + 3x - 1$ in such a way that the rate of change of its *x*-coordinate is constant, namely $x'(t) = 3$. Find the rate of change of its *y*-coordinate when the position of the particle is (1,4).

3. The radius r and height h of a circular cone change at a rate of 2 cm/s. How fast is the volume of the cone increasing when r = 10 and h = 20? (Recall that the volume of a cone is $\pi r^2 h/3$.)

■ 4.2 Extrema

Students should read Section 4.2 of Rogawski's *Calculus* [1] for a detailed discussion of the material presented in this section.

Next, let us consider finding critical points and inflection points to determine extrema. Remember that critical points of a function are those for which $f'(x) = 0$ or for which $f'(x)$ does not exist. Similarly, inflection points occur where either $f''(x) = 0$ or where $f''(x)$ does not exist. Extrema occur at critical points, but not all critical points are extrema (consult your calculus text). An inflection point is a point $(c, f(c))$ where concavity changes; this occurs where $f''(c) = 0$ or where $f''(x)$ does not exist, and like critical points, not all points where $f''(x) = 0$ (or where $f''(x)$ does not exist) are inflection points.

Example 4.2. Find all local extrema and inflection points of $f(x) = 1/(x^2 + 3)$.

Solution: We first define f in *Mathematica*:

In[272]:= **Clear [f, x]**

In[273]:= **f[x_] := 1 / (x^2 + 3)**

In[274]:= **Plot [f[x], {x, -4, 4}]**

Out[274]=

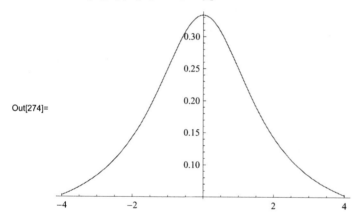

To find extrema of f, we locate its critical points, that is, those points where $f'(x) = 0$ or $f'(x)$ is undefined. We can solve the first case using *Mathematica*:

In[275]:= **f'[x]**
       Solve[f'[x] == 0, x]

Out[275]= $-\dfrac{2x}{\left(3 + x^2\right)^2}$

Out[276]= $\{\{x \to 0\}\}$

Since $f'(x)$ is defined everywhere, it follows that there is exactly one critical point at $x = 0$, and at that point, there is a maximum, as can be seen from the graph above. We could also have used the second derivative test to confirm this:

In[277]:= **f''[0]**

Out[277]= $-\dfrac{2}{9}$

Since the second derivative is negative at $x = 0$, the curve is concave down there. This, of course, means that we have a local maximum at $x = 0$.

To find the points of inflection, we locate zeros of the second derivative:

In[278]:= **Solve[f''[x] == 0, x]**

Out[278]= $\{\{x \to -1\}, \{x \to 1\}\}$

To determine if these solutions are indeed inflection points, we need to check if there is a sign change in $f''(x)$ on either side of each (at $x = -1$ and $x = 1$):

In[279]:= **Plot[f''[x], {x, -2, 2}]**

Out[279]=

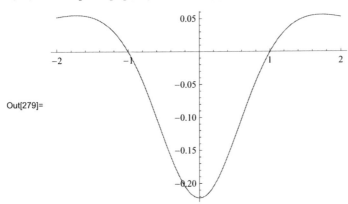

Notice from the graph above that $f''(x)$ changes from positive to negative at $x = -1$ and from negative to positive at $x = 1$. Thus both points $(-1, f(-1))$ and $(1, f(1))$ are inflection points.

■ **Exercises**

In Exercises 1 through 5, find all critical points and inflection points for:

1. $f(x) = x^3 - 3x^2 + 1$ 2. $f(x) = (x^2 - 3)e^x$ 3. $f(x) = \sin x$ on $[0, 2\pi]$

4. $f(x) = 2x^5 - 5x^4 + 5$ 5. $f(x) = \dfrac{x^2 + 4}{x}$

6. Consider the function $f(x) = x^n$ where n is a positive integer. For what values of n do we have
a) a relative minimum but not a point of inflection at the origin?
b) a point of inflection at the origin but not a relative minimum?
Sketch the graph of several power functions to support your reasoning.

■ 4.3 Optimization

Students should read Section 4.7 of Rogawski's *Calculus* [1] for a detailed discussion of the material presented in this section.

Extreme values of a function occur where $f'(x) = 0$ or where $f'(x)$ does not exist. This idea allows us to find maxima and minima, concepts that are crucial in many applications. For instance, in business, one wants to minimize costs or maximize profits. In government, one wants to track the flow of money in an economy, and when that flow is a minimum or a maximum.

In engineering design, we may want to know what shape of a conduit will generate maximum flow. Similar problems exist in many other fields. We will now look at some of these applications.

■ 4.3.1 Traffic Flow

Example 4.3. Traffic flow along a major highway in Boston between 6 AM and 10 AM can be modeled by the function $f(t) = 20\,t - 40\,\sqrt{t} + 50$ (in miles per hour), where $t = 0$ corresponds to 6 AM. Determine when the minimum traffic flow occurs.

Solution: Let us first plot the graph of $f(t)$.

In[280]:= **Clear[f, t]**

In[281]:= **f[t_] := 20 t - 40 $\sqrt{t}$ + 50**

In[282]:= **Plot[f[t], {t, 0, 4}]**

Out[282]=

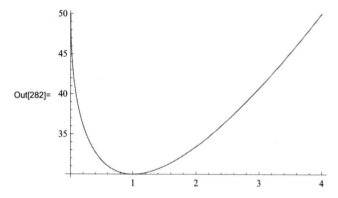

Note from the plot above that the average speed is decreasing between 6 AM and 7 AM and increasing after 7 AM.

At 6 AM the average speed is

In[283]:= **f[0]**

Out[283]= 50

or 50 mph. At 6:30 AM the average speed is

In[284]:= **f[.5]**

Out[284]= 31.7157

or 31.7 mph. To see how the average speed varies throughout the day we make a table of these values at each half hour from 6 AM to 10 AM:

In[285]:= **TableForm[Table[{t, f[t]}, {t, 0, 4, .5}]]**

Out[285]//TableForm=

0.	50.
0.5	31.7157
1.	30.
1.5	31.0102
2.	33.4315
2.5	36.7544
3.	40.718
3.5	45.1669
4.	50.

You can see from the table that the average speed quickly drops from 50 mph to 30 mph in the first hour and then gradually increases back up to 50 mph during the next 3 hours. If we want to verify that the minimum occurs at 7 AM (or $t = 1$), we can use calculus. Since extrema occur where the derivative is 0, we set the derivative equal to zero and solve for t:

In[286]:= **Solve[f'[t] == 0, t]**

Out[286]= $\{\{t \to 1\}\}$

Therefore the minimum does occur when $t = 1$ (7 AM) and from the table we see that the minimum average speed at this time is 30 mph.

▪ 4.3.2 Minimum Cost

Example 4.4. A friend of one of the authors owns some land on Long Island off the coast of Portland, Maine. He wants to build a house there, but there is no electricity. He is considering laying an underwater cable to connect up with the mainland. After a while I convince him of the ridiculousness of that idea. The cost is far more than he can afford, but it does get me thinking about mathematics. What would be the cheapest way of hooking up a cable to the municipal electrical system? Let us consider the following scenario:

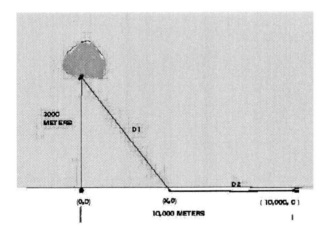

Imagine the island connection point at (0, 3000) and the mainline connection point at (10 000, 0) where the units are in meters. Assume it costs \$36 per meter to lay cable underwater and \$24 per meter to lay cable on land. You can lay cable underwater from (0, 3000) to (x, 0) and then lay cable on land from (x, 0) to (10 000, 0). The variable x can vary between 0 and 10000. What value of x would minimize the cost for laying this cable and what would that minimum cost be?

Solution: First, we need to determine the cost. There are two parts: the underwater part and the overland part. The cost of the underwater part is just \$36 times the distance D1 from (0, 3000) to (x, 0). We will call that cost $c1$:

In[287]:= `c1[x_] := 36 * ` $\sqrt{3000^2 + x^2}$

The overland cost is \$24 times the distance D2 from $(x, 0)$ to $(10\,000, 0)$. We will call that cost c2:

In[288]:= `c2[x_] := 24 * (10 000 - x)`

The total cost is then

In[289]:= `cost[x_] = c1[x] + c2[x]`

Out[289]= $24\ (10\,000 - x) + 36\ \sqrt{9\,000\,000 + x^2}$

We need to minimize this cost function. First, we graph it to see if it has a minimum:

In[290]:= `Plot[cost[x], {x, 0, 10 000}]`

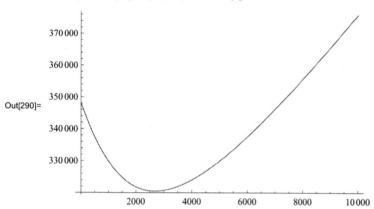

Out[290]=

Notice that this cost function has its minimum somewhere between 2000 and 4000. Also, you will note that as x gets close to that minimum the tangent lines of cost (x) are getting close to horizontal. In other words, the minimum will occur at a point x for which the derivative is zero or horizontal (i.e., the derivative at a point gives the slope of the tangent line at that point). This is a calculus problem that we can solve.

In[291]:= `Solve[cost'[x] == 0, x]`

Out[291]= $\left\{\left\{x \to 1200\ \sqrt{5}\ \right\}\right\}$

In[292]:= `N`$\left[\text{cost}\left[1200\ \sqrt{5}\ \right]\right]$

Out[292]= $320\,498.$

Therefore, the minimum occurs at $x = 1200\ \sqrt{5} \approx 2683.28$ meters and the minimum cost is approximately \$320,498.

NOTE: Another method in finding the minimum is to use the command **FindMinimum**. We will start our search near $x = 2000$:

In[293]:= `FindMinimum[cost[x], {x, 2000}, WorkingPrecision → 8]`

Out[293]= $\{320\,498.45,\ \{x \to 2683.2816\}\}$

Again, we get an answer that corroborates the previous answer.

▪ 4.3.3 Packaging (Minimum Surface Area)

Example 4.5. A major concern in business is to minimize the cost of packaging. This cost is related to the surface area of the package. If we can minimize that surface area, then we can minimize the cost. Let us assume that a company has a certain product that needs to be packaged in a rectangular box having a square base. If the volume of the box is required to be 1 cubic meter, then find the dimensions of the box that will minimize its surface area.

Solution: If the length of the sides of the square base is x and the height of the box is y, then the volume of the box is given by $x^2 y$ and must equal 1 cubic meter (this is our constraint):

In[294]:= **Clear[x, y, S]**

In[295]:= **constraint = x^2 * y == 1**

Out[295]= $x^2 y == 1$

The surface area of our package (box) is $S = 4xy + 2(x^2)$ and is the quantity that must be minimized (recall that the top and bottom sides each have area x^2 and the 4 sides each have area xy). Using our volume constraint, $x^2y = 1$, we can solve for y in terms of x:

$$y = \frac{1}{x^2}$$

In[296]:= **sol = Solve[constraint, y]**

Out[296]= $\left\{ \left\{ y \rightarrow \frac{1}{x^2} \right\} \right\}$

The surface area function can then be expressed as a function of x only:

$$S(x) = 4xy + 2x^2 = 4x(1/x^2) + 2x^2 = 4/x + 2x^2$$

In[297]:= **S[x_] = 4 x * y + 2 x^2 /. y → sol[[1, 1, 2]]**

Out[297]= $\frac{4}{x} + 2 x^2$

Using the idea again that extrema occur at points where the derivative is zero, we calculate:

In[298]:= **Solve[S'[x] == 0, x]**

Out[298]= $\left\{ \{x \rightarrow 1\}, \left\{x \rightarrow -(-1)^{1/3}\right\}, \left\{x \rightarrow (-1)^{2/3}\right\} \right\}$

This equation has 1 real and 2 imaginary solutions. We need only the real solution of $x = 1$. To see that this corresponds to an actual minimum, we plot the curve:

In[299]:= **Plot[S[x], {x, 0 , 5}]**

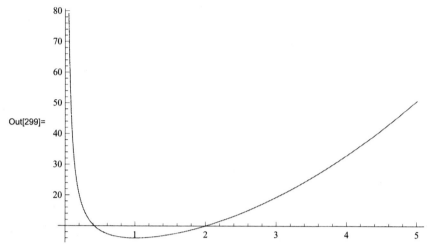

Out[299]=

Alternatively, we could have used the second derivative test to show that a minimum occurs at $x = 1$:

In[300]:= **S''[1]**

Out[300]= 12

Since $f''(1) > 0$, we know that the graph is concave up at $x = 1$ and hence must have a minimum there. Since $y = 1$ when $x = 1$, we conclude that the box with minimum surface area is a cube with sides of 1 meter.

■ 4.3.4 Maximize Revenue

The following application concerns optimizing group fares for charter flights.

Example 4.6. Suppose a travel agency charges $600 per person for a charter flight if exactly 100 people sign up. However, if more than 100 people sign up, then the fare is reduced by $2 per person for each additional person over the initial 100. The travel agency wants to know how many people they should book to maximize revenue. Also, determine what that maximum revenue is and what the corresponding fare is for each person.

We let x denote the number of passengers above 100. Keep in mind that revenue is the product of the number of people multiplied by the cost (fare) per person. If $R(x)$ is defined as the revenue function, then $R(x) = (100 + x)(600 - 2x)$. To determine the maximum value of $R(x)$ for $x \geq 0$, let us first examine its graph:

In[301]:= **R[x_] := (100 + x) (600 - 2 x)**

In[302]:= **Plot[R[x], {x, 0, 200}]**

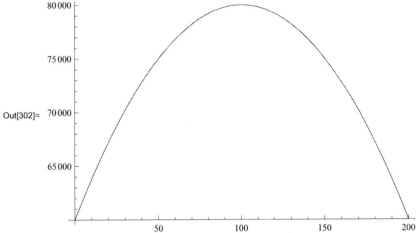

Out[302]=

From the plot above, we see that a maximum occurs at about $x = 100$. To confirm this, we first solve for the critical points:

In[303]:= **Solve[R'[x] == 0, x]**

Out[303]= $\{\{x \to 100\}\}$

Therefore the maximum does indeed occur at $x = 100$, and the maximum revenue is

In[304]:= **R[100]**

Out[304]= $80\,000$

or $80,000. Since $100 + x$ represents the number of customers, this occurs when 200 customers sign up for the flight. In this case, the cost per person is

In[305]:= **600 - 2 x /. x -> 100**

Out[305]= 400

or $400 per person.

■ Exercises

1. Assume traffic flow is given by a speed function $f(t) = 25\,t - 45\sqrt{t} + 55$. Analyze speed changes between 6 AM and 10 AM and calculate when traffic flow is minimized. What is that minimum speed?

2. Find the minimum value of $f(x) = 3\,x^4 + 4\,x^3$.

3. Assume that the average cost of producing compact discs is given by $c(x) = -.0002\,x + 3 + 2000/x$. Show that the average cost is always decreasing for x between 0 and 4000.

4. Suppose the population of a city is modeled by

$$p(t) = 4456\,t^3 + 8939\,t^2 + 23\,463\,t + 25\,528$$

where t is measured in years from 1990 to 2000.

a) Show that the population was always increasing in this decade.

b) Show that the population was increasing at its slowest rate in August of 1990. Hint: The population is increasing at its slowest rate when $p''(t) = 0$.

5. Given that the total cost for manufacturing x units of a particular product is described by the function $C(x) = 0.0025 x^2 + 80 x + 10\,000$, find the level of production that minimizes the total cost of manufacturing.

6. The total population of the planet is forecast by the function $P(t) = 0.00074 t^3 - 0.07 t^2 + 0.89 t + 6.04$ where t is measured in decades, $t = 0$ corresponds to the year 2000, and $P(t)$ is measured in billions of people. In what year will the population peak over the next 200 years?

7. A book designer has decided that the pages of a book are to have 1.5 inch margins top and bottom and 1 inch margins on each side. If each page is to have an area of 100 square inches, what are the dimensions of this page if its printed area is to be a maximum?

8. The owner of a farm wants to enclose a rectangular region with 3000 m of fencing while dividing the region into two parts, each of which is rectangular, by using part of the fencing to subdivide it and running a fence parallel to the sides (see figure that follows). What should be the dimensions of the region in order to maximize its area?

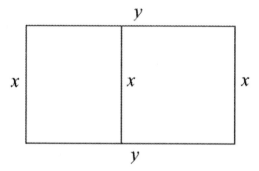

9. The owner of a cruise ship charges groups as follows: For a group of 40 people, the charge is $1,000 per person per day. If more than 40 people sign up, the fare is reduced by $8 for each addtional person.

a) Assuming at least 40 people sign up, determine the number necessary to maximize revenue.

b) What is the maximum revenue?

c) What would be the cost per person in this case?

■ 4.4 Newton's Method

Students should read Section 4.7 of Rogawski's *Calculus* [1] for a detailed discussion of the material presented in this section.

■ 4.4.1 Programming Newton's Method

Newton's Method is a technique for calculating zeros of a function based on the direction of its tangent lines. It is a recursive routine that is rather tedious to do by hand or even with a calculator, but simple with *Mathematica*. To start the procedure one should have an idea about the general location of each zero. This is because an initial approximation x_0 for that zero, say at $x = r$, is needed to start the recursion. For example, one can specify x_0 by examining the graph of the function to see where the zeros are approximately. Then the next approximation x_1 can be found by the recursive formula $x_1 = x_0 - f(x_0)/f'(x_0)$. This process can be iterated using the general formula

$$x_{n+1} = x_n - f(x_n)/f'(x_n)$$

Under suitable conditions, the sequence of approximations $\{x_0, x_1, x_2, \ldots\}$ (called the *Newton sequence*) will converge to r.

Example 4.7. Approximate the zeros of the function $f(x) = \ln(9 - x^2) - x$.

In[306]:= $\mathbf{f[x\_] := Log[9 - x^2] - x}$

In[307]:= $\mathbf{Plot[f[x], \{x, 0, 3\}]}$

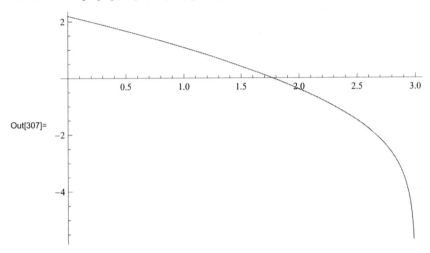

Out[307]=

Clearly, there is one zero between 1.5 and 2 based on the plot above. To approximate this zero, we define a function **newtn** to perform the recursion:

In[308]:= $\mathbf{newtn[x\_] := x - f[x] / f'[x]}$

To generate the corresponding Newton sequence, we compute 8 iterates of this function starting with an initial guess of $x = 1.6$. This iteration can be performed efficiently using the **NestList[f,x,n]** function, which is a recursive routine that outputs a list with **x** as its first value, followed by **f[x]**, **f[f[x]]**, **f[f[f[x]]]**, etc., up to **n** iterates as shown in the example below:

In[309]:= $\mathbf{approx = NestList[newtn, 1.6, 8]}$

Out[309]= $\{1.6, 1.77538, 1.76961, 1.7696, 1.7696, 1.7696, 1.7696, 1.7696, 1.7696\}$

From this we see that the root, accurate to 4 decimal places, is 1.7696. If greater accuracy is desired, say 12 decimal places, we can redisplay the values of **approx** if it is already accurate to 12 decimal places or else recalculate it using a higher number of iterations if necessary.

In[310]:= $\mathbf{NumberForm[approx // TableForm, 13]}$

Out[310]//NumberForm=
```
1.6
1.775382136758
1.769608467699
1.769601100211
1.769601100199
1.769601100199
1.769601100199
1.769601100199
1.769601100199
```

Discovery Exercise: The function $f(x) = \ln(9 - x^2) - x$ discussed above has a second zero. Locate it on the graph of $f(x)$ and use Newton's method to approximate it to 12 decimal places. Hint: First, plot the graph over a wide interval to locate the zero, and then zoom in to obtain an initial approximation.

Warning: Be sure that your initial approximation is sufficiently close to your zero; otherwise the Newton sequence may diverge or converge to another zero.

■ 4.4.2 Divergence

One interesting point about Newton's Method is that it does not always work. For instance, the function $y = x^{1/3}$ clearly has a root at $x = 0$:

In[311]:= **Plot$\left[\sqrt[3]{x}\ ,\ \{x,\ 0,\ 1\}\right]$**

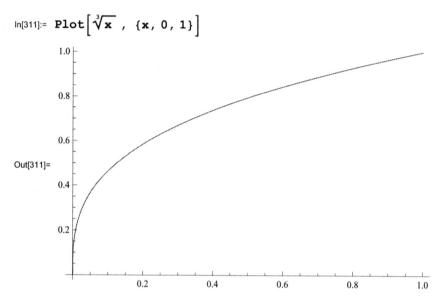

Out[311]=

Yet, Newton's Method fails for any guess $x \neq 0$:

In[312]:= **Clear[f]**

f[x_] := $\sqrt[3]{x}$

In[314]:= **NestList[newtn, 0.6, 6]**

Out[314]= $\{0.6,\ -1.2,\ 2.4 - 8.24861 \times 10^{-16}\ i,\ -4.8 + 1.64972 \times 10^{-15}\ i,$
$9.6 - 3.16674 \times 10^{-15}\ i,\ -19.2 + 6.33348 \times 10^{-15}\ i,\ 38.4 - 4.98733 \times 10^{-15}\ i\}$

NOTE: The extremely small imaginary values that appear in the answers earlier should be ignored (or treated as zero) since we expect our answers to be entirely real. This is due to *Mathematica*'s default algorithm for computing radicals in the domain of complex numbers, which may introduce extremely small numerical errors. To eliminate these imaginary parts, we use the **Re[expr]** command to extract the real part of **expr**.

In[315]:= **Re[NestList[newtn, 0.6, 6]]**

Out[315]= $\{0.6,\ -1.2,\ 2.4,\ -4.8,\ 9.6,\ -19.2,\ 38.4\}$

Question: Can you explain why Newton's Method fails in the above example?

■ 4.4.3 Slow Convergence

Even when Newton's Method works, sometimes the Newton sequence converges very slowly to the answer. Consider the following function:

In[316]:= `Clear[ f]`

`f[x_] := x³ - x - 1`

In[318]:= `Plot[f[x], {x, -3, 2}]`

Out[318]=

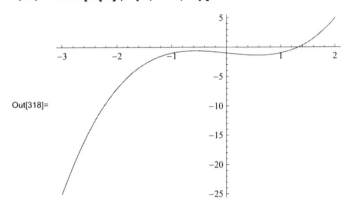

Clearly, there is a root between 1.2 and 1.4. If we use the **newtn** function with our guess as $x = 1$, we get quick convergence to the root:

In[319]:= `NestList[newtn, 1.0, 6]`

Out[319]= `{1., 1.5, 1.34783, 1.3252, 1.32472, 1.32472, 1.32472}`

But if we choose our initial guess near 0.6, the convergence is much slower as discussed in the following exercises.

■ Exercises

1. Compare the convergence in the above example (Section 4.4.3) for initial guesses of 0.5 and 0.6. Why does Newton's Method converge so slowly for these values? (Hint: Consider the tangent lines to the curve $f(x)$.)

2. Synthesizing the discussion in Sections 4.4.1 and 4.4.2 on the flaws in Newton's Method, can you come up with any general criteria that will tell us when Newton's Method will converge or diverge?

3. Use Newton's Method to find the postive zero of $f(x) = x^2 - 2$ accurate to 5 decimal places. Note: This demonstrates how Newton's Method can be used to approximate $\sqrt{2}$.

4. Consider the polynomial function $p(x) = x^4 - 8 x^2 + 15$.
a) Find all the roots of this function.
b) Graph this function over the interval $[-5, 5]$.
c) Explain why at $x = 2$ is not a good starting approximation for the root in the interval
d) Use Newton's Method to approximate the other three roots in the appropriate intervals.
e) Which other values of are not good seed (starting) values and why? (Hint : Consider points of horizontal tangency.)

5. Use Newton's Method to find a solution (accurate to 5 decimal places) to the following equations:

a) $\sin x = \cos (2 x)$ in the interval $[0, \pi/2]$ (Hint: Define $f(x) = \sin x - \cos(2 x)$.)   b) $e^x = 5 x$ c) $\cos x = x$

Chapter 5   Integration

▪ 5.1 Antiderivatives (Indefinite Integral)

Students should read Section 4.8 of Rogawski's *Calculus* [1] for a detailed discussion of the material presented in this section.

Integrate[*f*, *x*] gives the *indefinite integral* (or *antiderivative*) of *f* with respect to *x*. The command **Integrate** can evaluate all rational functions and a host of transcendental functions, including exponential, logarithmic, trigonometric, and inverse trigonometric functions. One can also use the palette button $\int \Box \, d \Box$ (BasicMathInput Palette) to evaluate integrals.

Example 5.1. Evaluate $\int (x^2 - 2x + 1)\, dx$.

Solution:

Method 1: (Palette buttons)

In[320]:= $\int \left(x^2 - 2\,x + 1\right) dx$

Out[320]= $x - x^2 + \dfrac{x^3}{3}$

NOTE: *Mathematica* does not explicitly include the constant of integration *C* in its answers for indefinite integrals; the user should always assume that this is implicitly part of the answer.

Method 2: (**Integrate** command)

In[321]:= **Integrate[(x^2 - 2 x + 1), x]**

Out[321]= $x - x^2 + \dfrac{x^3}{3}$

Example 5.2. Evaluate $\int x(x^2 + 1)^2\, dx$.

Solution:

Method 1: (Palette buttons)

In[322]:= $\int x \left(x^2 + 1\right)^2 dx$

Out[322]= $\dfrac{x^2}{2} + \dfrac{x^4}{2} + \dfrac{x^6}{6}$

NOTE: Observe that if the substitution $u = x^2 + 1$ is used to transform this integral, then the answer becomes $\int x(x^2 + 1)^2\, dx = \frac{1}{2} \int u^2\, du = \frac{1}{6}(1 + x^2)^3$. How does one reconcile this answer with the one obtained in the output above?

The following are examples of integrals that can be evaluated in a routine manner using the substitution method. The reader should perform the integration by hand to check answers.

Example 5.3. Evaluate $\int \dfrac{x}{\sqrt{x+1}}\, dx$.

Solution:

In[323]:= $\int \dfrac{x}{\sqrt{x+1}} \, dx$

Out[323]= $\dfrac{2}{3} \, (-2 + x) \, \sqrt{1 + x}$

Example 5.4. Evaluate $\int x^2 \sin(x^3) \, dx$.

Solution:

In[324]:= $\int x^2 \, \text{Sin}[x^3] \, dx$

Out[324]= $-\dfrac{1}{3} \, \text{Cos}[x^3]$

Note: *Mathematica* can certainly integrate much more complicated functions, including those that may require using any of the integration techniques discussed in your calculus textbook. We will consider some of these in Section 5.4.

- ■ **Exercises**

In Exercises 1 through 6, evaluate the integrals. Simplify your answers.

1. $\int (x^2 + 2) \, dx$ 　　　　2. $\int \cos 3\, x \, dx$ 　　　　3. $\int \sqrt{1 - x^2} \, dx$

4. $\int \sin^2 x \, dx$ 　　　　5. $\int \dfrac{3x^5 + 6x^4 - x + 1}{x^3} \, dx$ 　　　　6. $\int \dfrac{1}{1 + \sin 2x} \, dx$

In Exercises 7 and 8, evaluate the integrals by first using *Mathematica* to decompose the integrand as a sum of partial fractions (using the **Apart[expr]** command to perform this decomposition).

7. $\int \dfrac{x^2 + 2x - 1}{2x^3 + 3x^2 - 2x} \, dx$ 　　　　8. $\int \dfrac{1}{x(x+1)(2x+3)} \, dx$

- ■ **5.2 Riemann Sums and the Definite Integral**

Students should read Sections 5.1 and 5.2 of Rogawski's *Calculus* [1] for a detailed discussion of the material presented in this section.

There are two basic integration commands in *Mathematica* to evaluate definite integrals. **Integrate[f, {x, a, b}]** calculates the *definite integral* (area under the curve) of f on the interval $[a, b]$ using analytic methods. **NIntegrate[f, {x, a, b}]** calculates a numerical approximation of the definite integral of f on $[a, b]$ using numerical methods.

Review of Riemann Sums: A partition of a closed interval $[a, b]$ is a set $P = \{x_0, x_1, x_2, \ldots, x_n\}$ of points of $[a, b]$ such that

$$a = x_0 < x_1 < x_2 < \ldots .. < x_n = b.$$

Given a function f on a closed interval $[a, b]$ and a partition $P = \{x_0, x_1, \ldots, x_n\}$ of the interval $[a, b]$, recall that a *Riemann sum* of f over $[a, b]$ relative to P is a sum of the form

$$\sum_{i=1}^{n} f(x_i^*) \, \Delta x_i,$$

where $\Delta x_i = x_i - x_{i-1}$ and x_i^* is an arbitrary point in the ith subinterval $[x_{i-1}, x_i]$. For simplicity, we shall assume that $\Delta x_i = \Delta x = \frac{b-a}{n}$ for all i. A Riemann sum is therefore an approximation to the (signed) area of the region between the graph of f and the x-axis along the interval $[a, b]$. The exact area is given by the *definite integral of f over* $[a, b]$, which is defined to be the limit of its Riemann sums as $n \to \infty$ and is denoted by $\int_a^b f(x)\, dx$. In other words,

$$\int_a^b f(x)\, dx = \lim_{n \to \infty} \sum_{i=1}^n f(x_i^*)\, \Delta x.$$

This definite integral exists provided the limit exists. For a continuous function f, it can be shown that $\int_a^b f(x)\, dx$ exists.

■ 5.2.1 Riemann Sums Using Left Endpoints

A Riemann sum of f relative to a partition P can be obtained by considering rectangles whose heights are based on the left endpoint of each subinterval of P. This is achieved by setting $x_i^* = x_i = a + i(b - a)/n$ for $i = 0, 1, \ldots n - 1$, so that the corresponding height of each rectangle is given by $f(x_i)$. This leads to the following formula for a Riemann sum using left endpoints, which we denote by **LRSUM**. To use this function, we need to specify the values of a, b, and n as well as define f using *Mathematica*'s format.

In[325]:= **Clear[f]**
LRSUM[a_, b_, n_] := Sum[f[a + i * (b - a) / n] * (b - a) / n, {i, 0, n - 1}]

Example 5.4. Let $f(x) = x^2$ on $[0,1]$ and let $P = \{0, 1/n, 2/n, 3/n, \ldots, (n-1)/n, 1\}$ be a partition of $[0, 1]$.
a) Approximate $\int_0^1 f(x)\, dx$ by computing the Riemann sum relative to P using the left endpoint method.
b) Plot the graph of f and the rectangles corresponding to the Riemann sum in part (a).
c) Find the limit of the Riemann sum obtained in part a) by letting $n \to \infty$.

Solution: a) We define $f(x) = x^2$ in *Mathematica* and evaluate **LRSUM** using $a = 0$, $b = 1$, and various values for n. In the table below, the first column gives the value of n and the second column gives the corresponding Riemann sum.

In[327]:= **f[x_] := x^2**
TableForm[Table[{n, N[LRSUM[0, 1, n]]}, {n, 10, 100, 10}],
TableHeadings → {{}, {"n", "Riemann Sum"}}]

Out[328]//TableForm=

n	Riemann Sum
10	0.285
20	0.30875
30	0.316852
40	0.320938
50	0.3234
60	0.325046
70	0.326224
80	0.327109
90	0.327798
100	0.32835

Thus, $\int_0^1 x^2\, dx \approx 0.30875$ for $n = 20$ (rectangles). We leave it to the reader to use large values of n to investigate more accurate approximations using left endpoints.

b) The following program gives a plot of the rectangles corresponding to the Riemann sum in part (a) using left endpoints.

```
In[329]:= LEPT[f_, {a_, b_, n_}] := Module[
        {dx, k, xstar, lrect, plot},
        dx = N[(b - a) / n];
        xstar = Table[a + i * dx, {i, 0, n}];
        lrect = Table[Line[{{xstar[[i]], 0}, {xstar[[i]], f[xstar[[i]]] },
            {xstar[[i + 1]], f[xstar[[i]]] }, {xstar[[i + 1]], 0}}], {i, 1, n}];
        plot = Plot[f[x], {x, a, b}, Filling → Axis];
        Show[plot, Graphics[{Green, lrect}]]]
```

To demonstrate this for our example, we evaluate **LEPT** by specifying $f(x) = x^2$, $a = 0$, $b = 1$ and $n = 20$.

```
In[330]:= f[x_] := x^2
        LEPT[f, {0, 1, 20}]
```

Out[331]=

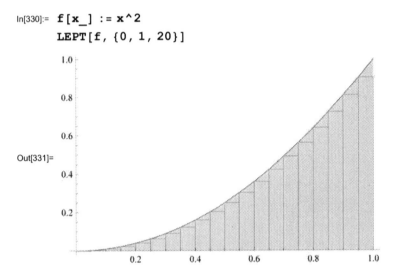

Here is a graphics animation of the plot above as n (number of rectangles) increases from 1 to 50.

Important Note: If you are reading the printed version of this publication, then you will not be able to view any of the animations generated from the **Animate** command in this chapter. If you are reading the electronic version of this publication formatted as a *Mathematica* Notebook, then evaluate each **Animate** command to view the corresponding animation. Just click on the arrow button to start the animation. To control the animation just click at various points on the sliding bar or else manually drag the bar.

In[332]:= **Animate[LEPT[f, {0, 1, a}] , {a, 1, 50, 5 }]**

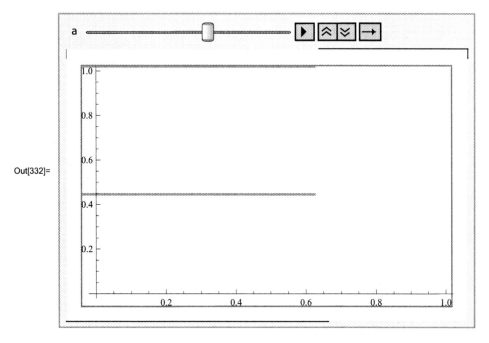

Out[332]=

NOTE: The underestimation given by **LRSUM** in this example can be explained from the above graph: The sum of the area of the rectangles is less than the area of the region under the graph of f since the rectangles are contained inside the same region. This is due to the fact that f is increasing on $[0, 1]$.

c) We evaluate **LRSUM** in the limit as $n \to \infty$.

In[333]:= **Limit[LRSUM[0, 1, n], n → Infinity]**

Out[333]= $\dfrac{1}{3}$

Thus, $\int_0^1 x^2 \, dx = 1/3 = 0.33....$

■ 5.2.2 Riemann Sums Using Right Endpoints

We can similarly define a Riemann sum of f relative to a partition P by considering rectangles whose heights are based on the right endpoint of each subinterval of P. This is achieved by setting $x_i^* = x_i = a + i(b-a)/n$ for $i = 1, 2, \ldots n,$ so that the corresponding height of each rectangle is given by $f(x_i)$. Note that i ranges from 1 to n in this case (as opposed to 0 to $n - 1$ for the left endpoint method). This leads to the following formula for the Riemann sum using right endpoints, which we denote by **RRSUM:**

In[334]:= **Clear[f]**
RRSUM[a_, b_, n_] := Sum[f[a + i * (b - a) / n] * (b - a) / n, {i, 1, n}]

Example 5.5. Let $f(x) = x^2$ on $[0,1]$ and let $P = \{0, \ 1/n, \ 2/n, \ 3/n, \ \ldots, \ (n-1)/n, \ 1\}$ be a partition of $[0, 1]$.

a) Approximate $\int_0^1 f(x) \, dx$ by computing the Riemann sum relative to P using the right endpoint method.

b) Plot the graph of f and the rectangles corresponding to the Riemann sum in part (a).

c) Find the limit of the Riemann sum obtained in part a) by letting $n \to \infty$.

Solution: a) We evaluate

In[336]:= **f[x_] := x^2**

TableForm$\Big[$Table[{n, N[RRSUM[0, 1, n]]}, {n, 10, 100, 10}],

TableHeadings → $\Big\{$ {}, {"n", "Riemann Sum"}$\Big\}\Big]$

Out[337]//TableForm=

n	Riemann Sum
10	0.385
20	0.35875
30	0.350185
40	0.345938
50	0.3434
60	0.341713
70	0.34051
80	0.339609
90	0.338909
100	0.33835

b) Similarly, we can write a program that gives a plot of the rectangles corresponding to the Riemann sum in part (a) using right endpoints.

In[338]:= **REPT[f_, {a_, b_, n_}] := Module[**
    {dx, i, xstar, rrect, plot},
    dx = N[(b - a) / n];
    xstar = Table[a + i * dx, {i, 0, n}];
    rrect = Table[Line[{{xstar[[i]], 0}, {xstar[[i]], f[xstar[[i + 1]]]},
        {xstar[[i + 1]], f[xstar[[i + 1]]]}, {xstar[[i + 1]], 0}}], {i, 1, n}];
    plot = Plot[f[x], {x, a, b}, Filling → Axis];
    Show[plot, Graphics[{Blue, rrect}]]]

For our example, we have:

In[339]:= **f[x_] := x^2**
    REPT[f, {0, 1, 20}]

Out[340]=

Important Note: If you are reading the printed version of this publication, then you will not be able to view any of the animations generated from the **Animate** command in this chapter. If you are reading the electronic version of this publication formatted as a *Mathematica* Notebook, then evaluate each **Animate** command to view the corresponding animation. Just click on the arrow button to start the animation. To control the animation just click at various points on the sliding bar or else manually drag the bar.

In[341]:= `Animate[REPT[f, {0, 1, a}] , {a, 1, 50, 5 }]`

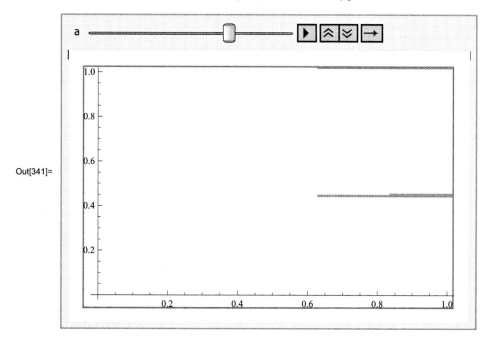

Out[341]=

NOTE: The overestimation of the **RRSUM** can be explained analogously as with the underestimation obtained from **LRSUM**.

c) We evaluate **RRSUM** in the limit as $n \to \infty$:

In[342]:= `Limit[RRSUM[0, 1, n], n → Infinity]`

Out[342]= $\dfrac{1}{3}$

NOTE: Here is a comparison between the two plots of the left-endpoint and right-endpoint rectangles:

In[343]:=
```
LREPT[f_ , {a_ , b_ , n_}] := Module[
    {dx, i, xstar, lrect, rrect, plot},
    dx = N[(b - a) / n];
    xstar = Table[a + i * dx, {i, 0, n}];
    lrect = Table[Line[{{xstar[[i]], 0}, {xstar[[i]], f[xstar[[i]]] },
        {xstar[[i + 1]], f[xstar[[i]]] }, {xstar[[i + 1]], 0}}], {i, 1, n}];
    rrect = Table[Line[{{xstar[[i]], 0}, {xstar[[i]], f[xstar[[i + 1]]]},
        {xstar[[i + 1]], f[xstar[[i + 1]]]}, {xstar[[i + 1]], 0}}], {i, 1, n}];
    plot = Plot[f[x], {x, a, b}, Filling → Axis];
    Show[plot, Graphics[{Blue, rrect}], Graphics[{Green, lrect}] ]
]
```

In[344]:= **f[x_] := x²**
      LREPT[f, {0, 1, 20}]

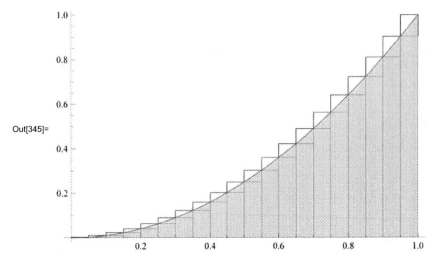

Out[345]=

In[346]:= **f[x_] := x²**
      Animate[LREPT[f, {0, 1, a}], {a, 1, 100, 5}]

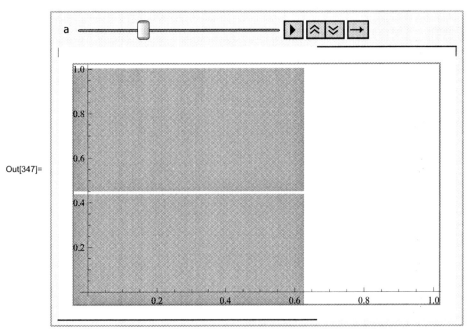

Out[347]=

■ 5.2.3 Riemann Sums Using Midpoints

The Riemann sum using the midpoints of each subinterval is given by the following formula. (We leave it to the student to verify that the midpoint of ith subinterval is given by $a + \left(i + \frac{1}{2}\right)\left(\frac{b-a}{n}\right)$ for $i = 1, \ldots, n$.)

In[348]:= **Clear[f]**
      MRSUM[a_, b_, n_] := Sum[f[a + (i + 1 / 2) * (b - a) / n] * (b - a) / n, {i, 1, n}]

Example 5.6. Let $f(x) = x^2$ on [0,1] and let $P = \{0, \ 1/n, \ 2/n, \ 3/n, \ \ldots, \ (n-1)/n, \ 1\}$ be a partition of [0, 1].

a) Approximate $\int_0^1 f(x)\, dx$ by computing the Riemann sum relative to P using the midpoint method.

b) Plot the graph of f and the rectangles corresponding to the Riemann sum in part (a).

c) Find the limit of the Riemann sum obtainded in part a) by letting $n \to \infty$.

Solution: a) We evaluate

In[350]:= **f[x_] := x^2**

    TableForm[Table[{n, N[MRSUM[0, 1, n]]}, {n, 10, 100, 10}],

      TableHeadings → {{}, {"n", "Riemann Sum"}}]

Out[351]//TableForm=

n	Riemann Sum
10	0.4425
20	0.385625
30	0.367685
40	0.358906
50	0.3537
60	0.350255
70	0.347806
80	0.345977
90	0.344558
100	0.343425

In[352]:= **Options[TableForm]**

Out[352]= {TableAlignments → Automatic, TableDepth → ∞,

    TableDirections → Column, TableHeadings → None, TableSpacing → Automatic}

b) Again, we can write a program that gives a plot of the rectangles corresponding to the Riemann sum in part (a) using midpoints.

In[353]:= **MIDPT[f_, {a_, b_, n_}] := Module[**

    {dx, i, xstar, mrect, plot},

    dx = N[(b - a) / n];

    xstar = Table[a + i * dx, {i, 0, n}];

    mrect =

     Table[Line[{{xstar[[i]], 0}, {xstar[[i]], f[(xstar[[i]] + xstar[[i + 1]]) / 2]},

       {xstar[[i + 1]], f[(xstar[[i]] + xstar[[i + 1]]) / 2]},

       {xstar[[i + 1]], 0}}], {i, 1, n}];

    plot = Plot[f[x], {x, a, b}, Filling → Axis];

    Show[plot, Graphics[{Red, mrect}]]

    ]

In[354]:= $\mathbf{f[x\_] := x^2}$
$\mathbf{MIDPT[f, \{0, 1, 10\}]}$

Out[355]=

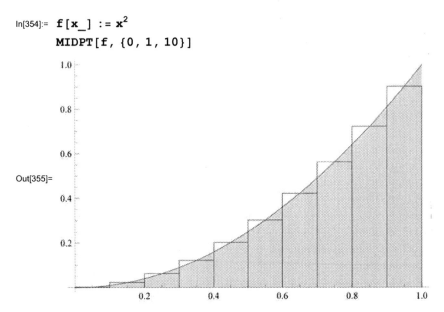

Important Note: If you are reading the printed version of this publication, then you will not be able to view any of the animations generated from the **Animate** command in this chapter. If you are reading the electronic version of this publication formatted as a *Mathematica* Notebook, then evaluate each **Animate** command to view the corresponding animation. Just click on the arrow button to start the animation. To control the animation just click at various points on the sliding bar or else manually drag the bar.

In[356]:= $\mathbf{f[x\_] := x^2}$
$\mathbf{Animate[MIDPT[f, \{0, 1, a\}], \{a, 1, 100, 5\}]}$

Out[357]=

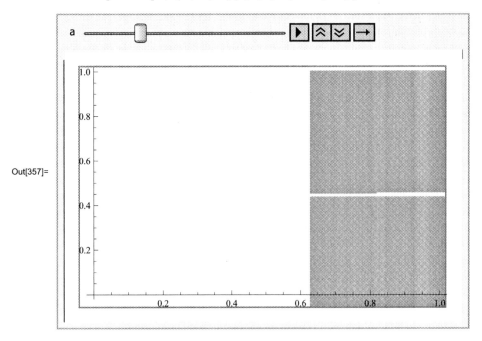

c) The limit of the Riemann sum using the midpoints is given by

In[358]:= `Limit[MRSUM[0, 1, n], n → Infinity]`

Out[358]= $\dfrac{1}{3}$

NOTE: Here is a visual comparison of all three Riemann sums in terms of rectangles:

```
In[359]:= ALL[f_, {a_, b_, n_}] := Module[
        {dx, i, xstar, lrect, rrect, mrect, plot},
        dx = N[(b - a) / n];
        xstar = Table[a + i * dx, {i, 0, n}];
        lrect = Table[Line[{{xstar[[i]], 0}, {xstar[[i]], f[xstar[[i]]] },
            {xstar[[i + 1]], f[xstar[[i]]] }, {xstar[[i + 1]], 0}}], {i, 1, n}];
        rrect = Table[Line[{{xstar[[i]], 0}, {xstar[[i]], f[xstar[[i + 1]]]},
            {xstar[[i + 1]], f[xstar[[i + 1]]]}, {xstar[[i + 1]], 0}}], {i, 1, n}];
        mrect = Table[Line[{{xstar[[i]], 0}, {xstar[[i]],
              f[(xstar[[i]] + xstar[[i + 1]]) / 2]}, {xstar[[i + 1]]},
              f[(xstar[[i]] + xstar[[i + 1]]) / 2]}, {xstar[[i + 1]], 0}}], {i, 1, n}];
        plot = Plot[f[x], {x, a, b}, Filling → Axis];
        Show[plot, Graphics[{Blue, rrect}],
          Graphics[{Green, lrect}], Graphics[ {Red, mrect}]]
      ]
```

In[360]:=

```
f[x_] := x^2
ALL[f, {0, 1, 10}]
```

Out[361]=

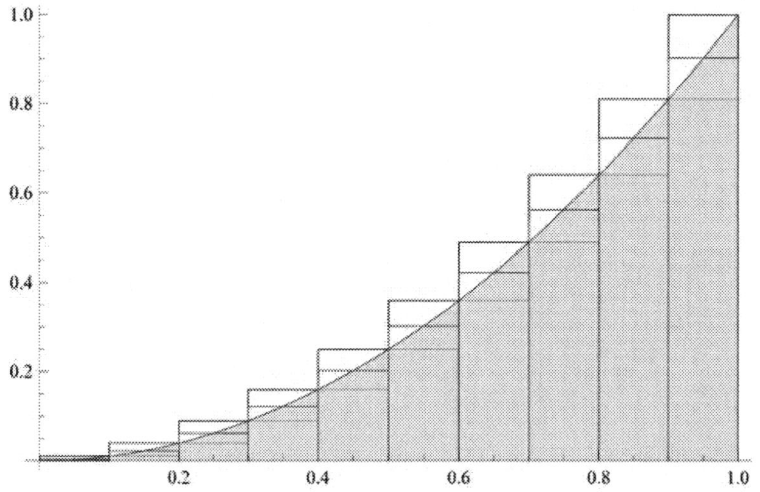

Here is how all three Riemann sums behave when we increase the number of rectangles.

In[362]:= **f[x_] := x^2**
Animate[ALL[f, {0, 1, a}], {a, 1, 100, 5}]

Out[363]=

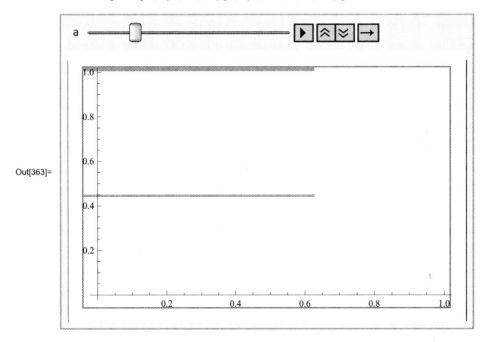

NOTE: All three limits from the left-endpoint, right-endpoint, and midpoint methods are equal. This is not surprising since each is equal to $\int_0^1 x^2 \, dx$ (remember that the existence of a definite integral requires that all Riemann sums converge to the same limit). However, the midpoint method tends to converge faster to the limit than the other two methods (discussed in your calculus text).

Example 5.7. Let $f(x) = x^3 + x^2 + 1$ on $[0, 1]$ and let $P = \{0, \ 1/n, \ 2/n, \ ...., \ n/n = 1\}$ be a partition of $[0, 1]$.
a) Find the Riemann sum of f relative to P using the left endpoints of the partition.
b) Find the Riemann sum of f relative to P using the right endpoints of the partition.
c) Show that the difference between the two sums goes to 0 at $n \to \infty$.
d) Find the limit of the Riemann sums in parts (a) and (b). Is this consistent with part (c)?
e) What do you conclude from part (d)?

Solution: a) The Riemann sum using left endpoints is given by

In[364]:= **Clear[f]**
LRSUM[a_, b_, n_] := Sum[f[a + i * (b - a) / n] * N[(b - a) / n], {i, 0, n - 1}]

In[366]:= **f[x_] := x^3 + x^2 + 1**
LRSUM[0, 1, n]

Out[367]= $\dfrac{5 - 12\,n + 19\,n^2}{12\,n^2}$

b) The Riemann sum using right endpoints is given by

In[368]:= **Clear[f]**
RRSUM[a_, b_, n_] := Sum[f[a + i * (b - a) / n] * N[(b - a) / n], {i, 1, n}]

In[370]:= $f[x_] := x^3 + x^2 + 1$
$\quad\quad$ RRSUM[0, 1, n]

Out[371]= $\dfrac{5 + 12\,n + 19\,n^2}{12\,n^2}$

c) We now evaluate and simplify the difference between the two Riemann sums:

In[372]:= $\textbf{Simplify[RRSUM[0, 1, n] - LRSUM[0, 1, n]]}$

Out[372]= $\dfrac{2}{n}$

As $n \to \infty$, observe that this difference goes to zero.

d) Next, we use the limit command to evaluate the limit of the two Riemann sums:

In[373]:= $\textbf{Limit[LRSUM[0, 1, n], n} \to \textbf{Infinity]}$

Out[373]= $\dfrac{19}{12}$

In[374]:= $\textbf{Limit[RRSUM[0, 1, n], n} \to \textbf{Infinity]}$

Out[374]= $\dfrac{19}{12}$

In light of (c), we should not be surprised that the two limits are the same. After all, their difference was seen to converge to zero!

e) By definition of a definite integral, we conclude from (d) that $\int_0^1 (x^3 + x^2 + 1)\,dx = 19/12$. We confirm this by evaluating

In[375]:= $\displaystyle\int_0^1 \left(x^3 + x^2 + 1\right) dx$

Out[375]= $\dfrac{19}{12}$

■ Exercises

1. Let $f(x) = \dfrac{x}{x^2+1}$ for $0 \le x \le 1$ and let $P = \{0/n,\ 1/n,\ 2/n,\ \ldots,\ n/n = 1\}$ be a partition of $[0, 1]$.

a) Find the Riemann sum of f using the left endpoints of P and plot the rectangles that approximate the integral of f over $[0, 1]$. Also, use the **Animate** command to see if the total area of the rectangles converges to the area of the region under the graph of f and above the x-axis.

b) Repeat (a) using right endpoints of P.

c) Repeat (a) using midpoints of P.

2. Let $f(x) = x \sin x$ on $[0, \pi]$. Use a uniform partition P and repeat Exercise 1 (immediately above) for this function.

■ 5.3 The Fundamental Theorem of Calculus

Students should read Sections 5.3 and 5.4 of Rogawski's *Calculus* [1] for a detailed discussion of the material presented in this section.

The crowning achievement in calculus is the **Fundamental Theorem of Calculus (FTC),** which reveals that integration and antidifferentiation are equivalent. This can be expressed in two parts:

FTC - Part I: Given a continuous function $f(x)$ on $[a, b]$, we have

$$\int_a^b f(x)\, dx = F(b) - F(a).$$

Here, $F(x)$ is *any* antiderivative of $f(x)$.

FTC - Part II: If $F(x) = \int_a^x f(t)\, dt$, then $F'(x) = f(x)$.

NOTE: Physically the Fundamental Theorem of Calculus tells us that the area under a velocity curve of an object is the same as the change in position of the object.

Mathematica naturally uses FTC to evaluate definite integrals whenever it is able to find an antiderivative. Of course, there are examples where it is not able to do this, as the latter examples following demonstrate.

Example 5.8. Evaluate $\int_1^5 \dfrac{x}{\sqrt{2\,x-1}}\, dx$.

Solution:

In[376]:= $\displaystyle\int_1^5 \frac{x}{\sqrt{2\,x-1}}\, dx$

Out[376]= $\dfrac{16}{3}$

Example 5.9. Evaluate $\int_{\sqrt{3}}^2 \dfrac{\sqrt{x^2-3}}{x}\, dx$.

Solution:

In[377]:= **Integrate[Sqrt[x^2 - 3] / x, {x, Sqrt[3], 2}]**

Out[377]= $1 - \dfrac{\pi}{2\sqrt{3}}$

In[378]:= **N[%]**

Out[378]= 0.0931003

Example 5.10. Approximate $\int_0^1 \tan x^2\, dx$.

Solution: Here is an example of an integral that *Mathematica* cannot evaluate exactly but returns the integral unevaluated because the precise answer is not expressible in terms of elementary functions.

In[379]:= **Integrate[Tan[x^2], {x, 0, 1}]**

Out[379]= $\displaystyle\int_0^1 \mathrm{Tan}\left[x^2\right]\, dx$

However, a numerical approximation is still possible through the command **N.**

In[380]:= **N[%]**

Out[380]= 0.398414

Or we could use the command **NIntegrate** to perform both steps at once:

In[381]:= **NIntegrate[Tan[x^2], {x, 0, 1}]**

Out[381]= 0.398414

Example 5.11. Use the fact that if $m \le f(x) \le M$ for all $x \in [a, b]$, then $m(b - a) \le \int_a^b f(x)\,dx \le M(b - a)$ to approximate $\int_0^2 \sqrt{x^3 + 1}\ dx$.

Solution: We note that the function $f(x) = \sqrt{x^3 + 1}$ is increasing on $[0, 2]$. This can be checked by finding $f'(x)$ and observing that $f'(x) > 0$ for all x (or by simply drawing the graph of f). Thus, $1 = f(0) \le f(x) \le f(2) = 3$ and so

$$1\,(2 - 0) \le \int_0^2 \sqrt{1 + x^3}\ dx \le 3\,(2 - 0)$$

or

$$2 \le \int_0^2 \sqrt{1 + x^3}\ dx \le 6$$

We can confirm this by evaluating

In[382]:= **Integrate$\left[\sqrt{x^3 + 1}\,, \{x, 0, 2\}\right]$**

Out[382]= $2\ \text{Hypergeometric2F1}\left[-\dfrac{1}{2}, \dfrac{1}{3}, \dfrac{4}{3}, -8\right]$

Since the function **Hypergeometric2F1** is not known to us, we use

In[383]:= **NIntegrate$\left[\sqrt{x^3 + 1}\,, \{x, 0, 2\}\right]$**

Out[383]= 3.24131

Example 5.12. Let $f(x) = \cos(x^2)$ on $[0, 2]$ and define $g(x) = \int_0^x f(t)\,dt = \int_0^x \cos(t^2)\,dt$.
a) Plot the graph of f.
b) Find the value(s) of x for which $g(x)$ starts to decrease.
c) Estimate $g(x)$ for $x = 0.2,\ 0.4,\ 0.6,\ 0.8,\ 1.0,\ 1.2,\ 1, 4,\ 1.6,\ 1.8,\ 2$.
d) Draw the graphs of $g(x)$ and $g'(x)$.
e) How do the graphs of $f(x)$ and $g'(x)$ compare?

Solution: a) We plot the graph of f.

In[384]:= **Clear[f]**

$$f[x\_] = Cos[x^2]$$

$$g[x\_] = \int_0^x f[t] \, dt$$

Out[385]= $Cos[x^2]$

Out[386]= $\sqrt{\dfrac{\pi}{2}} \; FresnelC\left[\sqrt{\dfrac{2}{\pi}} \; x\right]$

NOTE: The function **FresnelC** is called the Fresnel Cosine function and plays an important role in physics and engineering. The Fresnel Sine function is defined in the obvious manner.

In[387]:= **Plot[f[x], {x, 0, 2}]**

Out[387]=

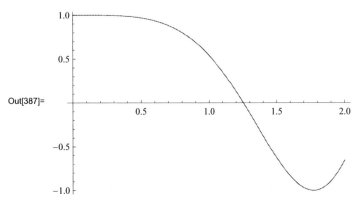

b) We note that the graph of f is above the x-axis (positive area) for x between 0 and $\sqrt{\pi/2}$ and below the x-axis for x between $\sqrt{\pi/2}$ and 2. Thus, the graph of g starts to decrease after $\sqrt{\pi/2}$. The following table of the Riemann sums of f on $[0, x]$ (for x varying from 0 to 2) shows this point.

In[388]:= **f[x_] := x²**

TableForm[Table[{n, N[MRSUM[0, 1, n]]}, {n, 10, 100, 10}]]

Out[389]//TableForm=

10	0.4425
20	0.385625
30	0.367685
40	0.358906
50	0.3537
60	0.350255
70	0.347806
80	0.345977
90	0.344558
100	0.343425

In[390]:= **LRSUM[a_, b_, n_] := Sum[f[a + i * (b - a) / n] * N[(b - a) / n], {i, 0, n - 1}]**

In[391]:= `TableForm[Table[{x, LRSUM[ 0, x, 100]}, {x, 0, 2, 0.1}],`
    `TableHeadings → {{}, {"x", "Riemann Sum"}}]`

Out[391]//TableForm=

x	Riemann Sum
0.	0.
0.1	0.00032835
0.2	0.0026268
0.3	0.00886545
0.4	0.0210144
0.5	0.0410438
0.6	0.0709236
0.7	0.112624
0.8	0.168115
0.9	0.239367
1.	0.32835
1.1	0.437034
1.2	0.567389
1.3	0.721385
1.4	0.900992
1.5	1.10818
1.6	1.34492
1.7	1.61318
1.8	1.91494
1.9	2.25215
2.	2.6268

NOTE: Since g is the integral, it should start to decrease at $x = \sqrt{\pi/2} \approx 1.25$. We can confirm this by examining the values of g in the neighborhood of this point:

In[392]:= `Table[{x, LRSUM[ 0, x, 100]}, {x, 1.2, 1.3, 0.01}] // TableForm`

Out[392]//TableForm=

1.2	0.567389
1.21	0.581692
1.22	0.596234
1.23	0.611016
1.24	0.62604
1.25	0.641309
1.26	0.656823
1.27	0.672587
1.28	0.6886
1.29	0.704865
1.3	0.721385

From the table above, we see that the function g does indeed start to decrease at approximately $x = 1.25$:

c) Here is the table of values for $g(x)$:

In[393]:= **TableForm[Table[{x, g[x]}, {x, 0.2, 2, 0.2}]]**

Out[393]//TableForm=

0.2	0.199968
0.4	0.398977
0.6	0.592271
0.8	0.767848
1.	0.904524
1.2	0.973945
1.4	0.949779
1.6	0.825517
1.8	0.635365
2.	0.461461

d) The graphs of the function $f(x)$ and $g'(x)$ are given below:

In[394]:= **Plot[{g[x], g'[x]}, {x, 0, 2}, PlotStyle → {Red, Blue}]**

Out[394]=

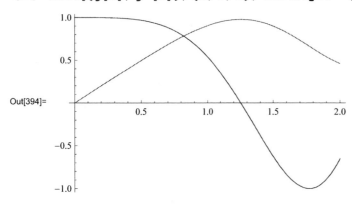

e) The graphs of the function $f(x)$ and $g'(x)$ are given below:

In[395]:= **Plot[{f[x], g'[x]}, {x, 0, 2}, PlotStyle → {Red, Blue}]**

Out[395]=

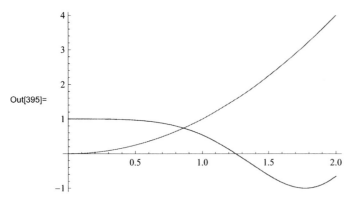

This means that the two graphs are the same. In fact, from the Fundamental Theorem of Calculus, we know that $g'(x) = f(x)$.

■ Exercises

In Exercies 1 troough 11, evalaute the given integrals.

1. $\int_0^1 (x^2 + 2)\, dx$ 2. $\int_0^\pi \cos 3x\, dx$ 3. $\int_0^1 \sqrt{1 - x^2}\ dx$ 4. $\int_{-\pi}^\pi \sin^2 x\, dx$

5. $\int_0^3 (x^3 - 4x^2 + x) \, dx$ 6. $\int_1^4 \left(\frac{1}{\sqrt{x}} + 2\sqrt{x}\right) dx$ 7. $\int_0^{\frac{\pi}{4}} \sec x \, dx$ 8. $\int_0^{\frac{\sqrt{2}}{4}} \frac{2}{\sqrt{1-4x^2}} \, dx$

9. $\int_0^3 \frac{1}{x+1} \, dx$ 10. $\int_1^4 \left(\frac{1}{x} + 2x^2\right) dx$ 11. $\int_0^{\pi} e^x \sin x \, dx$

12. Let $S(x) = \int_0^x \sin\left(\frac{1}{2}\pi t^2\right) dt$ ($S(x)$ is called the Fresnel sine)

a) Plot the graph of S and approximate the value of S as $x \to \infty$. Confirm your approximation by evaluating the limit as $x \to \infty$.

b) Find $S'(x)$ and use it to find the interval(s) on whcih $S(x)$ increase and decrease. Hint: Apply the Fundamental Theorem of Calculus.

c) On what intervals is S concave up? Concave down?

d) Find the value of x for which $S(x) = 0.7$.

13. Find an explicit formula for a continuous function f such that

$$\int_0^x f(t) \, dt = x e^x + \int_0^x \frac{f(t)}{2t^2+1} \, dt.$$

(Hint: First take the derivative of both sides and then solve for $f(x)$.)

■ 5.4 Integrals Involving Trigonometric, Exponential, and Logarithmic Functions

In your calculus text, you will learn how to evaluate integrals using different techniques. In *Mathematica,* we do not need to specify the technique. It chooses the technique appropriate for the problem. However, there are some integrals that cannot be evaluated in terms of elementary functions. In such cases, *Mathematica* will return the integal unevaluated or gives us a name for the integral.

Below, we will consider some examples of integrals that involve trigonometric functions, exponential, and logarithmic functions. If done by hand, some of these integrals require integration by parts, partial fraction decompositions, or trigonometric substitutions.

Example 5.13. Evaluate $\int \frac{x^2}{(x^3+1)^2} \, dx$.

Solution: If done by hand, this integral involves using the substitution method.

In[396]:= **Integrate[x^2 / (x^3 + 1)^2, x]**

Out[396]= $-\dfrac{1}{3\left(1+x^3\right)}$

Example 5.14. Evaluate $\int \frac{x^5+x^2+x+2}{x^2-1} \, dx$.

Solution: This integral involves long division and partial fraction decomposition.

In[397]:= $\int \dfrac{x^5 + x^2 + x + 2}{x^2 - 1} \, dx$

Out[397]= $x + \dfrac{x^2}{2} + \dfrac{x^4}{4} + \dfrac{5}{2} \, \text{Log}[1 - x] - \dfrac{1}{2} \, \text{Log}[1 + x]$

Example 5.15. Evaluate $\int \dfrac{x^4 + x^3 + x + 1}{(x^2 + 1)^2} \, dx$.

Solution: This integral involves long division, partial fraction decomposition, and inverse trigonometric functions.

In[398]:= $\int \dfrac{x^4 + x^3 + x + 1}{\left(x^2 + 1\right)^2} \, dx$

Out[398]= $x + \dfrac{x}{1 + x^2} - \text{ArcTan}[x] + \dfrac{1}{2} \, \text{Log}\left[1 + x^2\right]$

NOTE: All functions that appear as output are written in *Mathematica*'s notation. To convert the output to a more familiar form the command **TraditionalForm** can be used. Here is the "traditional" form of the output below (note that $\log x$ means the same as $\ln x$ in this case).

In[399]:= $\int \dfrac{x^4 + x^3 + x + 1}{\left(x^2 + 1\right)^2} \, dx$ **// TraditionalForm**

Out[399]//TraditionalForm=

$$\dfrac{x}{x^2 + 1} + \dfrac{1}{2} \log\left(x^2 + 1\right) + x - \tan^{-1}(x)$$

Example 5.16. Evaluate $\int x^2 \sin x \, dx$.

Solution: This integral involves integration by parts (twice).

In[400]:= $\int x^2 \, \text{Sin}[x] \, dx$

Out[400]= $-\left(-2 + x^2\right) \text{Cos}[x] + 2 \, x \, \text{Sin}[x]$

Example 5.17. Evaluate $\int \dfrac{-1}{\sqrt{1-x^2}} \, dx$.

Solution: This integral involves trigonometric substitution.

In[401]:= **Integrate[-1 / Sqrt[1 - x^2], x]**

Out[401]= $-\text{ArcSin}[x]$

NOTE: Your calculus textbook may give $\arccos x$ for the answer, as opposed to $-\arcsin x$ as above. Can you explain how the integration constant resolves the difference in these two answers?

Here are some examples of integrals that are important in applications but do not have an elementary antiderivative.

In[402]:= $\int \text{Sin}\left[\text{x}^2\right] \, d\text{x}$

Out[402]= $\sqrt{\dfrac{\pi}{2}} \ \text{FresnelS}\left[\sqrt{\dfrac{2}{\pi}} \ \text{x}\right]$

In[403]:= $\int \text{E}^{-\text{x}^2} \, d\text{x}$

Out[403]= $\dfrac{1}{2} \ \sqrt{\pi} \ \text{Erf}[\text{x}]$

In[404]:= **Integrate[Sin[x] / x, x]**

Out[404]= SinIntegral[x]

We can use **NIntegrate** to evaluate these integrals over any finite interval. For example:

In[405]:= **NIntegrate$\left[\text{E}^{-\text{x}^2}, \{\text{x}, 0, 10\}\right]$**

Out[405]= 0.886227

In[406]:= **NIntegrate[Log[x] / x, {x, 2, 100}]**

Out[406]= 10.3636

Example 5.18. Let $f_n(x) = \int_1^x t^n \, dt$. Investigate the limit graphically by plotting $f_n(x)$ for $n = 0, \, -0.3, \, -0.6,$ and -0.9 together with $g(x) = \ln x$ on a single plot.

In[407]:= **Clear[f, g]**
g[x_] := Log[x]
f[x_, n_] := $\int_1^{\text{x}} \text{t}^{\text{n}} \, d\text{t}$

In[410]:= **Plot[{f[x, n] /. n → {0, -0.3, -.6, -.9}, g[x]}, {x, 0, 10}, PlotStyle → {Red, Blue}]**

Out[410]=

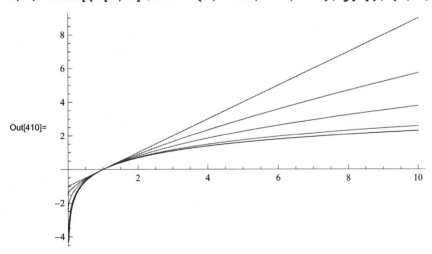

Exercises

In Exercises 1 though 5, evaluate the given integral.

1. $\int x \sqrt{2-x} \, dx$

2. $\int x^3 \sqrt{1+x^2} \, dx$

3. $\int \tan^2 x \sec^4 x \, dx$

4. $\int \frac{x^2-2x-1}{x^3+x} \, dx$

5. $\int \frac{x-1}{\sqrt{x^2+x-1}} \, dx$

In Exercises 6 through 11, use various values of *a*, *b*, and *n* to evaluate the given integral. Then make a conjecture for a general formula and prove your conjecture.

6. $\int \frac{1}{(x+a)(x+b)} \, dx$

7. $\int \cos(ax) \sin(bx) \, dx$

8. $\int x^n \ln x \, dx$

9. $\int x^n e^x \, dx$

10. $\int x^n \sin(x) \, dx$

11. $\int e^{ax} \cos(bx) \, dx$

Chapter 6   Applications of the Integral

Evaluating integrals can be tedious and difficult. *Mathematica* makes this work relatively easy. For example, when computing the area of a region the corresponding integral can be difficult to set up because the limits of integration are not known. *Mathematica*, with its powerful plotting capability, can turn this job into a very doable one. We will examine several applications that demonstrate this.

■ 6.1 Area Between Curves

Students should read Section 6.1 of Rogawski's *Calculus* [1] for a detailed discussion of the material presented in this section.

Let us consider the problem of finding the area between two curves.

Example 6.1. Determine the area of the region bounded between the curves $f(x) = \sin x$ and $g(x) = \csc^2 x$ on $[\pi/4, 3\pi/4]$.

Solution: To find the area here, we first plot the graphs of f and g.

In[411]:= **Clear[f, g]**

In[412]:= **f[x_] := Sin[x]**
        g[x_] := Csc[x]^2

In[414]:= **Plot[{f[x], g[x]}, {x, π / 4, 3 π / 4},**
        PlotStyle → {Red, Blue}, PlotRange → {-.5, 2.5},
        Filling → {1 → { 2}}]

Out[414]=

Looking at the plot above and recalling that $\csc x$ is always greater than or equal to 1 on this interval, it follows that $\csc^2 x$ is always greater than or equal to $\sin x$, which is less than or equal to 1 on the same interval. Hence, calculating the area between these two curves between $x = \pi/4$ and $x = 3\pi/4$ is straightforward:

In[415]:= $\int_{\pi/4}^{3\pi/4} (g[x] - f[x]) \, dx$

Out[415]= $2 - \sqrt{2}$

In[416]:= **N[%]**

Out[416]= 0.585786

Example 6.2. Determine the area of the region enclosed between the curves $f(x) = x(x^2 - 3x + 3)$ and $g(x) = x^2$.

Solution: To find the area between these two curves, we will need to see if they intersect and if so where by plotting their graphs.

In[417]:= **Clear[f, g, x]**

In[418]:= **f[x_] := x $\left(x^2 - 3x + 3\right)$**

In[419]:= **g[x_] := x^2**

In[420]:= **Plot[{f[x], g[x]}, {x, -2, 4},**
 PlotStyle → {Red, Blue}, PlotRange → {-2, 11},
 Filling → {1 → {2}}]

Out[420]=

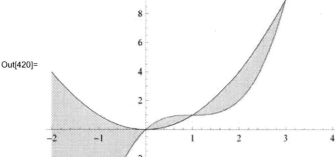

Notice that $f(x)$ is graphed in red, while $g(x)$ is graphed in blue. Also, the "Filling" option in the **Plot** command fills in the region between the two graphs (functions 1 and 2 in the Filling command) in gray. The bounded region between the two curves seems to lie between $x = 0$ and $x = 3$. To ascertain this, we solve for the intersection points:

In[421]:= **Solve[f[x] == g[x], x]**

Out[421]= **{{x → 0}, {x → 1}, {x → 3}}**

Hence, the intersection points are at $x = 0$, 1, and 3. Noting that $f(x)$ is greater than $g(x)$ on [0, 1] and $g(x)$ is greater than $f(x)$ on [1, 3], we need two integrals to calculate the (physical) area between the two curves since areas are always calculated by subtracting the smaller function from the larger one. In particular, on [0, 1] the area is given by $\int_0^1 [f(x) - g(x)]\, dx$ and on [1, 3] the area is given by $\int_1^3 [g(x) - f(x)]\, dx$.

In[422]:= $\int_0^1 (f[x] - g[x])\, dx + \int_1^3 (g[x] - f[x])\, dx$

Out[422]= $\dfrac{37}{12}$

In[423]:= **N[%]**

Out[423]= **3.08333**

Example 6.3. Determine the area of the region bounded between the curves $f(x) = |x|$ and $g(x) = \cos x$ on $[-\pi/2, \pi/2]$.

Solution: To find the area here, we first plot the graphs of f and g.

In[424]:= **Clear[f, g]**

In[425]:= `f[x_] := Abs[x]`
`g[x_] := Cos[x]`

In[427]:= `Plot[{f[x], g[x]}, {x, -π/2, π/2},`
`  PlotStyle → {Red, Blue}, PlotRange → {-1, 2},`
`  Filling → {1 → {2}}]`

Out[427]=
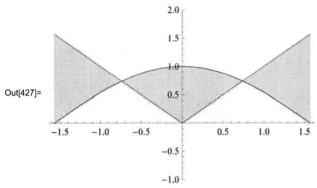

From the picture above, we will need to consider the total area as a sum of three separate regions. To this end, we first find the intersection points of these two curves in order to obtain the limits of integration. Make note of the fact that the **Solve** command does not work here because it is only able to solve algebraic equations. Instead, we use the **FindRoot** command to solve the equation $f(x) - g(x) = 0$ using an initial guess of $x = 0.75$ (based on the plot above):

In[428]:= `FindRoot[f[x] - g[x], {x, 0.75}]`

Out[428]= `{x → 0.739085}`

Thus our root is approximately $x = 0.739085$. By symmetry we see there is another root at $x = -0.739085$. Hence, the area between these two curves is the sum of the three integrals:

In[429]:= $\int_{-\pi/2}^{-0.739085} (f[x] - g[x]) \, dx + \int_{-0.739085}^{0.739085} (g[x] - f[x]) \, dx + \int_{0.739085}^{\pi/2} (f[x] - g[x]) \, dx$

Out[429]= `2.06936`

Hence the area of our bounded region is 2.06936.

NOTE: Observe that our region is symmetric about the y-axis and thus the same answer could have been found by computing the area of only half the region (the right half, say) and doubling the result.

■ Exercises

1. Find the area between the curves $y = \sin x$ and $y = \sin(2x)$ between $x = 0$ and $x = \pi$.

2. Find the area between the graphs of $x = \sin y$ and $x = 1 - \cos y$ between $y = 0$ and $y = \pi/2$.

3. Find the area above $y = 1 - x/\pi$ and below $y = \sin x$.

■ 6.2 Average Value

Students should read Sections 6.2 and 6.3 of Rogawski's *Calculus* [1] for a detailed discussion of the material presented in this section.

Remember that the average value of a function $f(x)$ on $[a, b]$ is defined as

$$f_{\text{ave}} = \frac{1}{b-a} \int_a^b f(x)\,dx.$$

Related to this notion is the Mean Value Theorem for Integrals (MVTI), which states that for any continuous function $f(x)$ on $[a, b]$ there exists a value $c \in [a, b]$ such that

$$f(c) = f_{\text{ave}}.$$

Example 6.4. Let $f(x) = 2\cos x - x$.
a) Find the only positive root α of f.
b) Calculate the average value of f on $[0, \alpha]$.
c) Determine a value c that satisfies the Mean Value Theorem for Integrals on $[0, \alpha]$.

Solution:
a) To calculate α, we first plot the graph of f and then use the **FindRoot** command with $x = 1$ as our initial guess:

In[430]:= `Clear[f]`

In[431]:= `f[x_] := 2 Cos[x] - x`

In[432]:= `Plot[f[x], {x, -π, π}]`

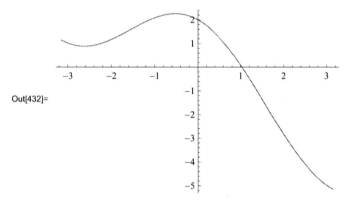

Out[432]=

In[433]:= `root = FindRoot[f[x], {x, 1}]`

Out[433]= $\{x \to 1.02987\}$

Therefore, $\alpha = 1.02987$ accurate to 5 decimal places.

b) We next calculate the average value of f on $[0, \alpha]$:

In[434]:= `α = root[[1, 2]]`

Out[434]= 1.02987

In[435]:= $\mathbf{fave} = \dfrac{1}{\alpha - 0} \int_0^\alpha \mathbf{f[x]\,dx}$

Out[435]= 1.14981

Thus, the average value is approximately $f_{\text{ave}} = 1.14981$.

c) By MVTI, there exists a value $c \in [0, \alpha]$ such that $f(c) = f_{\text{ave}}$. To find c, we solve this equation for c, or equivalently,

$$f(c) - f_{\text{ave}} = 0.$$

In[436]:= **FindRoot[f[c] - fave, {c, .5}]**

Out[436]= $\{c \to 0.55256\}$

◾ Exercises

1. Which of $f(x) = x \sin^2 x$ and $g(x) = x^2 \sin^2 x$ has a larger average value over [0, 2]? Over [2, 4]?

2. Let f_{ave} denote the average value of $f(x) = x^3 + x^2 + 5$ on [0, 4]. Find a value for c inside [0, 4] such that $f(c) = f_{ave}$.

◾ 6.3 Volume of Solids of Revolution

Students should read Sections 6.2-6.4 of Rogawski's *Calculus* [1] for a detailed discussion of the material presented in this section.

We recall that a definite integral can be evaluated by employing the definition

$$\int_a^b f(x)\,dx = \lim_{n \to +\infty} [\sum_{i=1}^n f(x_i^*)\,\Delta x_i].$$

Another application of the definite integral involves finding the volume of a *solid of revolution*, that is, a solid obtained by revolving a region in the plane about one of the coordinate axes.

◾ 6.3.1 The Method of Discs

Let S be a solid of revolution obtained by revolving the region bounded by the graphs of $y = f(x)$, $y = 0$, and the vertical lines $x = a$ and $x = b$, about the x-axis. To obtain the volume of S, we can approximate S by *discs*, i.e., cylinders obtained by revolving each rectangle, constructed by a Riemann sum of f relative to a partition $P = \{x_0, x_1, x_2, \ldots, x_n\}$ of $[a, b]$, about the x-axis. Using the fact that the volume of a cylinder with radius R and height h is given by

$$V = \pi R^2 h,$$

it follows that the volume of the ith cylinder (corresponding to the ith rectangle) is $V_i = \pi[f(x_i^*)]^2\,\Delta x$. Hence, an approximation to the volume of S is given by the Riemann sum

$$\text{Vol}(S) \approx \sum_{i=1}^n V_i = \pi \sum_{i=1}^n [f(x_i^*)]^2\,\Delta x.$$

In the limit as $n \to \infty$, we obtain the exact volume of S:

$$\text{Vol}(S) = \pi \lim_{n \to \infty} \sum_{i=1}^n [f(x_i^*)]^2\,\Delta x = \pi \int_a^b [f(x)]^2\,dx.$$

NOTE: If the region is revolved about the y-axis, then the volume of S is given by

$$\text{Vol}(S) = \pi \int_c^d [f(y)]^2\,dy.$$

Example 6.5. Find the volume of the solid of revolution obtained by rotating the region bounded by the graph of $f(x) = \sqrt{x}$, the x-axis, and the vertical line $x = 3$.

Solution: We define $f(x)$ in *Mathematica* and illustrate both the region and rectangles that are rotated to obtain the solid and discs, respectively. For this, we recall our program from Chapter 5 of this manual that was used to draw these rectangles.

```
In[437]:= LEPT[f_ , {a_ , b_ , n_}] := Module[
          {dx, k, xstar, lrect, plot},
          dx = N[(b - a) / n];
          xstar = Table[a + i * dx, {i, 0, n}];
          lrect = Table[Line[{{xstar[[i]], 0}, {xstar[[i]], f[xstar[[i]]] },
              {xstar[[i + 1]], f[xstar[[i]]] }, {xstar[[i + 1]], 0}}], {i, 1, n}];
          plot = Plot[f[x], {x, a, b}, Filling → Axis];
          Show[plot, Graphics[{Green, lrect}]]
         ]
```

```
In[438]:= f[x_] := √x
          plot = LEPT[f, {0, 3, 20}]
```

Out[439]=

The plot above shows our region shaded in gray and our rectangles outlined in green. We now rotate this shaded region about the x-axis to obtain a solid of revolution called a *paraboloid*. This is achieved in *Mathematica* using the **Revolution-Plot3D[{f,x},{x,a,b}]** command, which generates a surface of revolution having radius **f** at height **x**. This means that the vertical axis shown in the plot below is actually the x-axis.

In[440]:= **S = RevolutionPlot3D$\left[\left\{\sqrt{x}, x\right\}, \{x, 0, 3\}\right]$**

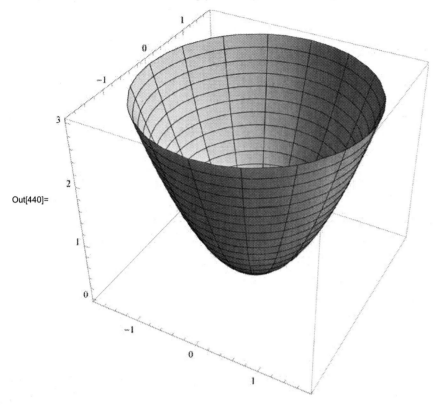

Out[440]=

The exact volume of the paraboloid is then given by

In[441]:= **V = $\pi \int_0^3 (f[x])^2 \, dx$**

Out[441]= $\dfrac{9\pi}{2}$

■ 6.3.2 The Method of Washers

For a solid of revolution S generated by revolving a region bounded between two curves $f(x)$ and $g(x)$ on $[a, b]$ about the x-axis, we employ washers (rings) instead of discs. Refer to your calculus textbook for a detailed treatment. The corresponding volume of S is given by (let's assume $g(x) \geq f(x)$)

$$\text{Vol}(S) = \pi \int_a^b \left\{ [g(x)]^2 - [f(x)]^2 \right\} dx.$$

Example 6.6. Find the volume of the solid generated by revolving about the x-axis the region enclosed by the parabola $y = x^2 + 1$ and the straight line $y = x + 3$.

Solution: Our initial goal is to find the points of intersection and secure the limits of integration.

In[442]:= **Clear[f, g, x]**
    f[x_] := $x^2 + 1$
    g[x_] := x + 3

In[445]:= **Plot[{f[x], g[x]}, {x, -2, 4}, PlotStyle → {Red, Blue},
   PlotRange → {-2, 8}, Filling → {1 → {2}}]**

Out[445]=

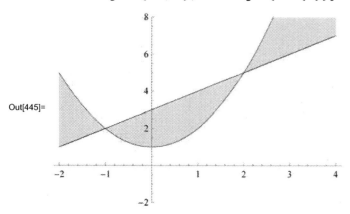

We notice that $f(x)$ is graphed in red, while $g(x)$ is graphed in blue. The following command solves for their intersection points:

In[446]:= **Solve[f[x] == g[x], x]**

Out[446]= $\{\{x \rightarrow -1\}, \{x \rightarrow 2\}\}$

One can easily verify that the intersection points are $(-1, 2)$ and $(2, 5)$. Thus, our limits of integration are $x = -1$ and $x = 2$.

Let P and Q denote the solids of revolution by revolving each of the regions lying under f and g, respectively, along the interval $[-1, 2]$. Our solid S, obtained by rotating the region between f and g on $[-1, 2]$ about the x-axis, can then be viewed as the difference of Q and P, i.e., the solid Q with the solid P removed from it. Following are surface plots of the three solids P, Q, and S. Again, note that the vertical axis shown in each of the plots below is actually the x-axis.

In[447]:= **P = RevolutionPlot3D[{f[x], x}, {x, -1, 2}, AspectRatio → Automatic]**
Q = RevolutionPlot3D[{g[x], x}, {x, -1, 2}, AspectRatio → Automatic]

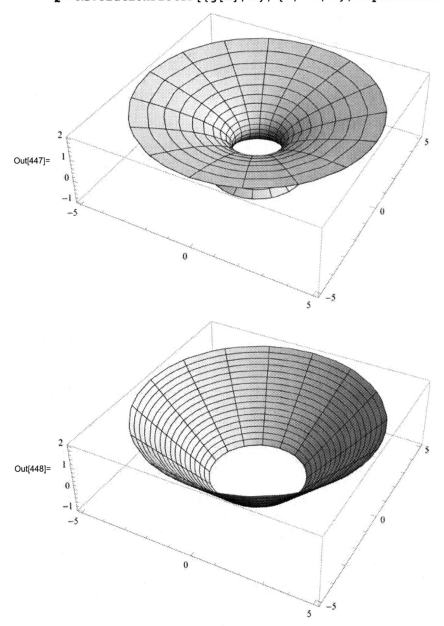

Out[447]=

Out[448]=

In[449]:= **S = Show[P, Q]**

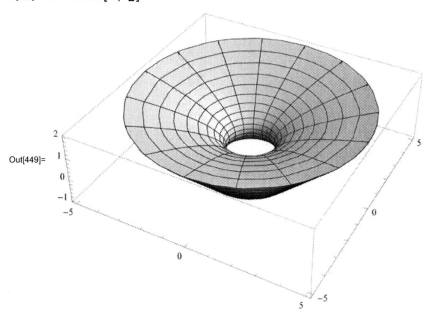

Out[449]=

Since the curve $y = f(x) = x + 3$ is lower than the curve $y = g(x) = x^2 + 1$, it follows that the volume of S is given by

In[450]:= $\mathbf{V = \pi \int_{-1}^{2} \left((g[x])^2 - (f[x])^2 \right) dx}$

Out[450]= $\dfrac{117\,\pi}{5}$

Observe that in the above discussion, the methods for calculating volumes of solids of revolution were via discs and washers. In other words, the element of volume is obtained by taking the rectangular element of area whose height is *perpendicular* to the axis of revolution and revolving it to construct a disc or washer.

■ 6.3.3 The Method of Cylindrical Shells

Students should read Section 6.4 of Rogawski's *Calculus* [1] for a detailed discussion of the material presented in this section.

Another approach to finding the volume of a solid of revolution is to approximate it using *cylindrical shells* in contrast to discs (or washers). Recall that a cylindrical shell element is one that is obtained by revolving a rectangular element of area whose height is *parallel* to the axis of revolution.

A cylindrical shell is by definition a solid contained between two concentric cylinders having the same axis of rotation. Suppose a cylindrical shell has inner radius r_1, outer radius r_2, and altitude h, then its volume V is given by

$$V = \pi\, r_2^2\, h - \pi\, r_1^2\, h = 2\,\pi\, h\!\left(\tfrac{r_2+r_1}{2}\right)(r_2 - r_1) = 2\,\pi\, \bar{r}\, h\, \Delta x,$$

where $\bar{r} = (r_2 + r_1)/2$ is the average radius and $\Delta x = r_2 - r_1$.

Let S denote denote the solid obtained by revolving the region bounded between a function $f(x)$, the x-axis, $x = a$, and $x = b$, about the y-axis. The volume of the ith shell corresponding to the ith rectangle is defined to be $V_i = 2\,\pi\, x_i^*\, f(x_i^*)\, \Delta x$, where $x_i^* = (x_i + x_{i-1})/2$. Hence, an approximation to the volume of S is given by the Riemann sum

$$\text{Vol}(S) \approx \sum_{i=1}^{n} V_i = 2 \pi \sum_{i=1}^{n} x_i^* f(x_i^*) \Delta x.$$

In the limit as $n \to \infty$, we obtain the exact volume of S:

$$\text{Vol}(S) = 2 \pi \lim_{n \to \infty} \sum_{i=1}^{n} x_i^* f(x_i^*) \Delta x = 2 \pi \int_a^b x f(x) \, dx.$$

NOTE: If the region is revolved about the x-axis using cylindrical shells, then the volume of S is given by

$$\text{Vol}(S) = 2 \pi \int_c^d y f(y) \, dy.$$

Example 6.7. Consider the region bounded by the curve $y = x^2$, the x-axis, and the line $x = 2$. Find the volume of the solid generated by revolving this region about the y-axis using the method of cylindrical shells.

Solution: Let us first plot the region bounded by the given curves (shaded in the plot below):

In[451]:= `f[x_] = x^2;`
`Plot[f[x], {x, 0, 2}, Filling → Axis]`

Out[452]=
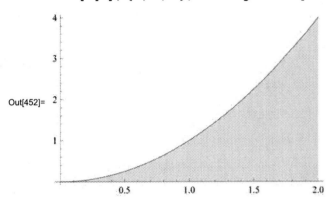

We then revolve this shaded region about the y-axis to obtain our solid S (parabolic bowl). This can be seen in the three plots following, which illustrate S as the difference of the solids Q (cylinder) and P (paraboloid), that is, Q with P removed from it.

In[453]:= **P = RevolutionPlot3D[{f[x]} , {x, 0, 2}]**

Q = RevolutionPlot3D[{{2, y}} , {y, 0, 4}]

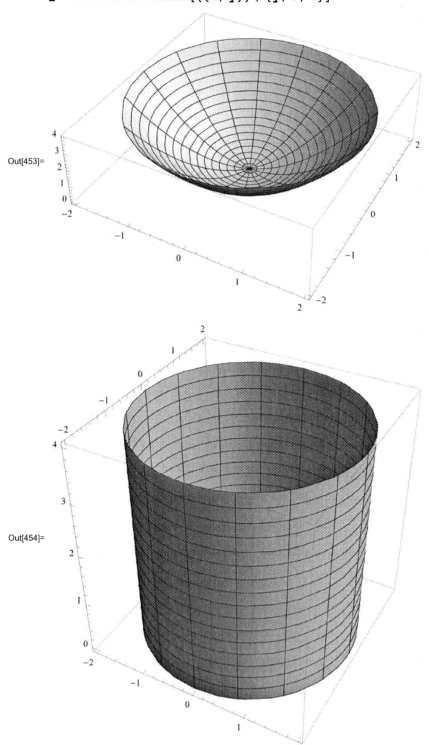

Out[453]=

Out[454]=

In[455]:= **S = Show[P, Q]**

Out[455]=

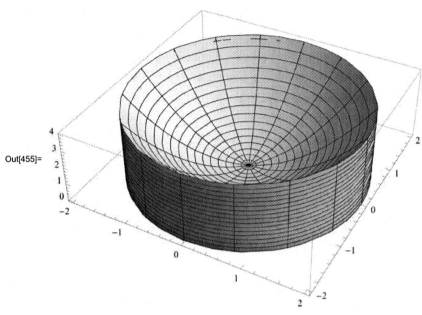

The volume of *S* is given by

In[456]:= $\mathbf{V = 2\,\pi \int_0^2 x \ast f[x]\; dx}$

Out[456]= $8\,\pi$

NOTE: The volume in this example can also be calculated using the washer method. However, one would first have to solve the equation $y = x^2$ for *x*, yielding $x = \sqrt{y}$. Moreover, the limits of integration (with respect to *y*) would have to be determined, which in this case would be $y = 0$ and $y = 4$ corresponding to $x = 0$ and $x = 2$, respectively. Hence,

In[457]:= $\mathbf{V = \pi \int_0^4 \left(2^2 - \left(\sqrt{y}\right)^2\right) dy}$

Out[457]= $8\,\pi$

The two answers from both methods agree as they should.

Example 6.8. Sketch the *ellipse* $\frac{x^2}{a^2} + \frac{y^2}{b^2} = 1$ and find the volume of the solid obtained by revolving the region enclosed by the ellipse about the *x*-axis.

Solution: We will use the **ContourPlot** command to plot the ellipse for $a = 2$ and $b = 3$. The reader should experiment with other values of *a* and *b*.

In[458]:= **a = 2;**

b = 3;

ContourPlot$\left[\dfrac{x^2}{a^2} + \dfrac{y^2}{b^2} == 1, \{x, -a-1, a+1\}, \{y, -b-1, b+1\},\right.$

AspectRatio → Automatic, Axes → True, Frame -> False$\Big]$

Out[460]=

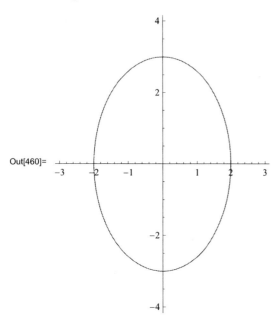

To plot the corresponding solid of revolution (*ellipsoid*), we first solve $\dfrac{x^2}{a^2} + \dfrac{y^2}{b^2} = 1$ for y.

In[461]:= **Clear[a, b]**

sol = Solve$\left[\dfrac{x^2}{a^2} + \dfrac{y^2}{b^2} == 1, y\right]$

Out[462]= $\left\{\left\{y \to -\dfrac{b\sqrt{a^2 - x^2}}{a}\right\}, \left\{y \to \dfrac{b\sqrt{a^2 - x^2}}{a}\right\}\right\}$

The positive and negative solutions above correspond to the upper half and lower half, respectively, of the ellipse. We shall consider the upper half in plotting the ellipsoid and computing its volume by defining

$$f(x) = \sqrt{b^2 - \dfrac{b^2 x^2}{a^2}} = b\sqrt{1 - \dfrac{x^2}{a^2}}.$$

In[463]:= **f[x_] = sol[[2, 1, 2]]**

Out[463]= $\dfrac{b\sqrt{a^2 - x^2}}{a}$

Here is a plot of *S* (rotated 90 degrees about the *x*-axis).

In[464]:= **a = 2;**
b = 3;
RevolutionPlot3D[{f[x], x} , {x, -a, a}]

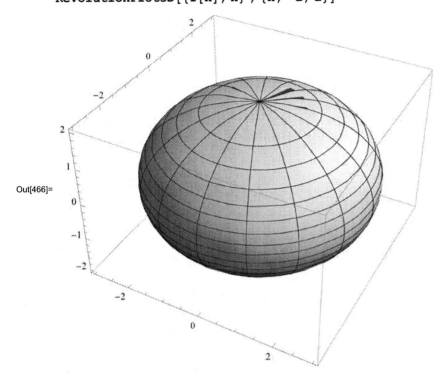

Out[466]=

To find the volume of the ellipsoid, we can employ either method, disc or shell, but in this case the disc method is preferable from a computational standard. This is because the disc formula for volume contains the square term $[f(x)]^2$, which lets us avoid having to deal with radical terms if the shell method were used. Since the ellipsoid is defined along the integral $[-a, a]$, its volume based on the disc method is therefore

In[467]:= $V = \pi \int_{-a}^{a} (f[x])^2 \, dx$

Out[467]= 24π

More generally, the volume of the ellipsoid for arbitrary positive values of a and b is given by

In[468]:= **Clear[a, b]**

$V = \pi \int_{-a}^{a} (f[x])^2 \, dx$

Out[469]= $\frac{4}{3} a b^2 \pi$

Thus, $V = \frac{4}{3} \pi a b^2$.

NOTE: If we let $a = b$, then the ellipsoid becomes a sphere and the formula above reduces to the classic formula $V = \frac{4}{3} \pi a^3$, where a is the radius of the sphere.

■ Exercises

1. Plot the solid of revolution obtained by rotating the region enclosed by the graphs about the given axis and calculate its volume.

a) $y = \frac{9}{x^2}$, $y = 10 - x^2$ about the x-axis

b) $y = 16 - x^4$, $y = 0$, $x = 2$, $x = 3$ about the y−axis

2. Plot the *hypocycloid* $x^{2/3} + y^{2/3} = 1$ and find the volume of the solid obtained by revolving the region enclosed by the hypocycloid about the y-axis. Is the volume of the solid obtained by revolving the same region about the x-axis the same? Justify your answer. (Hint: Use the **ContourPlot** command.)

3. Use the Shell Method to find the volume of the solid obtained by rotating the region enclosed by the graphs in each part below about the y-axis.

a) $y = x^2$, $y = 8 - x^2$, and $x = 0$

b) $y = \frac{1}{2} x^2$ and $y = \sin(x^2)$

4. The solid generated by revolving the region between the two branches of the *hyperbola* $y^2 - x^2 = 1$ from $x = -a$ to $x = a$ about the x-axis is called a *hyperboloid*. Find the volume of the hyperboloid for $a = 2$ and then for any arbitrary value of a.

Chapter 7   Techniques of Integration

■ 7.1 Numerical Integration

Students should read Section 7.1 of Rogawski's *Calculus* [1] for a detailed discussion of the material presented in this section.

Numerical integration is the process of approximating a definite integral using appropriate sums of function values. We already saw in Chapter 5 of this text formulas for Right, Left, and Midpoint Rules and their subroutines **LRSUM**, **RRSUM**, and **MRSUM**, respectively. In this section, we will develop two additional rules: the Trapezoidal Rule and Simpson's Rule.

■ 7.1.1 Trapezoidal Rule

The Trapezoidal Rule approximates the definite integral $\int_a^b f(x)\,dx$ by using areas of trapezoids and is given by the formula:

$$T_n = .5\,((b-a)/n)\,(y_0 + 2\,y_1 + \ldots + 2\,y_{n-1} + y_n)$$

where n is the number of trapezoids and $y_i = f(a + i\,(b-a)/n)$. This formula can be found in your calculus text. Here is a *Mathematica* subroutine, called **TRAP**, for implementing the Trapezoidal Rule:

In[470]:= **Clear[f, a, b, n]**

In[471]:= **TRAP[a_, b_, n_] :=**
   (f[a] + 2 Sum[f[a + i * (b - a) / n], {i, 1, n - 1}] + f[b]) (.5 (b - a) / n)

Example 7.1. Calculate the area under the function $f(x) = x^2$ on [0, 1] using the Trapezoidal Rule for various values of n.

Solution: The following output gives a table of approximations of $\int_0^1 x^2\,dx$ based on the Trapezoidal Rule for $n = 10, 20, \ldots, 100$.

In[472]:= **f[x_] := x^2**
   TableForm[Table[{n, N[TRAP[0, 1, n]]}, {n, 10, 100, 10}],
   TableHeadings → {{}, {"n", " T_n"}}]

Out[473]//TableForm=

n	T_n
10	0.335
20	0.33375
30	0.333519
40	0.333438
50	0.3334
60	0.33338
70	0.333367
80	0.333359
90	0.333354
100	0.33335

It is clear that these values are converging to 1/3, which is the exact value of our definite integral:

In[474]:= $\int_0^1 x^2 \, dx$

Out[474]= $\dfrac{1}{3}$

▪ 7.1.2 Simpson's Rule

One difference between Simpson's Rule and all the other rules we have developed so far (**TRAP**, **LRSUM**, **RRSUM**, and **MRSUM**) is that the number of partition points, n, in this case, must be even. The other difference is that Simpson's Rule is a quadratic approximation based on parabolas, whereas the other rules are linear approximations based on lines. The formula for Simpson's Rule is given by (refer to your calculus text for details):

$$S_n = (1/3)\,[y_0 + 4\,y_1 + 2\,y_2 + 4\,y_3 + 2\,y_4 + ... + 4\,y_{n-3} + 2\,y_{n-2} + 4\,y_{n-1} + y_n]\,(b-a)/n$$
$$= (1/3)[(y_0 + 4\,y_1 + y_2) + (y_2 + 4\,y_3 + y_4) + ... + (y_{n-2} + 4\,y_{n-1} + y_n)]\,(b-a)/n$$

where $y_i = f(a + i\,(b-a)/n)$. Here is a *Mathematica* subroutine, called **SIMP**, for implementing Simpson's Rule:

In[475]:= `Clear[a, b, n]`

In[476]:= `SIMP[a_, b_, n_] :=`
`    (1 / 3) Sum[f[a + (2 i - 2) (b - a) / n] + 4 f[a + (2 i - 1) (b - a) / n] +`
`        f[a + 2 i (b - a) / n], {i, 1, n / 2}] (b - a) / n`

Example 7.2. Calculate the area under the function $f(x) = x^2$ on [0, 1] using Simpson's Rule for various values of n.

Solution: We use the same set of values of n as in the previous example. This will allow us to compare Simpson's Rule with the Trapezoidal Rule.

In[477]:= `f[x_] := x`^{2}
`    TableForm[Table[{n, N[SIMP[0, 1, n]]}, {n, 10, 100, 10}],`
`      TableHeadings → {{}, {"n", " s`$_n$`"}}]`

Out[478]//TableForm=

n	s_n
10	0.333333
20	0.333333
30	0.333333
40	0.333333
50	0.333333
60	0.333333
70	0.333333
80	0.333333
90	0.333333
100	0.333333

Notice how fast SIMP converges to the actual value of the integral (1/3) compared to TRAP.

Example 7.3. Calculate the definite integral of $f(x) = \sin(25\,x^2)$ on [0, 1] using Simpson's Rule and approximate it to five decimal places. What is the minimum number of partition points needed to obtain this level of accuracy?

Solution: We first evaluate SIMP using values for n in increments of 20.

In[479]:= $f[x_] := Sin[25 x^2]$

$TableForm[Table[\{n, N[SIMP[0, 1, n]]\}, \{n, 20, 200, 20\}],$

$TableHeadings \rightarrow \{\{\}, \{"n", " s_n"\}\}]$

Out[480]//TableForm=

n	s_n
20	0.0958943
40	0.10526
60	0.105526
80	0.105566
100	0.105576
120	0.10558
140	0.105582
160	0.105582
180	0.105583
200	0.105583

Based on the output our approximation, accurate to five decimal places, is 0.10558. This first occurs between $n = 100$ to $n = 120$. We evaluate SIMP inside this range to zoom in on the minimum number of partition points needed.

In[481]:= $f[x_] := Sin[25 x^2]$

$TableForm[Table[\{n, N[SIMP[0, 1, n]]\}, \{n, 100, 120, 2\}],$

$TableHeadings \rightarrow \{\{\}, \{"n", " s_n"\}\}]$

Out[482]//TableForm=

n	s_n
100	0.105576
102	0.105577
104	0.105577
106	0.105578
108	0.105578
110	0.105579
112	0.105579
114	0.105579
116	0.10558
118	0.10558
120	0.10558

Thus, we see that the minimum number of points needed is $n = 116$. How does this compare with the minimum number of points needed by TRAP to obtain the same level of accuracy?

NOTE: Observe that SIMP does not converge as fast in this example as in the previous example. This is because the function $f(x) = \sin(25 x^2)$ is oscillatory as the following graph demonstrates:

In[483]:= **Plot[f[x], {x, 0, 1}]**

Out[483]=

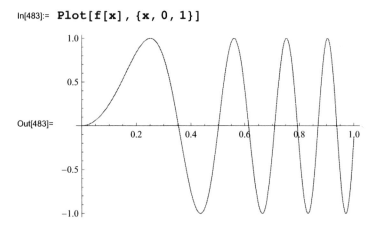

Try increasing the frequency of this function, say to $\sin(100\,x^2)$, to see how well SIMP performs.

■ 7.1.3 Midpoint Rule

Since most calculus texts include again the Midpoint Rule in the section on numerical integration, for completeness, we will too. The Riemann sum using the midpoints of each subinterval is given by the following formula:

In[484]:= **Clear[f]**
MRSUM[a_, b_, n_] := Sum[f[a + (i - 1 / 2) * (b - a) / n] * (b - a) / n, {i, 1, n}]

Example 7.4. Calculate the area under the function $f(x) = x^2$ on [0, 1] using the Midpoint Rule for various values of n.

Solution:

In[486]:= **f[x_] := x²**
TableForm[Table[{n, N[MRSUM[0, 1, n]]}, {n, 10, 100, 10}],
TableHeadings → {{}, {"n", "Midpoint rule"}}]

Out[487]//TableForm=

n	Midpoint rule
10	0.3325
20	0.333125
30	0.333241
40	0.333281
50	0.3333
60	0.33331
70	0.333316
80	0.33332
90	0.333323
100	0.333325

■ Exercises

1. Consider the definite integral $\int_1^2 \ln(x)\,dx$.

a) Using the Trapezoidal Rule, Simpson's Rule, and Midpoint Rule, approximate this integral for $n = 10, 20, \ldots, 100$.

b) Compare how fast each subroutine (**TRAP, SIMP, MRSUM**) converges to $\int_a^b \ln(x)\,dx$ and decide which of these rules is "best."

2. Repeat Exercise 1 for the following definite integrals:

a) $\int_0^2 \frac{e^x}{x+1}\,dx$ b) $\int_0^1 \cos(x^2)\,dx$ c) $\int_0^1 e^{x^2}\,dx$

Can you make any general conclusions about which rule (Trapezoidal, Simpson's, Midpoint) is best?

3. For each of the functions given below, set up a definite integral for the volume of the solid of revolution obtained by revolving the region under $f(x)$ along the given interval and about the given axis. Then use the subroutines **TRAP**, **SIMP**, and **MRSUM** to approximate the volume of each solid accurate to two decimal places (use various values of n to obtain the desired accuracy).

a) $f(x) = \cos x$; $[0, \pi/2]$; x-axis b) $f(x) = e^{-x^2}$; $[0, 1]$; y-axis c) $f(x) = \sin x$, $[0, \pi]$, x – axis

■ 7.2 Techniques of Integration

Students should read Sections 7.2 trhough 7.4 and 7.6 of Rogawski's *Calculus* [1] for a detailed discussion of the material presented in this section.

All calculus texts have at least a chapter devoted to "Techniques of Integration." When using *Mathematica*, these techniques are usually not necessary since *Mathematica* automatically gives you the answer.

■ 7.2.1 Substitution

On occasion, we do need to use techniques of integration, even when using *Mathematica*.

Example 7.5. Evaluate the following integral: $\int 2^x \sqrt{(2^x)^2 - 1}\,dx.$

Solution: We evaluate this integral in *Mathematica*:

In[488]:= $\int 2^x \sqrt{(2^x)^2 - 1}\,dx$

Out[488]= $\dfrac{2^x \sqrt{-1 + 4^x} - \text{Log}\left[2^x + \sqrt{-1 + 4^x}\right]}{\text{Log}[4]}$

To students in a first-year calculus course, this answer makes no sense. There are many integrals that *Mathematica* cannot evaluate at all, or cannot evaluate in terms of elementary functions (such as the integral above). Some of these integrals are doable in terms we should understand, once we first use an appropriate technique of integration. In the above example, all we need to do is first make the following substitution: $u = 2^x$ and $du = (\ln 2)\, 2^x\, dx$, which transforms the integral to:

In[489]:= $\dfrac{1}{\text{Log}[2]} \int \sqrt{u^2 - 1}\,du$

Out[489]= $\dfrac{\frac{1}{2} u \sqrt{-1 + u^2} - \frac{1}{2} \text{Log}\left[u + \sqrt{-1 + u^2}\right]}{\text{Log}[2]}$

This is the correct answer. All we need to do is substitute 2^x for u, and add the arbitrary constant of integration, getting:

$\frac{1}{2\,\text{Log}[2]} \left(2^x \sqrt{-1 + (2^x)^2} - \text{Log}[2^x + \sqrt{-1 + (2^x)^2}\,] \right) + C$

Note that the *Mathematica* function Log[x] is equivalent to the standard form ln x.

■ 7.2.2 Trigonometric Substitution

Example 7.6. Evaluate $\int \frac{1}{x^2 \sqrt{x^2-9}} \, dx$.

Solution: By hand, the integral $\int \frac{1}{x^2 \sqrt{x^2-9}} \, dx$ would normally be evaluated with a trigonometric substitution of the form $x = 3 \sec\theta$. But with *Mathematica*, we can do this directly:

In[490]:= $\int \dfrac{1}{x^2 \sqrt{x^2 - 9}} \, dx$

Out[490]= $\dfrac{\sqrt{-9 + x^2}}{9\,x}$

This, of course, is the correct answer, when we remember that *Mathematica* does not add an arbitrary constant to indefinite integrals.

- **7.2.3 Method of Partial Fractions**

Integrals of rational expressions often require the Method of Partial Fraction Decomposition to evaluate them (by hand). For example:

$$\int \frac{3x-3}{x^2+5x+4} \, dx = \int \left(\frac{5}{x+4} - \frac{2}{x+1} \right) dx = 5 \ln|x+4| - 2 \ln|x+1| = \ln \left| \frac{(x+4)^5}{(x+1)^2} \right|$$

On the other hand, *Mathematica* will give us essentially the same answer for this integral, but does its work behind the scenes without revealing its technique:

In[491]:= $\mathbf{Simplify}\left[\int \dfrac{3\,x - 3}{x^2 + 5\,x + 4} \, dx \right]$

Out[491]= $-2 \, \text{Log}[1 + x] + 5 \, \text{Log}[4 + x]$

If we would like to see the partial fraction decomposition of the integrand, $\frac{3x-3}{x^2+5x+4}$, *Mathematica* will also do that for us without strain by using the **Apart** command:

In[492]:= $\mathbf{Apart}\left[\dfrac{3\,x - 3}{x^2 + 5\,x + 4} \right]$

Out[492]= $-\dfrac{2}{1 + x} + \dfrac{5}{4 + x}$

Example 7.7. Evaluate $\int \frac{2x^3+x^2-2x+2}{(x^2+1)^2} \, dx$.

Solution: We simply evaluate this integral using *Mathematica*:

In[493]:= $\int \dfrac{2\,x^3 + x^2 - 2\,x + 2}{\left(x^2 + 1 \right)^2} \, dx$

Out[493]= $\dfrac{4 + x}{2 \left(1 + x^2 \right)} + \dfrac{3 \, \text{ArcTan}[x]}{2} + \text{Log}\left[1 + x^2 \right]$

But again, if we would like to see the partial fraction decomposition of the integrand, $\frac{2x^3+x^2-2x+2}{(x^2+1)^2}$, then this is straightforward with *Mathematica*:

In[494]:= **Apart$\left[\dfrac{2\,x^3 + x^2 - 2\,x + 2}{\left(x^2 + 1\right)^2} \right]$**

Out[494]= $\dfrac{1 - 4\,x}{\left(1 + x^2\right)^2} + \dfrac{1 + 2\,x}{1 + x^2}$

■ Exercises

1. Evaluate $\int (1 + \ln(x)) \sqrt{1 + (x \ln (x))^2} \; dx$ with *Mathematica*. If it doesn't give an understandable answer, use a technique of integration that changes the integral into one that *Mathematica* will evaluate.

In Exercises 2 through 5, use *Mathematica* to find the partial fraction decomposition of the given functions and then integrate them:

2. $\dfrac{x^2+3\,x-44}{(x-3)\,(x+5)\,(3\,x-2)}$ 3. $\dfrac{3\,x^2-4\,x+5}{(x-1)\,(x^2+1)}$ 4. $\dfrac{25}{x\,(x^2+2\,x+5)}$ 5. $\dfrac{10}{x(x^2+2\,x+5)^2}$

In Exercises 6 through 10, use *Mathematica* to evaluate the given integrals.

6. $\int \dfrac{x^2}{(x^2-4)^{3/2}} \; dx$ 7. $\int x^3 \sqrt{9-x^2} \; dx$ 8. $\int \dfrac{1}{\sqrt{25+x^2}} \; dx$

9. $\int \sin^5 x \, dx$ 9. $\int \dfrac{\tan^{-1} t}{1+t^2} \; dt$ 10. $\int \sinh^3 x \cosh x \, dx$

■ 7.3 Improper Integrals

Students should read Section 7.7 of Rogawski's *Calculus* [1] for a detailed discussion of the material presented in this section.

Recall that there are two types of improper integrals.

Type I: If we assume that $f(x)$ is integrable over $[a, b]$ for all $b \geq a$, then the improper integral of $f(x)$ over $[a, \infty)$ is defined as
$$\int_a^\infty f(x) \, dx = \lim_{t \to \infty} \int_a^t f(x) \, dx,$$
provided this limit exists. Similarly, we define
$$\int_{-\infty}^b f(x) \, dx = \lim_{t \to -\infty} \int_t^b f(x) \, dx,$$
provided this limit exists.

Type II: If $f(x)$ is continuous on $[a, b)$ but discontinuous at $x = b$, we define
$$\int_a^b f(x) \, dx = \lim_{t \to b-} \int_a^t f(x) \, dx \, ,$$
provided this limit exists. Similarly, if $f(x)$ is continuous on $(a, b]$ but discontinuous at $x = a$,
$$\int_a^b f(x) \, dx = \lim_{t \to a+} \int_t^b f(x) \, dx,$$
provided this limit exists. Finally, if $f(x)$ is continuous for all x on $[a, b]$ except at $x = c$, where $a < c < b$, we define
$$\int_a^b f(x) \, dx = \lim_{t \to c-} \int_a^t f(x) \, dx + \lim_{t \to c+} \int_t^b f(x) \, dx,$$
provided both of these limits exist.

By using the **Limit** command in *Mathematica* along with **Integrate**, *Mathematica* eliminates the drudgery of having to evaluate these integrals by hand.

Example 7.8. Evaluate the following improper integrals:

a) $\int_{20}^{\infty} \frac{1}{y} \, dy$

b) $\int_{2}^{\infty} e^{-2x} \, dx$

c) $\int_{0}^{1} x \ln x \, dx$

d) $\int_{-\infty}^{\infty} \frac{1}{1+x^2} \, dx$

Solution:

a) We evaluate

In[495]:= $\int_{20}^{\infty} \frac{1}{y} \, dy$

Integrate::idiv : Integral of $\frac{1}{y}$ does not converge on {20, ∞}. ≫

Out[495]= $\int_{20}^{\infty} \frac{1}{y} \, dy$

Thus, evaluating this integral directly using *Mathematica* tells us it does not exist. Alternatively, we could have used the limit definition:

In[496]:= $\mathbf{Limit}\left[\int_{20}^{t} \frac{1}{y} \, dy, \, t \to \infty\right]$

Out[496]= ∞

Observe the difference in the two outputs above. Both correctly express the answer as divergent; however, the second answer is better since it reveals the nature of the divergence (infinity), which is the answer we would expect if solving this problem by hand.

b) We evaluate

In[497]:= $\int_{2}^{\infty} e^{-2x} \, dx$

Out[497]= $\frac{1}{2 \, e^4}$

Again, we obtain the same answer using the limit definition (as it should):

In[498]:= $\mathbf{Limit}\left[\int_{2}^{t} e^{-2x} \, dx, \, t \to \infty\right]$

Out[498]= $\frac{1}{2 \, e^4}$

Mathematica will similarly handle discontinuities. In the following example, the function has a discontinuity at $x = 0$.

c) We evaluate

In[499]:= $\int_0^1 x \, \text{Log}[x] \, dx$

Out[499]= $-\dfrac{1}{4}$

In[500]:= $\text{Limit}\left[\int_t^1 x \, \text{Log}[x] \, dx, \; t \to 0, \; \text{Direction} \to -1\right]$

Out[500]= $\text{ConditionalExpression}\left[-\dfrac{1}{4}, \; (t \notin \text{Reals} \;||\; 0 < \text{Re}[t] < 1 \;||\; \text{Re}[t] > 1) \; \&\& \right.$

$\left. \left(\dfrac{t}{1-t} \notin \text{Reals} \;||\; \text{Re}\left[\dfrac{t}{1-t}\right] \geq 0 \;||\; \text{Re}\left[\dfrac{t}{1-t}\right] \leq -1\right)\right]$

d) We evaluate

In[501]:= $\int_{-\infty}^{\infty} \dfrac{1}{1 + x^2} \, dx$

Out[501]= π

Note that *Mathematica* does not require us to break the integral up into two integrals, which would be required according to its definition, if evaluated by hand. On the other hand, there is nothing wrong with dividing this integral into two in *Mathematica*:

In[502]:= $\int_{-\infty}^{0} \dfrac{1}{1 + x^2} \, dx \; + \; \int_{0}^{\infty} \dfrac{1}{1 + x^2} \, dx$

Out[502]= π

NOTE: Observe that it does not matter where we divide the integral. It is valid to express $\int_{-\infty}^{a} \frac{1}{1+x^2} \, dx + \int_{a}^{\infty} \frac{1}{1+x^2} \, dx$ for the integral $\int_{-\infty}^{\infty} \frac{1}{1+x^2} \, dx$ for any real value a as long as they are convergent. However, evaluating this sum in *Mathematica* yields different expressions for the answer, which depend on the sign of a and whether it is real or complex. This is shown in the following output:

In[503]:= $\text{Clear}[a]$

$\int_{-\infty}^{a} \dfrac{1}{1 + x^2} \, dx \; + \; \int_{a}^{\infty} \dfrac{1}{1 + x^2} \, dx$

Out[504]= $\text{ConditionalExpression}\left[\right.$

$\dfrac{1}{2}\left(\pi + i \, \text{Log}[1 + i \, a] - i \left(\begin{array}{ll} \text{Conjugate}[\text{Log}[1 - i \, a]] & \text{Re}[a] == 0 \; \&\& \; \text{Im}[a] < 0 \\ \text{Log}[1 - i \, a] & \text{True} \end{array}\right)\right) \; +$

$\dfrac{1}{2}\left(\pi + i \, \text{Log}[1 - i \, a] - i \left(\begin{array}{ll} \text{Conjugate}[\text{Log}[1 + i \, a]] & \text{Re}[a] == 0 \; \&\& \; \text{Im}[a] > 0 \\ \text{Log}[1 + i \, a] & \text{True} \end{array}\right)\right), \; -1 \leq$

$\text{Im}[a] \leq 1\Big]$

If instead, a is given a fixed value, then *Mathematica* will give us our answer of π:

In[505]:= **a = 1**

$$\int_{-\infty}^{a} \frac{1}{1+x^2} \, dx \; + \; \int_{a}^{\infty} \frac{1}{1+x^2} \, dx$$

Out[505]= 1

Out[506]= π

■ Exercises

In Excercises 1 through 8, evaluate the given improper integrals:

1. $\int_{-\infty}^{4} e^{.01\,t} \, dt$

2. $\int_{-3}^{\infty} \frac{1}{(x+4)^{3/2}} \, dx$

3. $\int_{-2}^{4} \frac{1}{(x+2)^{1/3}} \, dx$

4. $\int_{-\infty}^{\infty} x \, e^{-x^2} \, dx$

5. $\int_{0}^{3} \frac{1}{x-1} \, dx$

6. $\int_{-\infty}^{\infty} \frac{1}{e^x + e^{-x}} \, dx$

7. $\int_{1}^{\infty} \frac{1}{x^{.999}} \, dx$

8. $\int_{1}^{\infty} \frac{1}{x^{1.003}} \, dx$

11. Find the volume of the solid obtained by rotating the region below the graph of $y = e^{-x}$ about the x-axis for $0 \le x < \infty$.

12. Determine how large the number b has to be in order that $\int_{b}^{\infty} \frac{1}{x^2+1} \, dx < .0001$.

13. Evaluate the improper integral $\int_{-1}^{1} \frac{1}{\left| \sqrt[3]{x} \right|} \, dx$.

14. Determine how large the number b should be so that $\int_{b}^{\infty} \frac{1}{x^2+1} \, dx \; < \; .0001$.

15. Consider the function defined by

$$G(x) = \int_{0}^{\infty} t^{x-1} \, e^{-t} \, dt$$

a) Evaluate $G(n)$ for $n = 0, \ 2, \ , \ 3, \ 4, \ ...., \ 10$. Make a conjecture about these values. Verify your conjecture.
b) Evaluate $G((2\,n-1)/2)$, for $n = 1, \ 2, \ 3, \ ... \ 10$. Make a conjecture about these values. Verify your conjecture.
c) Plot the graph of $G(x)$ on the interval $[0, \ 5]$.

NOTE: The function G is called the *gamma* function and is denoted by $\Gamma[x]$. In *Mathematica* it is denoted by **Gamma[x]**. The gamma function was first introduced by Euler as a generalization of the factorial function.

■ 7.4 Hyperbolic and Inverse Hyperbolic Functions

Students should read Section 7.5 of Rogawski's *Calculus* [1] for a detailed discussion of the material presented in this section.

■ 7.4.1. Hyperbolic Functions

The *hyperbolic* functions are defined in terms of the exponential functions. They have a direct connection to engineering mathematics, including bridge construction. For example, cables from suspension bridges typically form a curve called a *catenary* (derived from the Latin word *catena*, which means chain) that is described by these functions.

The six hyperbolic functions are denoted and defined as follows:

$$\sinh x = \frac{e^x - e^{-x}}{2}, \qquad \cosh x = \frac{e^x + e^{-x}}{2}, \qquad \tanh x = \frac{e^x - e^{-x}}{e^x + e^{-x}}$$

$$\coth x = \frac{e^x + e^{-x}}{e^x - e^{-x}}, \qquad \operatorname{sech} x = \frac{2}{e^x + e^{-x}}, \qquad \operatorname{csch} x = \frac{2}{e^x - e^{-x}}$$

The reason these functions are called hyperbolic functions is due to their connection with the *equilateral hyperbola* $x^2 - y^2 = 1$. Here, one defines $x = \cosh t$ and $y = \sinh t$. Hence, one obtains the basic hyperbolic identity $\cosh^2 t - \sinh^2 t = 1$, much the same manner as the corresponding trigonometric identity $\cos^2 t + \sin^2 t = 1$, when one considers the unit circle $x^2 + y^2 = 1$ with $x = \cos t$ and $y = \sin t$.

In *Mathematica*, we use the same notation with the obvious convention that the first letter of each function is capitalized and square brackets must be used in place of parentheses. Thus, $\sinh x$ will be entered as **Sinh[x]**.

Example 7.9. Consider the hyperbolic sine function $f(x) = \sinh x$.
a) Plot the graph of f.
b) From the graphs deduce the domain and range of the function.
c) Is f bounded?
d) Does f attain an absolute minimum? Maximum?
e) Repeat a) through d) for the hyperbolic function $g(x) = \cosh x$
f) Repeat a) through d) for the hyperbolic function $h(x) = \tanh x$.

Solution: We begin by defining f in *Mathematica*:

In[507]:= **Clear[f, x]**
      f[x_] = Sinh[x]

Out[508]= Sinh[x]

a) We next plot its graph on the interval $[-3, 3]$.

In[509]:= **Plot[f[x], {x, -3, 3}]**

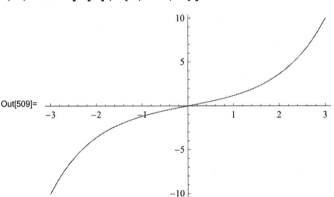

Out[509]=

b) The preceding graph indicates that the domain and range of $\sinh x$ is $(-\infty, \infty)$. To convince yourself, you should plot the graph over wider intervals. We should also expect this from the definition of $\sinh x$ itself. Can you explain why?

c) The function $\sinh x$ is not bounded. The graph earlier should not be used as a proof of this. However, we can evaluate its limit at $-\infty$ and ∞ to see that this is indeed true.

In[510]:= **Limit[f[x], x → -∞]**
      Limit[f[x], x → ∞]

Out[510]= $-\infty$

Out[511]= ∞

d) The limits just computed show that $\sinh x$ has no absolute maximum or minimum since it is unbounded.

e) Next, we consider the hyperbolic cosine function denoted by $\cosh x$.

In[512]:= **Clear[g, x]**
g[x_] = Cosh[x]

Out[513]= Cosh[x]

In[514]:= **Plot[g[x], {x, -3, 3}]**

Out[514]=

The preceding graph indicates that the domain of cosh x is $(-\infty, \infty)$. The range appears to be $[1, \infty)$. Can you prove this?

The hyperbolic cosine function, cosh x, is not bounded from above. This can be seen from the following limits:

In[515]:= **Limit[Cosh[x], x → -∞]**
Limit[Cosh[x], x → ∞]

Out[515]= ∞

Out[516]= ∞

Again, since cosh x is not bounded from above, it follows that cosh x has no absolute maximum. As we have observed in part b) of this example, cosh x has absolute minimum value 1, attained at $x = 0$.

f) Finally, we consider the hyperbolic tangent function, tanh x:

In[517]:= **Clear[h, x]**
h[x_] = Tanh[x]

Out[518]= Tanh[x]

In[519]:= **Plot[h[x], {x, -3, 3}]**

Out[519]=

Again, the preceding graph indicates that the domain of $\tanh x$ is $(-\infty, \infty)$. The range appears to be $(-1, 1)$. This can be seen from the following limits:

In[520]:= **Limit[Tanh[x], x → -∞]**
     Limit[Tanh[x], x → ∞]

Out[520]= -1

Out[521]= 1

The graph of $\tanh x$ also indicates that it is strictly increasing on its domain. This can be proven by showing that its derivative, which we will calculate later, is strictly positive. It is clear that $\tanh x$ has no absolute extrema.

NOTE: The reader will notice some similarities between the hyperbolic functions and the associated trigonometric functions. Moreover, if one studies the theory of functions of a complex variable, the relationship between these classes of transcendental functions becomes even more transparent; for numerous identities exist between the classes of functions.

■ 7.4.2 Identities Involving Hyperbolic Functions

It is immediate that the ratio and reciprocal identities for the hyperbolic functions coincide with their trigonometric counterparts. In fact, for each trigonometric identity, there is a corresponding (not necessarily the same) hyperbolic identity. Following are some examples.

Example 7.10. Show that the following identities hold true.
a) $1 - \tanh^2 x = \operatorname{sech}^2 x$ b) $\cosh(x + y) = \cosh x \cosh y + \sinh x \sinh y$

Solution:

a) We use the definitions for $\tanh x$ and $\operatorname{sech} x$ to express each side of the identity in terms of exponentials:

In[522]:= **Simplify[(1 - Tanh[x]²) /. Tanh[x] → (E^x - E^(-x)) / (E^x + E^(-x))]**

Out[522]= $\dfrac{4 e^{2x}}{\left(1 + e^{2x}\right)^2}$

In[523]:= **Simplify[Sech[x]² /. Sech[x] → 2 / (E^x + E^(-x))]**

Out[523]= $\dfrac{4}{\left(e^{-x} + e^{x}\right)^2}$

We leave it for the reader to verify that both of these outputs agree, that is, $\dfrac{4 e^{2x}}{(1+e^{2x})^2} = \dfrac{4}{(e^{-x}+e^x)^2}$ (cross-multiply and then simplify).

The identity can also be confirmed in *Mathematica* by evaluating the difference between its left- and right-hand sides, which should equal zero:

In[524]:= **Simplify[1 - Tanh[x]² - Sech[x]²]**

Out[524]= 0

NOTE: We can also confirm the identity graphically by plotting the graphs of each side of the identity, which should coincide.

In[525]:= **Plot[{1 - Tanh[x]^2, Sech[x]^2}, {x, -2, 2}]**

Out[525]=

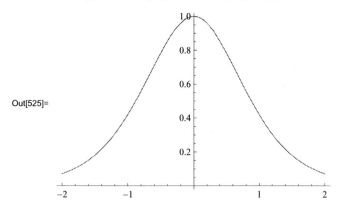

b) We again evaluate the difference between the left- and right-hand sides of the identity:

In[526]:= **Simplify[Cosh[x + y] - (Cosh[x] Cosh[y] + Sinh[x] Sinh[y])]**

Out[526]= 0

■ 7.4.3 Derivatives of Hyperbolic Functions

We next contrast the formulas for the derivatives of the trigonometric functions versus the formulas for the derivatives of the companion hyperbolic functions.

Example 7.11. Compare the derivatives of the given pair of functions.
a) $\sinh x$ and $\sin x$ b) $\cosh x$ and $\cos x$ c) $\tanh x$ and $\tan x$

Solution: We use the derivative command, **D**, to evaluate derivatives of each pair.

a)

In[527]:= **D[Sinh[x], x]**
          D[Sin[x], x]

Out[527]= Cosh[x]

Out[528]= Cos[x]

b)

In[529]:= **D[Cosh[x], x]**
          D[Cos[x], x]

Out[529]= Sinh[x]

Out[530]= -Sin[x]

b)

In[531]:= **D[Tanh[x], x]**
          D[Tan[x], x]

Out[531]= Sech[x]^2

Out[532]= Sec[x]^2

It is clear that derivatives of hyperbolic and trigonometric functions are quite similar.

■ 7.4.4 Inverse Hyperbolic Functions

In light of the fact that hyperbolic functions are defined in terms of the exponential functions, it is readily apparent that the inverse hyperbolic functions are defined in terms of the natural logarithmic function. The inverses of the hyperbolic functions have notation similar to those of inverse trigonometric functions. Thus, the inverse of $\sinh x$ is denoted by $\operatorname{arcsinh} x$ or $\sinh^{-1} x$. In *Mathematica*, the notation is $\sinh^{-1} x$ is **ArcSinh[x]**.

Example 7.12. Plot the graphs of $\sinh^{-1} x$ and $\sinh x$ on the same axis.

Solution: Recall that the graph of a function and the graph of its inverse are reflections of each other across the line $y = x$. This is confirmed by the following plot of $\sinh^{-1} x$ (in blue) and $\sin x$ (in red).

In[533]:= **Plot[{Sinh[x], x, ArcSinh[x]}, {x, -3, 3},**
      PlotStyle → {Blue, Green, Red}, AspectRatio → Automatic, PlotRange → {-3, 3}]

Out[533]=

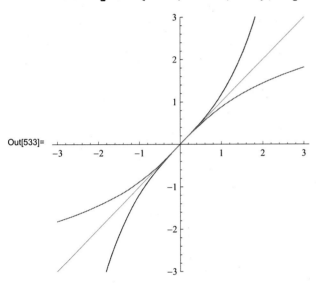

Example 7.13. Show that $\tanh^{-1} x = \frac{1}{2} \ln\left(\frac{1+x}{1-x}\right)$ for $-1 < x < 1$.

Solution: We plot the graphs of $y = \tanh^{-1} x$ and $y = \frac{1}{2} \ln\left(\frac{1+x}{1-x}\right)$ on the same axes. Note that *Mathematica*'s notation of $\tanh^{-1} x$ is **ArcTanh [x]** and $\ln y$ is entered as **Log[y]**:

In[534]:= $\texttt{Plot}\Big[\Big\{\texttt{ArcTanh[x]}, \frac{1}{2}\ \texttt{Log}\Big[\frac{1+x}{1-x}\Big]\Big\}, \{x, -2, 2\}\Big]$

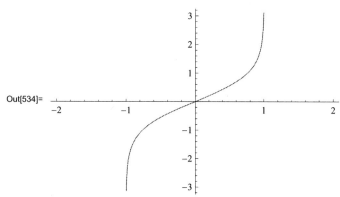

Out[534]=

The fact that there is only one graph indicates that the functions are the same. We prove this by letting $y = \tanh^{-1} x$ and solving for y as follows. From $y = \tanh^{-1} x$ we get $x = \tanh y = \frac{e^y - e^{-y}}{e^y + e^{-y}}$. Now solving this last equation for y in *Mathematica* yields:

In[535]:= $\texttt{Solve[x == (E\^y - E\^(-y)) / (E\^y + E\^(-y)), y]}$

Solve::ifun : Inverse functions are being used by Solve, so
some solutions may not be found; use Reduce for complete solution information. ≫

Out[535]= $\Big\{\Big\{y \to \texttt{Log}\Big[-\frac{\sqrt{-1-x}}{\sqrt{-1+x}}\Big]\Big\}, \Big\{y \to \texttt{Log}\Big[\frac{\sqrt{-1-x}}{\sqrt{-1+x}}\Big]\Big\}\Big\}$

The first solution in the preceding output is imaginary, which we ignore, and consider only the second solution. Hence,

$$\tanh^{-1} x = y = \ln\frac{\sqrt{-1-x}}{\sqrt{-1+x}} = \ln\sqrt{\frac{1+x}{1-x}} = \frac{1}{2}\ln\left(\frac{1+x}{1-x}\right).$$

NOTE: The message in the previous output refers to the fact that when solving equations involving inverse functions, not all solutions are necessarily found by *Mathematica* since there may be infinitely many of them or they depend on the domain of definition. For example, the equation $\sin x = 1$ has infinitely many solutions, in particular all values of the form $x = \pi/2 + 2\pi n$, where n is any integer. On the other hand, solving this equation in *Mathematica* yields only the solution in its principal domain, that is, $x = \pi/2$:

In[536]:= $\texttt{Solve[Sin[x] == 1, x]}$

Solve::ifun : Inverse functions are being used by Solve, so
some solutions may not be found; use Reduce for complete solution information. ≫

Out[536]= $\Big\{\Big\{x \to \frac{\pi}{2}\Big\}\Big\}$

■ Exercises

In Exercises 1 through 5, verify the given hyperbolic identities using the **Simplify** command. Also state the corresponding trigonometric identity.

1. $\sinh(x + y) = \sinh x \cosh y + \cosh x \sinh y$

2. $\cosh 2x = \cosh^2 x + \sinh^2 x$

3. $\tanh 2x = \frac{2\tanh x}{1+\tanh^2 x}$

4. $\cosh(x + y) = \cosh x \cosh y + \text{sonh } x \sinh y$

5. $\tanh(x + y) = \frac{\tanh x + \tanh y}{1 + \tanh x \tanh y}$

6. Determine the first few positive integral powers of $\cosh x + \sinh x$. Can you form a general conjecture for the nth case, namely $(\cosh x + \sinh x)^n$, where n is any natural number? Then justify your conclusion via mathematical induction.

 In Exercises 7 through 12, determine the derivatives of thegiven functions and simplify your answers where possible. Compare your solution via paper and pencil methods with the one generated by *Mathematica*.

7. $f(x) = \tanh\left(1 + x^2\right)$

8. $f(x) = x \sinh x - \cosh x$

9. $f(x) = \sqrt{\frac{1+\tanh x}{1-\tanh x}}$

10. $f(x) = x^2 \sinh^{-1}(2x)$

11. $f(x) = x \tanh^{-1} x + \ln\left(\sqrt{1 - x^2}\right)$

12. $f(x) = x \coth x - \operatorname{sech} x$

13. The Gateway Arch in St. Louis was designed by Eero Saarinen and was constructed using the equation

$$y = 211.49 - 20.96 \cosh(0.03291765 x)$$

for the central curve of the arch, where x and y are measured in meters and $|x| \le 91.20$.

a) Plot the graph of the central curve.
b) What is the height of the arch at its center?
c) At what points is the arch 100 meters in height?
d) What is the slope of the arch at the points in part (c)?

14. A flexible cable always hangs in the shape of a catenary $y = c + a \cosh(x/a)$, where c and a are constants and $a > 0$. Plot several members of the family of functions $y = a \cosh(x/a)$ for various values of a. How does the graph change as a varies?

In Exercises 15 through 17, evaluate each of the given integrals:

15. $\int \sinh x \cosh^n x \, dx$

16. $\int \frac{\cosh x}{\cosh^2 x - 1} \, dx$

17. $\int \frac{\operatorname{sech}^2 x}{2 + \tanh x} \, dx$

18. Let $t = \ln\left(\frac{1+\sqrt{5}}{2}\right)$ and define

$$f(n) = \begin{cases} \frac{2}{\sqrt{5}} \cosh(t n), & \text{if } n \text{ is odd} \\ \frac{2}{\sqrt{5}} \sinh(t n), & \text{if } n \text{ is even} \end{cases}$$

Evaluate $f(n)$ for $n = 1, 2, 3, \ldots, 20$. Do these values seem familiar? If not, we highly recommend the interesting article by Thomas Osler, *Vieta-like products of nested radicals with Fibonacci and Lucas numbers*, to appear in the journal *Fibonacci Quarterly*.

Chapter 8   Further Applications of Integration

■ 8.1 Arc Length and Surface Area

Students should read Section 8.1 of Rogawski's *Calculus* [1] for a detailed discussion of the material presented in this section.

■ 8.1.1 Arc Length

The integrals for calculating arc length and surface area are generally difficult to do by hand. Thus, *Mathematica* is the appropriate tool for evaluating these integrals.

If y is a function of x, that is, $y = f(x)$, and $f'(x)$ exists and is continuous on $[a, b]$, then the arc length of the graph of $f(x)$ over the interval $[a, b]$ is

$$L = \int_a^b \sqrt{1 + f'(x)^2} \, dx$$

If x is a function of y, that is, $x = g(y)$, and $g'(y)$ exists and is continuous on $[c, d]$, then the arc length of the graph of $g(y)$ over the interval $[c, d]$ is

$$L = \int_c^d \sqrt{f'(y)^2 + 1} \, dy$$

Example 8.1. Estimate the arc length of $y = \frac{1}{x}$ over the interval $[1, 2]$.

Solution: Finding the arc length of this simple rational function by hand is virtually impossible. This is because $f'(x) = -\frac{1}{x^2}$ and thus the arc length integral is $L = \int_1^2 \sqrt{1 + \frac{1}{x^4}} \, dx$, which cannot be evaluated in terms of elementary functions, as the following answer illustrates.

In[537]:= $\int_1^2 \sqrt{1 + \frac{1}{x^4}} \, dx$

Out[537]= $\dfrac{\sqrt{2\pi}\ \text{Gamma}\left[\frac{7}{4}\right]}{3\ \text{Gamma}\left[\frac{5}{4}\right]} - \dfrac{1}{2}\ \text{Hypergeometric2F1}\left[-\frac{1}{2}, -\frac{1}{4}, \frac{3}{4}, -16\right]$

However, there are numerical techniques that we can use. For example, the *Mathematica* command **NIntegrate** uses sophisticated algorithms to gives us a good estimate for this definite integral:

In[538]:= **NIntegrate** $\left[\sqrt{1 + \frac{1}{x^4}}, \{x, 1, 2\}\right]$

Out[538]= 1.13209

A more elementary method of estimating this arc length is Simpson's Rule as shown in Section 7.1 of this text.

In[539]:= `Clear[f, a, b, n]`
`SIMP[a_, b_, n_, f_] :=`
`(1 / 3) Sum[f[a + (2 i - 2) (b - a) / n] + 4 f[a + (2 i - 1) (b - a) / n] +`
`f[a + 2 i (b - a) / n], {i, 1, n / 2}] (b - a) / n`

In[541]:= $f[x\_] := \sqrt{1 + \dfrac{1}{x^4}}$

`TableForm[Table[{n, N[SIMP[1, 2, n, f]]}, {n, 10, 100, 10}],`
`TableHeadings → {{}, {"n", "`S_n`"}}]`

Out[542]//TableForm=

n	S_n
10	1.1321
20	1.13209
30	1.13209
40	1.13209
50	1.13209
60	1.13209
70	1.13209
80	1.13209
90	1.13209
100	1.13209

Thus, we see that Simpson's Rule gives us as accurate an estimate of the arc length, as does the **NIntegrate** command for *n* as small as 20.

Example 8.2. Consider the the ellipse whose equation is given by

$$\frac{x^2}{a^2} + \frac{y^2}{b^2} = 1$$

Assume that $a > b$. Find the arc length of the upper half of the ellipse.

Solution: To plot the ellipse for various values of *a* and *b*, we define a plotting command **plot[a,b]** as follows.

In[543]:= `Clear[a, b, x, y, eq, plot]`
$eq[x\_, y\_, a\_, b\_] := \dfrac{x^2}{a^2} + \dfrac{y^2}{b^2} - 1$
`plot[a_, b_] := ContourPlot[eq[x, y, a, b] == 0, {x, -a, a}, {y, -b, b},`
`AspectRatio → Automatic, Axes → True, Frame → False]`

Here is a plot of the ellipse for $a = 2$ and $b = 3$.

In[546]:= **plot[2, 3]**

Out[546]=

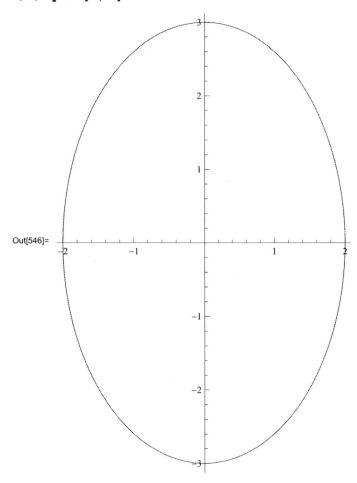

On the upper half of the ellipse, we have $y \geq 0$. Thus, we can solve for y and and take the positive solution. We will denote this positive solution as a function of x, a, and b.

In[547]:= **sol = Solve$\left[\dfrac{x^2}{a^2} + \dfrac{y^2}{b^2} == 1, y\right]$;**

f[x_, a_, b_] = sol[[2, 1, 2]]

Out[548]= $\dfrac{b\sqrt{a^2 - x^2}}{a}$

Clearly, the domain of f is $[-a, a]$. The natural thing to do would be to evaluate the integral $\int_{-a}^{a} \sqrt{1 + (f'(x))^2}\ dx$. Try this yourself, but be prepared to wait awhile. Moreover, *Mathematica* will give the following output:

$$\text{If}\left[\text{Im}[a] == 0\ \&\&\ \left(a\,\text{Im}\left[\dfrac{1}{\sqrt{-a^2 + b^2}}\right] \geq 1\ ||\right.\right.$$

$$\left.\left. 1 + a\,\text{Im}\left[\dfrac{1}{\sqrt{-a^2 + b^2}}\right] \leq 0\ ||\ a\,\text{Im}\left[\dfrac{1}{\sqrt{-a^2 + b^2}}\right] == 0\ ||\ a\,\text{Re}\left[\dfrac{1}{\sqrt{-a^2 + b^2}}\right] \neq 0\right),$$

$$\frac{2\,(-a)^{3/2}\,\sqrt{b^2}\;\text{EllipticE}\!\left[1-\frac{b^2}{a^2}\right]\text{Sign}[a]}{\sqrt{-a\,b^2}}\,,\;\text{Integrate}\!\left[\sqrt{1+\frac{b^2\,x^2}{a^4-a^2\,x^2}}\,,\;\{x,\,-a,\,a\}\,,\right.$$

$$\left.\text{Assumptions}\to(\text{Re}[b]==0\;\&\&\;\text{Re}[a]\neq0\;\&\&\;\text{Im}[a]==0\;\&\&\;\text{Im}[b]\neq0)\;||\;\text{Im}[a]<0\;||\;\text{Im}[a]>0\right]$$

To understand this output, let us make a change of variable $x = a \sin t$. Then the integral becomes (verify this)

$$\int_{-a}^{a}\sqrt{1+(f'(x))^2}\;dx = a\int_{-\pi/2}^{\pi/2}\sqrt{1+\frac{b^2\sin^2 t}{a^2\cos^2 t}}\;\cos t\,d t$$

The latter integral can be expressed as

$$2\,a\int_{0}^{\pi/2}\sqrt{1+\frac{b^2\sin^2 t}{a^2\cos^2 t}}\;\cos t\,d t = 2\,a\int_{0}^{\pi/2}\sqrt{\cos^2 t+\left(b^2/a^2\right)\sin^2 t}\;d t = 2\,a\int_{0}^{\pi/2}\sqrt{1-c^2\sin^2 t}\;d t,$$

where $c = \sqrt{1-(b/a)^2}$ and we have used the identity $\cos^2 t = 1 - \sin^2 t$.

To simplify our notation, let us define the integrand in the preceding far left integral as

In[549]:= **g[t_, a_, b_] = $\sqrt{1-\left(1-(b/a)^2\right)(\text{Sin}[t])^2}$**

Out[549]= $\sqrt{1-\left(1-\dfrac{b^2}{a^2}\right)\text{Sin}[t]^2}$

Here are some values of the arc length of the upper half of the ellipse.

In[550]:= **TableForm$\left[\text{Table}\!\left[2\,a\int_{0}^{\pi/2}\text{g}[t,\,a,\,b]\;dt,\,\{a,\,1,\,3\},\,\{b,\,1,\,3\}\right],\right.$**

TableHeadings $\to$ {{"a=1", "a=2", "a=3"}, {"b=1", "b=2", "b=3"}}$\Big]$

Out[550]//TableForm=

	b=1	b=2	b=3
a=1	π	$2\,\text{EllipticE}[-3]$	$2\,\text{EllipticE}[-8]$
a=2	$4\,\text{EllipticE}\!\left[\frac{3}{4}\right]$	$2\,\pi$	$4\,\text{EllipticE}\!\left[-\frac{5}{4}\right]$
a=3	$6\,\text{EllipticE}\!\left[\frac{8}{9}\right]$	$6\,\text{EllipticE}\!\left[\frac{5}{9}\right]$	$3\,\pi$

Observe that we obtain exact values for the arc length when $a = b$. Can you explain why?

The approximate values of the numbers appearing in the preceding table are as follows:

In[551]:= **TableForm$\left[\text{N}\!\left[\text{Table}\!\left[2\,a\int_{0}^{\pi/2}\text{g}[t,\,a,\,b]\;dt,\,\{a,\,1,\,3\},\,\{b,\,1,\,3\}\right],\,10\right],\right.$**

TableHeadings $\to$ {{"a=1", "a=2", "a=3"}, {"b=1", "b=2", "b=3"}}$\Big]$

Out[551]//TableForm=

	b=1	b=2	b=3
a=1	3.141592654	4.844224110	6.682446610
a=2	4.844224110	6.283185307	7.932719795
a=3	6.682446610	7.932719795	9.424777961

NOTE: The integral $\int \sqrt{1 - c^2 \sin^2 t}\ dt$ is known as an *elliptic integral*. It is very useful in mathematics and has many applications. In *Mathematica*, it is denoted by **Elliptic[t,c^2]**. The command **Elliptic[x,m]** gives $\int_0^x \sqrt{1 - m \sin^2 t}\ dt$, while **Elliptic[m]** gives $\int_0^{\pi/2} \sqrt{1 - m \sin^2 t}\ dt$.

■ 8.1.2 Surface Area

If $f'(x)$ exists and is continuous on $[a, b]$, then the surface area of revolution obtained by rotating the graph of $f(x)$ about the x-axis for $a \le x \le b$ is

$$S = 2\pi \int_a^b f(x) \sqrt{1 + [f'(x)]^2}\ dx$$

Similarly, if $x = g(y)$ and $g'(y)$ exists and is continuous on $[c, d]$, then the surface area of revolution obtained by rotating $g(y)$ about the y-axis for $c \le y \le d$ is

$$S = 2\pi \int_c^d g(y) \sqrt{[g'(y)]^2 + 1}\ dy$$

Again, evaluating these complicated integrals is what *Mathematica* does best, as the following examples illustrate.

Example 8.3. Determine the surface area of revolution obtained by rotating the region under $y = e^{-x}$ along the interval $[0, 2]$ about the x-axis.

Solution: We calculate

In[552]:= **Clear[f, x]**
f[x_] := e^{-x}
S = 2 π $\int_0^2$ f[x] $\sqrt{1 + f'[x]^2}$ dx

Out[554]= $\frac{1}{2} \pi \left(4 + 2\sqrt{2} - \frac{2}{\sqrt{1+e^4}} - \frac{2}{e^4 \sqrt{1+e^4}} + \text{Log}\left[3 + 2\sqrt{2}\right] - \text{Log}\left[2 + e^4 + 2\sqrt{1+e^4}\right] \right)$

In[555]:= **N[%]**

Out[555]= 6.35887

Here is the corresponding surface of revolution (rotated $90°$ about the y-axis):

In[556]:= **RevolutionPlot3D[E⁻ˣ, {x, 0, 2}]**

Out[556]=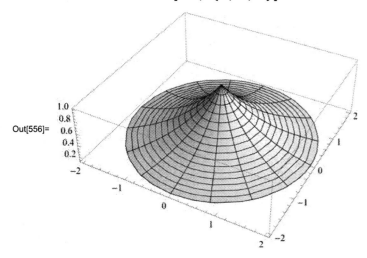

NOTE: Observe that in this case *Mathematica* was able to find an anti-derivative of the integrand. However, not all integrals of this form can be evaluated analytically as the next example illustrates.

Example 8.4. Determine the surface area of revolution obtained by rotating the region under $y = \tan x$ along the interval $\left[0, \frac{\pi}{4}\right]$ about the *x*-axis.

Solution: As in the previous example, we evaluate

In[557]:= **Clear[f, x]**
f[x_] := Tan[x]
NIntegrate$\left[2 \pi \, f[x] \sqrt{1 + f'[x]^2}\, , \{x, 0, Pi / 4\}\right]$

Out[559]= 3.83908

To appreciate the complexity of the integral and understand why we used the command **NIntegrate**, we advise the reader to define the anti-derivative **F[t]** below and evaluate **F[π/4]** (be prepared to wait awhile).

In[560]:= **F[t_] := Integrate$\left[f[x] \sqrt{1 + f'[x]^2}\, , \{x, 0, t\}\right]$**

Here is the corresponding surface of revolution:

In[561]:= **RevolutionPlot3D[Tan[x], {x, 0, Pi / 4}]**

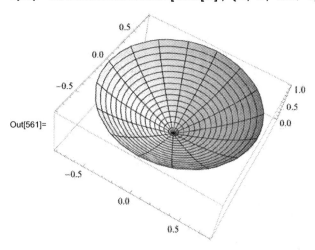

Out[561]=

■ Exercises

In Exercises 1 and 2, calculate the arc length of the given function over the given interval:

1. $y = x^4$, over $[1, 2]$ 2. $y = \sin x$, over $\left[0, \frac{\pi}{2}\right]$

3. Calculate the arc length of the astroid $x^{2/3} + y^{2/3} = 1$. Below is a plot of its graph. Hint: By symmetry it suffices to calculate only the portion in the first quadrant.

In[562]:= **ContourPlot[(x^2) ^ (1 / 3) + (y^2) ^ (1 / 3) == 1, {x, -1, 1}, {y, -1, 1}]**

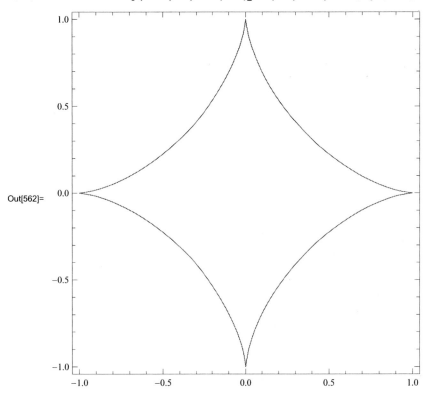

Out[562]=

4. Show that the circumference of the unit circle is 2π by calculating its arc length. Use the fact that the equation of the unit circle is given by $x^2 + y^2 = 1$.

In Exercises 5 through 7, compute the surface area of the given functions rotated about the *x*-axis over the given intervals:

5. $y = x^3 + \frac{1}{x}$, over [1, 4]   6. $y = \left(4 - x^{2/3}\right)^{2/3}$ over [0, 8]   7. $y = \cos x$, over [0, π]

8. Show that the surface area of the unit sphere is 4π by rotating the top half of the unit circle $x^2 + y^2 = 1$ about the *x*-axis.

■ 8.2 Center of Mass

Students should read Section 8.3 of Rogawski's *Calculus* [1] for a detailed discussion of the material presented in this section.

A *lamina* is a thin plate whose mass is distributed throughout a region in the plane. Suppose a lamina has a constant density ρ and that the lamina occupies a region in the plane under the graph of a continuous function f over the interval [*a*, *b*], where $f(x) \geq 0$ for all *x*.

The *mass* of the lamina is given by

$$M = \rho \int_a^b f(x)\, dx$$

Then the *moments* of the lamina with respect to *x*-axis and *y*-axis are denoted by M_x and M_y and are defined by

$$M_x = \frac{1}{2} \rho \int_a^b [f(x)]^2\, dx$$

$$M_y = \rho \int_a^b x\, f(x)\, dx$$

The *center of mass* (also called the *centroid*) of the lamina is defined to be $(\overline{x}, \overline{y})$, where

$$\overline{x} = \frac{M_y}{M} \text{ and } \overline{y} = \frac{M_x}{M}$$

NOTE: If the lamina described above as a density ρ that continuously depends on *x*, that is, if $\rho = \rho(x)$ for *x* in the interval [*a*, *b*], then the moments, the total mass, and the center of mass are given by

$$M = \int_a^b \rho(x)\, f(x)\, dx$$

$$M_x = \frac{1}{2} \int_a^b \rho(x)[f(x)]^2\, dx$$

$$M_y = \int_a^b x\, \rho(x)\, f(x)\, dx$$

$$\overline{x} = \frac{M_y}{M} \text{ and } \overline{y} = \frac{M_x}{M}$$

Example 8.5. Suppose a lamina lies underneath the graph of $y = 16 - x^2$ and over the interval [−4, 4].

a) Assume the density of the lamina is $\rho = 3$. Find the mass, moments, and the center of mass of the lamina.
b) Assume the density of the lamina is $\rho = \frac{x}{2} + 2$. Find the mass, moments, and the center of mass of the lamina.

Solution:

a) We use the above formulas with $\rho = 3$:

In[563]:= $\mathbf{f[x\_] = 16 - x^2}$

Out[563]= $16 - x^2$

The mass is given by

In[564]:= $\mathbf{M = 3 \int_{-4}^{4} f[x] \, dx}$

Out[564]= 256

The moment with respect to the *x*-axis is

In[565]:= $\mathbf{Mx = (3/2) \int_{-4}^{4} (f[x])^2 \, dx}$

Out[565]= $\dfrac{8192}{5}$

The moment with respect to the *y*-axis is

In[566]:= $\mathbf{My = 3 \int_{-4}^{4} x \, f[x] \, dx}$

Out[566]= 0

The coordinates for the center of mass are

In[567]:= $\mathbf{xbar = My / M}$
$\mathbf{ybar = Mx / M}$

Out[567]= 0

Out[568]= $\dfrac{32}{5}$

Observe that the region of the lamina is symmetric with respect to the *y*-axis. Hence, the fact that $\bar{x} = 0$ is also clear from the fact that the density is a constant.

Below is the plot of the lamina and its center of mass:

In[569]:= $\mathbf{plot1 = Plot[f[x], \{x, -4, 4\}, Filling \rightarrow Axis];}$
$\mathbf{plot2 = ListPlot[\{\{xbar, ybar\}\}, PlotStyle \rightarrow \{PointSize[0.02], Red\}];}$
$\mathbf{Show[plot1, plot2]}$

Out[571]=

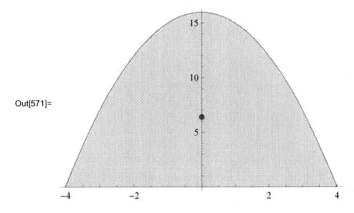

b) Here, $\rho = x + 4$. With the above notation we have

In[572]:= $f[x\_] = 16 - x^2$
$\rho[x\_] = \dfrac{x}{2} + 2$

Out[572]= $16 - x^2$

Out[573]= $2 + \dfrac{x}{2}$

The mass is

In[574]:= $Mv = \displaystyle\int_{-4}^{4} \rho[x]\, f[x]\, dx$

Out[574]= $\dfrac{512}{3}$

The moment with respect to the *x*-axis is

In[575]:= $Mxv = (1 / 2) \displaystyle\int_{-4}^{4} \rho[x]\, (f[x])^2\, dx$

Out[575]= $\dfrac{16\,384}{15}$

The moment with respect to the *y*-axis is

In[576]:= $Myv = \displaystyle\int_{-4}^{4} \rho[x]\, x\, f[x]\, dx$

Out[576]= $\dfrac{2048}{15}$

The coordinates for the center of mass are

In[577]:= $xbarv = Myv / M$
$ybarv = Mxv / M$

Out[577]= $\dfrac{8}{15}$

Out[578]= $\dfrac{64}{15}$

Here is a plot of the lamina showing the center of masses with the uniform density of $\rho = 3$ and variable density of $\rho = \frac{x}{2} + 2$ represented by the red and green dots, respectively.

In[579]:= `plot3 = ListPlot[{{ xbarv, ybarv}}, PlotStyle → {Green, PointSize[.02]}];`
`Show[plot1, plot2, plot3]`

Out[580]=

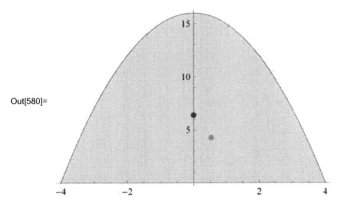

NOTE: Observe that the center of mass with variable density (green dot) is shifted to the right, as expected, since the density is more weighted to the right.

Example 8.6. Suppose a lamina covers the top half of the ellipse

$$\frac{x^2}{a^2} + \frac{y^2}{b^2} = 1$$

a) Assume the density of the lamina is $\rho = 1$. Find the mass, moments and the center of mass of the lamina.
b) Assume the density of the lamina is $\rho = e^{-x}$. Find the mass, moments and the center of mass of the lamina.

Solution: To distinguish between the uniform and variable density cases in parts a) and b), respectively, we attach the letter **u** and **v** to the notation in this solution. Thus, **Mu** will be the mass corresponding to the uniform density while **Mv** is the mass corresponding the variable density.

a) We solve the equation of the ellipse for y:

In[581]:= `Clear[a, b, x, y]`

$$sol = Solve\left[\frac{x^2}{a^2} + \frac{y^2}{b^2} == 1, y\right]$$

Out[582]= $\left\{\left\{y \rightarrow -\frac{b\sqrt{a^2 - x^2}}{a}\right\}, \left\{y \rightarrow \frac{b\sqrt{a^2 - x^2}}{a}\right\}\right\}$

In the top half of the ellipse , we have $y \geq 0$. Thus, we take the second solution, simplify, and define it as a function of x, a, and b

In[583]:= `fa[x_, a_, b_] := b`$\sqrt{1 - \frac{x^2}{a^2}}$

Let the mass, the moment with respect to the x-axis, the moment with respect to the $y-$ axis , and the center of mass be denoted by $M(a, b)$, $M_x(a, b)$, $M_y(a, b)$, and $(\bar{x}(a, b), \bar{y}(a, b))$, respectively. We now compute these quantities assuming $\rho = 1$.

In[584]:= **Clear[a, b, Mua, Mxua, Myua, xbaru, ybaru]**

Mua[a_ , b_] = $\int_{-a}^{a}$ fa[x, a, b] dx

Mxua[a_ , b_] = (1 / 2) $\int_{-a}^{a}$ (fa[x, a, b])^2 dx

Myua[a_ , b_] = $\int_{-a}^{a}$ x fa[x, a, b] dx

Out[585]= $\dfrac{a\,b\,\pi}{2}$

Out[586]= $\dfrac{2\,a\,b^2}{3}$

Out[587]= 0

In[588]:= **xbarua[a_ , b_] = $\dfrac{\text{Myua[a, b]}}{\text{Mua[a, b]}}$**

ybarua[a_ , b_] = $\dfrac{\text{Mxua[a, b]}}{\text{Mua[a, b]}}$

Out[588]= 0

Out[589]= $\dfrac{4\,b}{3\,\pi}$

That $\bar{x} = 0$ is also clear from the fact that the density is a constant and the upper half of the ellipse is symmetric with respect to the y−axis.

The mass of the lamina, the moments of the lamina with respect to the x- and y-axis for various values of a and b are as follows:

```
In[590]:= umassa = TableForm[Table[Mua[a, b], {a, 1, 3}, {b, 1, 3}],
            TableHeadings → {{"a=1", "a=2", "a=3"}, {"b=1", "b=2", "b=3"}}];
        uxmomenta = TableForm[ Table[Mxua[a, b] , {a, 1, 3}, {b, 1, 3}] ,
            TableHeadings → {{"a=1", "a=2", "a=3"}, {"b=1", "b=2", "b=3"}}];
        uymomenta = TableForm[ Table[Myua[a, b] , {a, 1, 3}, {b, 1, 3}] ,
            TableHeadings → {{"a=1", "a=2", "a=3"}, {"b=1", "b=2", "b=3"}}];
        TableForm[{umassa, uxmomenta, uymomenta},
          TableHeadings → {{"Mass", "x-moment", "y-moment"}, {}}]
```

Out[593]//TableForm=

		b=1	b=2	b=3
	a=1	$\frac{\pi}{2}$	π	$\frac{3\pi}{2}$
Mass	a=2	π	2π	3π
	a=3	$\frac{3\pi}{2}$	3π	$\frac{9\pi}{2}$
		b=1	b=2	b=3
	a=1	$\frac{2}{3}$	$\frac{8}{3}$	6
x-moment	a=2	$\frac{4}{3}$	$\frac{16}{3}$	12
	a=3	2	8	18
		b=1	b=2	b=3
	a=1	0	0	0
y-moment	a=2	0	0	0
	a=3	0	0	0

The corresponding *y*-coordinate of the center of mass in each case is (recall that $\bar{x} = 0$ for all cases)

```
In[594]:= centermassua = Table[ Mxua[a, b] / Mua[a, b] , {a, 1, 3}, {b, 1, 3}];

        TableForm[centermassua,
          TableHeadings → {{"a=1", "a=2", "a=3"}, {"b=1", "b=2", "b=3"}}]
```

Out[595]//TableForm=

	b=1	b=2	b=3
a=1	$\frac{4}{3\pi}$	$\frac{8}{3\pi}$	$\frac{4}{\pi}$
a=2	$\frac{4}{3\pi}$	$\frac{8}{3\pi}$	$\frac{4}{\pi}$
a=3	$\frac{4}{3\pi}$	$\frac{8}{3\pi}$	$\frac{4}{\pi}$

The following animation shows how the center of mass changes as *a* and *b* varies.

```
In[596]:= plot4a[a_, b_] :=
          Plot[f[x, a, b], {x, -a, a}, PlotRange → {{-5, 5}, {-15, 15}}, Filling → Axis];

        plot5a[a_, b_] := ListPlot[{{ Myua[a, b] / Mua[a, b] , Mxua[a, b] / Mua[a, b] }},

          PlotStyle → {Red, PointSize[0.02]}]

        plotua[a_, b_] := Show[plot4a[a, b], plot5a[a, b]]
```

Important Note:: If you are reading the printed version of this publication, then you will not be able to view any of the animations generated from the **Animate** command in this chapter. If you are reading the electronic version of this publication formatted as a *Mathematica* Notebook, then evaluate each **Animate** command to view the corresponding animation. Just click on the arrow button to start the animation. To control the animation just click at various points on the sliding bar or else manually drag the bar.

In[599]:= **Animate[plotua[a, b], {a, 1, 8}, {b, 1, 10}]**

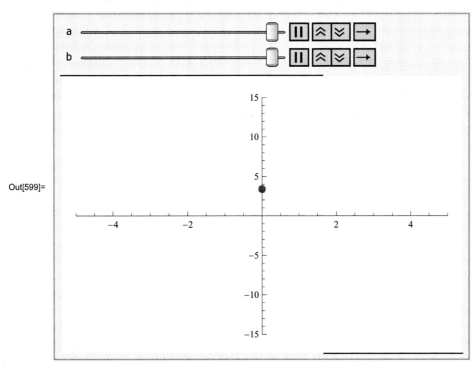

Out[599]=

b) Here, $\rho = e^{-x}$. With the above notations modified to reflect variable density, we have

In[600]:= **Clear[a, b, Mv, Mxv, Myv, xbarv, ybarv]**

ρ[x_] = E^{-x}

Mvb[a_, b_] = $\int_{-a}^{a} \rho$[x] fa[x, a, b] dx

Mxvb[a_, b_] = (1 / 2) $\int_{-a}^{a} \rho$[x] (fa[x, a, b])^2 dx

Myvb[a_, b_] = $\int_{-a}^{a} \rho$[x] x fa[x, a, b] dx

Out[601]= e^{-x}

Out[602]= ConditionalExpression[b π BesselI[1, a], a > 0]

Out[603]= $\dfrac{2 b^2 (a \, Cosh[a] - Sinh[a])}{a^2}$

Out[604]= ConditionalExpression[-a b π BesselI[2, a], a > 0]

In[605]:= $\texttt{xbarvb[a\_, b\_]} = \dfrac{\texttt{Myvb[a, b]}}{\texttt{Mvb[a, b]}}$

$\texttt{ybarv[a\_, b\_]} = \dfrac{\texttt{Mxvb[a, b]}}{\texttt{Mvb[a, b]}}$

Out[605]= $\texttt{ConditionalExpression}\left[-\dfrac{a\,\texttt{BesselI}[2, a]}{\texttt{BesselI}[1, a]}, a > 0\right]$

Out[606]= $\texttt{ConditionalExpression}\left[\dfrac{2\,b\,(a\,\texttt{Cosh}[a] - \texttt{Sinh}[a])}{a^2\,\pi\,\texttt{BesselI}[1, a]}, a > 0\right]$

Observe that the formulas for the mass and moments of the lamina are no longer elementary. Here is a table of numerical values for these quantities assuming various choices for a and b:

In[607]:= ```
umassb = TableForm[Table[Mvb[a, b], {a, 1, 3}, {b, 1, 3}],
    TableHeadings → {{"a=1", "a=2", "a=3"}, {"b=1", "b=2", "b=3"}}];
uxmomentb = TableForm[Table[Mxvb[a, b] , {a, 1, 3}, {b, 1, 3}] ,
    TableHeadings → {{"a=1", "a=2", "a=3"}, {"b=1", "b=2", "b=3"}}];
uymomentb = TableForm[Table[Myvb[a, b] , {a, 1, 3}, {b, 1, 3}] ,
    TableHeadings → {{"a=1", "a=2", "a=3"}, {"b=1", "b=2", "b=3"}}];
TableForm[N[{umassb, uxmomentb, uymomentb}],
  TableHeadings → {{"Mass", "x-moment", "y-moment"}, {}}]
```

Out[610]//TableForm=

| | | b=1 | b=2 | b=3 |
|---|---|---|---|---|
| Mass | a=1 | 1.7755 | 3.551 | 5.3265 |
| | a=2 | 4.99713 | 9.99427 | 14.9914 |
| | a=3 | 12.4199 | 24.8398 | 37.2596 |
| | | b=1 | b=2 | b=3 |
| x-moment | a=1 | 0.735759 | 2.94304 | 6.62183 |
| | a=2 | 1.94877 | 7.79506 | 17.5389 |
| | a=3 | 4.48558 | 17.9423 | 40.3702 |
| | | b=1 | b=2 | b=3 |
| y-moment | a=1 | −0.426464 | −0.852928 | −1.27939 |
| | a=2 | −4.32879 | −8.65758 | −12.9864 |
| | a=3 | −21.1606 | −42.3213 | −63.4819 |

The coordinates for the center of mass are

In[611]:= $\texttt{centermassvb} = \texttt{N}\left[\texttt{Table}\left[\left\{\dfrac{\texttt{Myvb[a, b]}}{\texttt{Mvb[a, b]}}, \dfrac{\texttt{Mxvb[a, b]}}{\texttt{Mvb[a, b]}}\right\}, \{a, 1, 3\}, \{b, 1, 3\}\right]\right]$

Out[611]= {{{-0.240194, 0.414395}, {-0.240194, 0.828791}, {-0.240194, 1.24319}},
    {{-0.866255, 0.389977}, {-0.866255, 0.779953}, {-0.866255, 1.16993}},
    {{-1.70377, 0.361161}, {-1.70377, 0.722323}, {-1.70377, 1.08348}}}

Here is a plot showing the two centers of mass with for uniform and variable density.
```

In[612]:=
```
plot4b[a_, b_] := Plot[f[x, a, b], {x, -a, a},
    PlotRange → {{-8, 8}, {-1, 8}}, AspectRatio → Automatic, Filling → Axis];
plot5b[a_, b_] := ListPlot[{{Myvb[a, b]/Mvb[a, b], Mxvb[a, b]/Mvb[a, b]}},
    PlotStyle → {Green, PointSize[0.02]}]
plotvb[a_, b_] := Show[plot4b[a, b], plot5b[a, b]]
```

Important Note: If you are reading the printed version of this publication, then you will not be able to view any of the animations generated from the **Animate** command in this chapter. If you are reading the electronic version of this publication formatted as a *Mathematica* Notebook, then evaluate each **Animate** command to view the corresponding animation. Just click on the arrow button to start the animation. To control the animation just click at various points on the sliding bar or else manually drag the bar.

In[615]:= **Animate[plotvb[a, b], {a, 1, 8}, {b, 1, 8}]**

Out[615]=

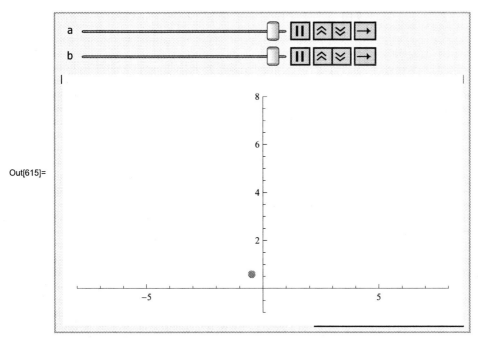

■ Exercises

1. Suppose a lamina is lying underneath the graph of $y = 1 + x^2$ over the interval $[0, 2]$.
a) Assume the density of the lamina is $\rho = 3$. Find the mass, moments, and the center of mass of the lamina.
b) Assume the density of the lamina is $\rho = 2x$. Find the mass, moments, and the center of mass of the lamina.
c) Plot the lamina and the center of mass on the same axes for both parts a) and b) above.

2. Suppose a lamina of constant density $\rho = 2$ is in the shape of the astroid $x^{2/3} + y^{2/3} = 1$. Find its mass, moments, and center of mass. Plot the lamina with its center of mass.

Chapter 9   Introduction to Differential Equations

■ 9.1 Solving Differential Equations

Students should read Section 9.1 of Rogawski's *Calculus* [1] for a detailed discussion of the material presented in this section.

An *ordinary differential equation* is an equation that involves an unknown function, its derivatives, and an independent variable. Differential equations are useful for modeling many physical phenomena some of which are discussed in the next section.

Given a differential equation, our objective is to find all functions that satisfy it. *Mathematica*'s command for solving a differential equation is **DSolve[eqn,y[x],x]** where **eqn** is the differential equation to be solved and **y[x]** is the unknown function that depends on the independent variable **x**.

If the differential equation has initial conditions, we use braces { } to group the equation as well as the initial conditions (separated by commas): **DSolve[{eqn,cond1,cond2,...,condn},y[x],x]**, where **cond1, cond2,...,condn** are initial conditions.

■ 9.1.1. Separation of Variables

As discussed in your textbook, there is a special class of first-order differential equations that can be solved by hand using the method of separation of variables. *Mathematica* can help in applying this method but of course it can solve the differential equation outright. This makes *Mathematica* useful for verifying solutions obtained by other methods or for solving more complicated differential equations. Since your textbook focuses on solving differential equations by hand, we will primarily discuss how to solve them using *Mathematica*.

Example 9.1. Solve the given differential equation and plot the graph of the solutions.

a) $y' = 2(4 - y)$, $y(0) = 1$ b) $\sqrt{1 - x^2}\ y' = x y$ c) $y\dfrac{dy}{dx} + 5x = 0$

Solution:

a) This is an initial value problem. Let us first solve this differential equation by hand using the method of separation of variables:

$$\frac{dy}{dx} = 2(4 - y) \quad \Longrightarrow \quad \frac{dy}{y-4} = -2\,dx$$

$$\int \frac{dy}{y-4} = -\int 2\,dx$$

$$\log|y - 4| = -2x + C$$

$$|y - 4| = e^{-2x+C} = e^C e^{-2x}$$

$$y - 4 = \pm e^C e^{-2x} = C e^{-2x} \ (\pm e^C \text{ replaced by } C)$$

This shows that the general solution is given by

$$y = C e^{-2x} + 4$$

It remains to determine the value of the constant C using the initial condition $y(0) = 1$ (recall from your textbook that each value of C corresponds to a particular solution):

$$1 = y(0) = C e^{-2\cdot0} + 4 = C + 4$$

Thus, $C = -3$ and the unique solution is

$$y = -3 e^{-2x} + 4$$

Next, let us confirm this solution using *Mathematica*. Recall that when entering a differential equation in *Mathematica*, we write $y[x]$ instead of y to make explicit the dependence on x.

In[616]:= **sola = DSolve[{y'[x] == 2 (4 - y[x])}, y[x], x]**

Out[616]= $\left\{\left\{y[x] \to 4 + e^{-2x} C[1]\right\}\right\}$

This solution agrees with the solution obtained earlier by hand (the arbitrary constant $C[1]$ is the same to the constant C). We can visualize the behavior of the particular solutions by plotting some of their graphs for different values of $C[1]$. First, let us define the general solution to be $g(x, c)$, where $c = C[1]$ as follows (see Section 1.2.3 to learn how to extract elements from lists):

In[617]:= **Clear[g, x, c]**
   g[x_, c_] = sola[[1, 1, 2]] /. C[1] → c

Out[618]= $4 + c\, e^{-2x}$

We then plot the one-parameter family of solution curves by combining the graphs of $g(x, c)$ for $c = -5, -4, \ldots, 5$.

In[619]:= **plotgeneralsolution =**
   Plot[Table[g[x, c], {c, -5, 5}], {x, -2, 2}, PlotRange → {-20, 20}, ImageSize → 250]

Out[619]=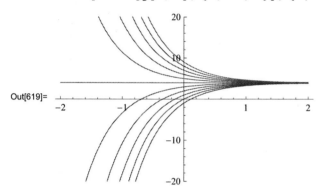

Can you explain how the graph of $g(x, c)$ varies as c varies? Which c value corresponds to the top graph?

Next, to find the unique particular solution satisfying the given initial condition $y(0) = 1$, we solve the equation $g(0, c) = 1$ for c:

In[620]:= **Solve[g[0, c] == 1, c]**

Out[620]= $\{\{c \to -3\}\}$

Thus, our unique solution is $y = -3\, e^{-2x} + 4$. This agrees with the solution we obtained earlier by hand. Of course, *Mathematica* can solve for the unique solution on its own, bypassing the algebraic steps involved:

In[621]:= **sola = DSolve[{y'[x] == 2 (4 - y[x]), y[0] == 1}, y[x], x]**

Out[621]= $\left\{\left\{y[x] \to e^{-2x} \left(-3 + 4\, e^{2x}\right)\right\}\right\}$

However, this unique solution does not appear to be the same as the one we obtained earlier. To remedy this, let us extract solution from the output and define it as $y = f(x)$:

In[622]:= **f[x_] = sola[[1, 1, 2]]**

Out[622]= $e^{-2x} \left(-3 + 4\, e^{2x}\right)$

We then apply the Expand command to simplify $f(x)$:

In[623]:= **Expand[f[x]]**

Out[623]= $4 - 3 e^{-2x}$

Thus, the unique solution obtained by *Mathematica* is the same as the one obtained by hand. Here is the plot of the unique solution:

In[624]:= **plotuniquesolution = Plot[f[x], {x, -2, 2},**
      PlotRange → {-20, 20}, PlotStyle → Thickness[0.01], ImageSize → 250]

Out[624]=
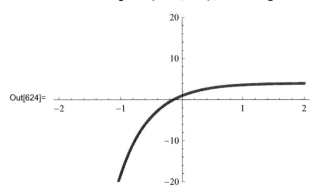

Lastly, we combine plots of the general solution and the unique solution to show where the latter (bold graph) is situated in the former:

In[625]:= **Show[{plotgeneralsolution, plotuniquesolution}, ImageSize → 250]**

Out[625]=
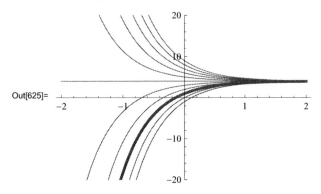

b) From this point on, we shall skip using the method of separation of variables, which we leave for the reader to employ, and proceed directly to solving all differential equations using *Mathematica* as in part a) above.

In[626]:= **solb = DSolve$\left[\sqrt{1-x^2}\ y'[x] == x\,y[x], y[x], x\right]$**

Out[626]= $\left\{\left\{y[x] \to e^{-\sqrt{1-x^2}}\ C[1]\right\}\right\}$

Again, we can visualize the behavior of these particular solutions by plotting graphs of some particular solutions corresponding to different values of $C[1]$. As before, we define the general solution to be $g(x, c)$, where $c = C[1]$.

In[627]:= **Clear[g, x, c]**
      g[x_, c_] = solb[[1, 1, 2]] /. C[1] → c

Out[628]= $c\ e^{-\sqrt{1-x^2}}$

We then make a combined plot of the graphs of $g(x, c)$ for $c = -5, -4, ..., 5$.

In[629]:= `Plot[Table[g[x, c], {c, -5, 5}], {x, -2, 2}, ImageSize → 250]`

Out[629]=

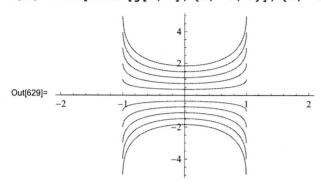

c) We again use *Mathematica* to directly obtain the solution:

In[630]:= `Clear[y]`
`solde = DSolve[ y[x] y'[x] - 5 x == 0, y[x], x]`

Out[631]= $\left\{ \left\{ y[x] \rightarrow -\sqrt{5 x^2 + 2 C[1]} \right\}, \left\{ y[x] \rightarrow \sqrt{5 x^2 + 2 C[1]} \right\} \right\}$

Observe that the two solutions, which we denote by $f(x, c)$ and $g(x, c)$, differ only in sign:

In[632]:= `f[x_, c_] = solde[[2, 1, 2]] /. C[1] → c`
`g[x_, c_] = solde[[1, 1, 2]] /. C[1] → c`

Out[632]= $\sqrt{2 c + 5 x^2}$

Out[633]= $-\sqrt{2 c + 5 x^2}$

The following two plots show the graphs of $f(x, c)$ and $g(x, c)$ corresponding to $c = -50, -40, ..., 0, ..., 40, 50$.

In[634]:= `Plot[Table[f[x, c], {c, -50, 50, 10}],`
`{x, -5, 5}, PlotRange → {0, 10}, ImageSize → 250]`

Out[634]=

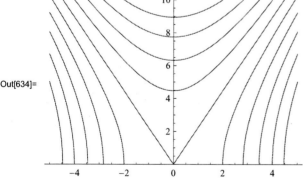

In[635]:= **Plot[Table[g[x, c], {c, -50, 50, 10}],**
   {x, -5, 5}, PlotRange → {-10, 0}, ImageSize → 250]

Out[635]=

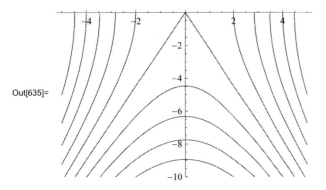

Observe that the two solutions $y = -\sqrt{5x^2 + 2c}$ and $y = \sqrt{5x^2 + 2c}$ can be represented by a single equation:

$$y^2 - 5x^2 = 2c$$

which describes a family of hyperbolas. Here is a contour plot of this equation. Observe that it nothing more than a combination of the two plots above as to be expected.

In[636]:= **ContourPlot[$y^2 - 5x^2$, {x, -5, 5}, {y, -10, 10}, Frame → False,**
   Axes -> True, ContourShading → False, Contours → 10, ImageSize → 250]

Out[636]=

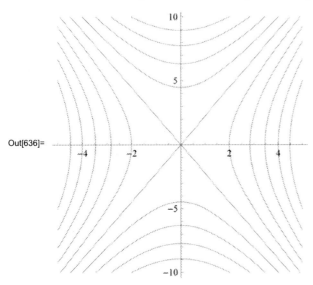

■ Exercises

In Exercises 1 through 8, solve the given differential equations. If initial conditions are also given, then plot the unique solution. If not, then make a combine plot of several particular solutions by choosing various values of the arbitrary constant. Then describe the graphs and explain how they vary as the arbitrary constant varies.

1. $\left(1 + x^2\right) y' = x^2 \, y; \; y(0) = 2$ 2. $y' + 3 x^4 y^2 = 0; \; y(0) = 1$

3. $y' + y^2 = -1; \; y(0) = -1$ 4. $y' + 3 y = \sin x; \; y(0) = 0$

5. $y' = -2\,x\,y$ (bell-shaped curves)   6. $16\,y\,y' + 9\,x = 0$

7. $y' - y = y^2$ 8. $2\,x\,y\,y' - y^2 + x^2 = 0$

9. Consider the differential equation

$$(3 + 2\,y)\,y' = 2 - e^x, \quad y(0) = a$$

a) Solve the equation.
b) Plot the graphs for values of $a = -2, -1, 0, 1, 2$.
c) Plot the graphs for the values of $a = -.5, -.1, .1, .5$.
NOTE: For parts b) and c), make sure to use a sufficiently large interval for x.

10. Consider the differential equation

$$y = x\,y\,(b - y)/(4 + x), \quad y(0) = a$$

a) Solve the equation.
b) Plot the graphs for values of $a = -2, -1, 0, 1, 2$ and $b = -2, -1, 0, 1, 2$.
c) Plot the graphs for the values of $a = -.5, -.1, .1, .5$ and $b = -.5, -.1, .1, .5$
d) Show that the limit as $x \to \infty$ of the solution does not depend on a. Does the limit depend on b? If so, how?

11. Suppose a skydiver falls from rest toward the earth and assume that the air resistance caused by his open parachute is proportional to the square of his velocity v with proportionality constant k (we neglect air resistance due to the skydiver himself). A model for describing the skydiver's velocity after his parachute opens is then given by the differential equation

$$v' = -\frac{k}{m}\left(v^2 - \frac{m\,g}{k}\right)$$

where m is the mass of the skydiver and $g = 9.8$ meters/sec^2 is his acceleration due to gravity.

a) Solve the equation assuming an initial velocity $v(0) = v_0$.
b) Suppose that for a particular skydiver $m = 70$ kg and $k = 30$ kg/meter. Solve the equation again using these values and plot the particular solutions for the following values of v_0: 0, 2, ..., 10.
c) What is the skydiver's limiting (terminal) velocity as $t \to \infty$ for each of the particular solutions in part b)? Does it depend on v_0?
d) Find a formula for the terminal velocity in terms of m, g, and k.

12. Recall that the first-order linear differential equation $y' + y = 0$ has solution $y = C\,e^{-x}$. Solve the following higher-order generalizations of this equation:

a) $y'' + 2\,y' + y = 0$
b) $y''' + 3\,y'' + 3\,y' + y = 0$
c) $y^{(4)} + 4\,y''' + 6\,y'' + 4\,y' + y = 0$
d) Do you recognize the coefficients involved in the differential equations above? What would be the next differential equation (of order 5) that follows this pattern? Solve this differential equation to verify that its solution follows that same pattern exhibited in parts a) through c).

▪ 9.2 Models of the Form $y' = k(y - b)$

Students should read Section 9.2 of Rogawski's *Calculus* [1] for a detailed discussion of the material presented in this section.

NOTE: The differential equations we encounter in this section can be solved by the method of separation of variables and is discussed in the text. We leave it to the reader to solve the examples in this section by hand to verify the solutions obtained using

Mathematica.

■ 9.2.1. Bacteria Growth

The growth of bacteria in a culture is known to be proportional to the amount of the bacteria present at time t. Suppose the initial amount of the bacteria is y_0 and the amount at time t is $y(t)$. Then the above physical law is modeled by the differential equation

$$y' = k\,y, \qquad y(0) = y_0$$

where k is the proportionality (growth) constant. Such a model exhibits exponential growth as can be seen from its solution below:

In[637]:= `Clear[k]`
`DSolve[{y'[x] == k*y[x], y[0] == y0}, y[x], x]`

Out[638]= $\left\{\left\{y[x] \rightarrow e^{k\,x}\,y0\right\}\right\}$

NOTE: Since the bacteria is growing in number, $y(t)$ is increasing and hence $y'(t) > 0$. Thus, k must be a positive number.

Example 9.2. Suppose the amount of bacteria in a culture was 200 at time $t = 0$. It was found that there were 450 bacteria after 2 minutes.
a) Find the amount of the bacteria at any time t.
b) At what time will the number of bacteria exceed 10,000?

Solution:

a) First, note that $y(0) = 200$ and $y(2) = 450$. We solve the differential equation $y' = k\,y$ with the former as the initial condition:

In[639]:= `Clear[y, t, k]`
`solde = DSolve[{y'[t] == k y[t], y[0] == 200}, y[t], t]`

Out[640]= $\left\{\left\{y[t] \rightarrow 200\,e^{k\,t}\right\}\right\}$

In[641]:= `f[t_] = solde[[1, 1, 2]]`

Out[641]= $200\,e^{k\,t}$

To find the value of k we solve $f(2) = 450$ for k.

In[642]:= `solk = Solve[f[2] == 450, k]`

Solve::ifun : Inverse functions are being used by Solve, so
some solutions may not be found; use Reduce for complete solution information. »

Out[642]= $\left\{\left\{k \rightarrow \dfrac{1}{2}\,Log\left[\dfrac{9}{4}\right]\right\}\right\}$

In[643]:= `N[%]`

Out[643]= $\{\{k \rightarrow 0.405465\}\}$

Thus, the proportionality constant is $k = \frac{1}{2}\ln(9/4) \approx 0.405465$. Substituting this value into $y(t)$, we see that the amount of bacteria at a given time t is

$$y(t) = 200\,e^{0.405465\,t}$$

b) To find the amount of time it takes for the bacteria to exceed 10,000, we solve

In[644]:= **k = solk[[1, 1, 2]]**
Solve[f[t] == 10 000, t]

Out[644]= $\frac{1}{2} \text{Log}\left[\frac{9}{4}\right]$

Solve::ifun : Inverse functions are being used by Solve, so
some solutions may not be found; use Reduce for complete solution information. ≫

Out[645]= $\left\{\left\{t \to -\frac{\text{Log}[50]}{\text{Log}[2] - \text{Log}[3]}\right\}\right\}$

We can approximate this value for *t* by

In[646]:= **N[%]**

Out[646]= $\{\{t \to 9.64824\}\}$

Thus, it takes about 9.64824 minutes for the bacteria to reach 10,000. To visually see this, we plot the graphs of the solution $y(t) = 200\, e^{0.405465\, t}$ (blue curve) and $y = 10\,000$ (red line) on the same axes.

In[647]:= **Plot[{f[t], 10 000}, {t, 0, 15}, PlotStyle → {Blue, Red}, ImageSize → 250]**

Out[647]=

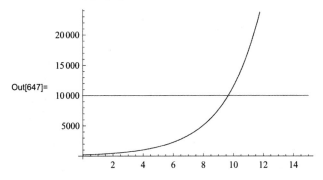

NOTE: The solution $y(t) = 200\, e^{0.405465\, t}$ is only approximate since we approximated the growth constant *k*. By using the exact value for $k = \frac{1}{2}\ln(9/4) = \ln(3/2)$, we can derive the exact solution:

$$y(t) = 200\, e^{k\, t} = 200\, e^{t\ln\frac{3}{2}} = 200\, e^{\ln\left(\frac{3}{2}\right)^{t}} = 200\left(\frac{3}{2}\right)^{t}$$

This agrees with the answer obtained by *Mathematica*:

In[648]:= **f[t]**

Out[648]= $25 \times 2^{3-t}\, 3^{t}$

■ 9.2.2. Radioactive Decay

The differential equation $y' = k\, y$ is also used to model the amount of a radioactive substance whose rate of decay is proportional to the amount present. However, in this case we note that the proportionality constant $k < 0$. (Explain this!)

Example 9.3. Carbon dating is a method used to determine the age of a fossil based on the amount of radioactive Carbon-14 in it compared to the amount normally found in the living environment. Suppose that a bone fossil contains 5 % of the amount of Carbon-14 normally found in living animals. If the half-life of Carbon-14 is 5600 years, estimate the age of the bone.

Solution: Let $y(t)$ be the amount of Carbon-14 in the bone and let y_0 be the initial amount of Carbon-14. Then the differential equation we need to solve is

In[649]:= `Clear[k, y, y0]`
`solde = DSolve[{y'[t] == k y[t], y[0] == y0}, y[t], t]`

Out[650]= $\{\{y[t] \to e^{k\,t}\,y0\}\}$

Thus, the solution to the differential equation is $y(t) = y_0\,e^{k\,t}$. The half-life of Carbon-14 is 5600 implies that $y(5600) = \frac{1}{2}\,y_0$. We solve this equation for k:

In[651]:= `y[t_] = solde[[1, 1, 2]]`
$$\text{solk} = \text{Solve}\left[y[5600] == \frac{1}{2}\,y0,\,k\right]$$

Out[651]= $e^{k\,t}\,y0$

Solve::ifun : Inverse functions are being used by Solve, so
some solutions may not be found; use Reduce for complete solution information. ≫

Out[652]= $\left\{\left\{k \to -\dfrac{\text{Log}[2]}{5600}\right\}\right\}$

In[653]:= `N[%]`

Out[653]= $\{\{k \to -0.000123776\}\}$

Thus, $k = -0.000123776$. To find the age of the bone, we solve $y(t) = 0.05\,y_0$ (5% of the initial amount) for t.

In[654]:= $k = -\dfrac{\text{Log}[2]}{5600};$
`Solve[y[t] == 0.05 y0, t]`

Solve::ifun : Inverse functions are being used by Solve, so
some solutions may not be found; use Reduce for complete solution information. ≫

Out[655]= $\{\{t \to 24\,202.8\}\}$

Thus, the bone is about 24,203 years old. Observe that it not necessary to know the original amount y_0 of Carbon-14 in the bone.

■ 9.2.3. Annuity

An *annuity* is an investment in which a principal amount of money is placed in a bank account that earns interest at an annual rate (compounded continuously) and the money is withdrawn at a regular interval. The differential equation that models an annuity is given by the annuity equation (rate of change = growth due to interest − withdrawal rate):

$$P'(t) = r\,P(t) - W = r\left(P(t) - \frac{W}{r}\right)$$

where $P(t)$ is the balance in the annuity at time t, r is the interest rate, and W is the rate (dollars per year) at which money is withdrawn continuously.

Example 9.4. Find the general solution of the annuity equation for $P(t)$ and then use it to calculate the following:
a) Assume $r = 6\%$ and $W = \$6000$ per year and $P(0) = \$50\,000$. Find $P(t)$ and determine if and when the annuity runs out of money.
b) Assume $r = 6\%$ and $W = \$6000$ per year and $P(0) = \$100\,000$. Find $P(t)$ and determine if and when the annuity runs out of money.
c) Assume $r = 6\%$ and $W = \$12\,000$ per year. If we want the annuity to run out of money after 20 years, how much should be

invested now?

Solution: We solve

In[656]:= $\text{DSolve}\left[P'[t] == r\left(P[t] - \dfrac{W}{r}\right), P[t], t\right]$

Out[656]= 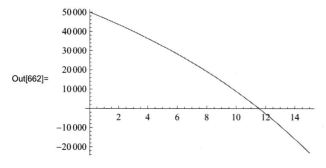 $\left\{\left\{ \qquad [t] \to \dfrac{W}{r} + e^{r\,t}\,C[1]\right\}\right\}$

Thus, the general solution is $P(t) = W/r + c\,e^{rt}$.

a) We set $r = 0.06$, $W = 6000$, and solve the initial value problem:

In[657]:= $\text{Clear}[r, W, P]$
$r = 0.06;$
$W = 6000;$
$\text{solde} = \text{DSolve}\left[\left\{P'[t] == r\left(P[t] - \dfrac{W}{r}\right), P[0] == 50\,000\right\}, P[t], t\right]$

Out[660]= $\left\{\left\{P[t] \to 100\,000. - 50\,000.\ e^{0.06\,t}\right\}\right\}$

We then define $P(t)$ to be the solution above and plot it to see when the money will run out.

In[661]:= $P[t\_] = \text{solde}[[1, 1, 2]]$
$\text{Plot}[P[t], \{t, 0, 15\}, \text{ImageSize} \to 250]$

Out[661]= $100\,000. - 50\,000.\ e^{0.06\,t}$

Out[662]=

As the graph indicates, the money runs out after approximately 11.5 years. We can confirm this by solving $P(t) = 0$:

In[663]:= $\text{NSolve}[P[t] == 0, t]$

NSolve::ifun : Inverse functions are being used by NSolve, so
some solutions may not be found; use Reduce for complete solution information. »

Out[663]= $\{\{t \to 11.5525\}\}$

b) We repeat the procedure in part a) with the obvious modifications:

```
In[664]:= Clear[r, W, P]
        r = 0.06;
        W = 6000;
        solde = DSolve[{P'[t] == r (P[t] - W/r), P[0] == 100 000}, P[t], t];
        P[t_] = solde[[1, 1, 2]]
        Plot[P[t], {t, 0, 80}, ImageSize → 250]
```

Out[668]= 100 000.

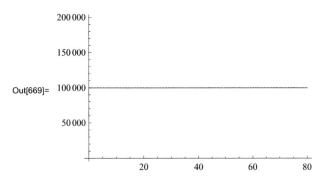

Out[669]=

Observe that the balance $P(t) = 100,000$ remains constant (can you explain why?) and thus the account will never run out of money. What happens if we invest $100,001? $99,999?

c) In this case, we have $r = 0.06$ and $W = 10\,000$ per year. The general solution is then given by

```
In[670]:= Clear[r, W, P, c]
        r = 0.06;
        W = 12 000;
        dsol = DSolve[{P'[t] == r (P[t] - W/r), P[0] == c}, P[t], t];
        P[t_] = dsol[[1, 1, 2]]
```

Out[674]= $200\,000. - 200\,000. e^{0.06\,t} + 1. c e^{0.06\,t}$

To determine the principal amount that will make the account run out of money in 20 years, we solve $P(20) = 0$ for c:

```
In[675]:= NSolve[P[20] == 0, c]
```

Out[675]= $\{\{c \to 139\,761.\}\}$

Thus, we need to invest $139,761.00 now.

■ 9.2.4. Newton's Law of Cooling

Newton's Law of Cooling states that the rate of change in the temperature of an object is proportional to the difference between its temperature and that of the surrounding environment (known as the *ambient temperature*). If A is the ambient temperature and $T(t)$ is the temperature of the object at time t, then the differential equation that models this law is

$$T'(t) = -k(T(t) - A), \quad T(0) = T_0$$

where T_0 is the initial temperature of the object and k is a positive proportionality constant.

Example 9.6. The temperature in an oven is $350°$ F when the oven is turned off. After 15 minutes, the temperature is $250°$ F.

Assume the temperature in the house is $70°$ F.

a) Find the temperature of the oven at any time t.

b) At what time will the temperature become $75°$ F?

c) What will the temperature be in the limit as $t \to \infty$?

d) Does your answer in c) conform with your physical intuition?

Solution:

a) The ambient temperature here is room temperature. Hence, $A = 70$. The initial temperature is $T_0 = 350$. Newton's Law of Cooling then gives the model

$$T'(t) = -k(T(t) - 70)), \quad T(0) = 350$$

We solve this equation to get

In[676]:= **Clear[T, k]**
  sol = DSolve[{T'[t] == -k (T[t] - 70), T[0] == 350}, T[t], t]

Out[677]= $\left\{\left\{ T[t] \to 70\, e^{-k\,t}\left(4 + e^{k\,t}\right)\right\}\right\}$

In[678]:= **T[t_] = sol[[1, 1, 2]]**

Out[678]= $70\, e^{-k\,t}\left(4 + e^{k\,t}\right)$

Thus, the solution is $T(t) = 70\, e^{-k\,t}\left(4 + e^{k\,t}\right)$ or $T(t) = 70 + 280\, e^{-k\,t}$. To find the value of k, we solve $T(15) = 250$ for k:

In[679]:= **solk = Solve[T[15] == 250, k]**

  Solve::ifun : Inverse functions are being used by Solve, so
      some solutions may not be found; use Reduce for complete solution information. ≫

Out[679]= $\left\{\left\{ k \to \dfrac{1}{15}\, \text{Log}\left[\dfrac{14}{9}\right]\right\}\right\}$

In[680]:= **k = solk[[1, 1, 2]]**

Out[680]= $\dfrac{1}{15}\, \text{Log}\left[\dfrac{14}{9}\right]$

In[681]:= **N[%]**

Out[681]= 0.0294555

Thus, $k = \frac{\ln(14/9)}{15} = 0.0294555$. Hence, the temperature of the oven at any time t is given by

$$T(t) = 20 + 280\, e^{-0.0294555\, t}$$

b) We solve $T(t) = 75$ for t:

In[682]:= **NSolve[T[t] == 75, t]**

  NSolve::ifun : Inverse functions are being used by NSolve, so
      some solutions may not be found; use Reduce for complete solution information. ≫

Out[682]= $\{\{t \to 136.659\}\}$

Thus, the temperature will be $75°$ F after about two hours and 17 minutes.

c) We make a plot of the solution:

In[683]:= **Plot[T[t], {t, 0, 100}, AxesOrigin → {0, 0}, ImageSize → 250]**

Out[683]=

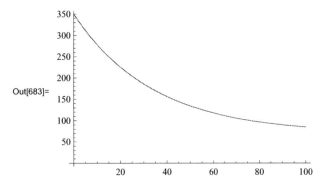

To find the limiting temperature, we evaluate

In[684]:= **Limit[T[t], t → Infinity]**

Out[684]= 70

d) Since heat flows from a region of higher temperature to a region of lower temperature, it is intuitively clear that the oven will cool down to the room (ambient) temperature. Hence, the limit should be 70° F as expected.

■ Exercises

1. Mass of bacteria in a culture grow at a rate proportional to its size. Suppose the culture contains 200 cells intially and there are 800 cells after 3 hours.

a) Find the formula for the number of cells in the culture at time t.
b) Find the amount of bacteria after 2 hours.
c) At what time will the bacteria exceed 10,000 cells?

2. A mummy excavated from an archaelogical site in Egypt is found to contain 20% of Carbon-14 normally found in living humans. Use carbon dating to estimate the age of the mummy.

3. Plutonium-239 is a highly radioactive element generated from waste in nuclear power plants and has a half-life of approximately 24,000 years. How many years would it take for Plutonium-239 to decay to a safe level of 1/1000 its original amount?

4. Solve the following using the annuity differential eqaution discussed in this section.
a) Assume $r = 6\%$ and $W = \$500$ per year and $P(0) = \$5,000$. Find $P(t)$ and determine when the annuity runs out of money.
b) Assume $r = 6\%$ and $W = \$500$ per year and $P(0) = \$9,000$. Find $P(t)$ and determine when the annuity runs out of money.
c) Assume $r = 6\%$ and $W = \$20,000$ per year. If we want the annuity to run out after 40 years, how much should we invest now?

5. Suppose a retired worker wants to invest in an annuity that will pay out $10,000 per year.
a) Assuming the annuity has an interest rate of 5%, find the minimum principal amount that should be invested so that the annuity never runs out of money.
b) Assuming the principal amount of money invested is $250,000, find the minimum interest rate that the annuity should bear so that it never runs out of money.

6. A hot metal rod is placed in a water bath whose temperature is 40° F. The rod cools from 300° F to 200° F in 1 minute. How long will take the rood to cool down to 150° F? 45° F?

■ 9.3 Numerical Methods Using Slope Fields

Students should read Section 9.3 of Rogawski's *Calculus* [1] for a detailed discussion of the material presented in this section.

■ 9.3.1. Slope Fields

Consider a differential equation in the form

$$y' = f(x, y)$$

Since y' represents the slope of the line tangent to the graph of the solution y, we can think of $f(x, y)$ as the slope of the same tangent line at the point (x, y), which we indicate by drawing a segment of it at the point of tangency. The set of all such line segments (normalized to have the same length) is called the *slope* (or *direction*) *field* of the differential equation. Note that the slope field gives a graphical approximation to the solution. It enables us to draw or visualize the graph of the unique solution of the equation passing through a given point. We will illustrate this in an upcoming example.

To plot the slope field of the differential equation $y' = f(x, y)$ along the intervals (a, b) and (c, d) on the x- and y-axis, respectively, we use the command **VectorPlot[{1, f[x, y]}, {x, a, b}, {y, c, d}]**, where slope is represented as a two-dimensional vector $(1, f(x, y))$ with the change in x normalized to equal 1.

NOTE: The command **VectorPlot** replaces the command **VectorFieldPlot**, which is obsolete in version 7 of *Mathematica*.

Example 9.9. Consider the differential equation $y' = x^2 - 2y$, $y(0) = -1$.

a) Draw the slope fields for the differential equation.
b) Solve the differential equation.
c) Plot both the slope field and the solution on the same axes.
d) Redo parts b) and c) for the same equation but with initial condition given by $y(a) = b$. Choose various values for a and b.

Solution:

a) Here, $f(x, y) = x^2 - 2y$. We use the **VectorPlot** command to plot the corresponding slope field:

In[685]:= **f[x_, y_] := x² - 2 y**

In[686]:= **plot1 = VectorPlot[{1, f[x, y]}, {x, -5, 5}, {y, -10, 10}, Axes → True,
Frame → False, VectorScale → {Tiny, Tiny, None}, ImageSize → 250]**

Out[686]=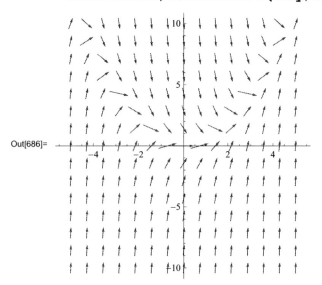

b) We use the **DSolve** command to find the exact solution of the differential equation.

In[687]:= **Clear[y, x, g]
sol = DSolve[{y'[x] == f[x, y[x]], y[0] == -1}, y[x], x]
g[x_] = sol[[1, 1, 2]]**

Out[688]= $\left\{\left\{ y[x] \to \frac{1}{4} e^{-2x} \left(-5 + e^{2x} - 2 e^{2x} x + 2 e^{2x} x^2\right)\right\}\right\}$

Out[689]= $\frac{1}{4} e^{-2x} \left(-5 + e^{2x} - 2 e^{2x} x + 2 e^{2x} x^2\right)$

c) We now plot the slope field together with the solution above passing through the point $(0, -1)$:

In[690]:= **plot2 = Plot[g[x], {x, -5, 5}, PlotRange → {-10, 10}, ImageSize → 250]**

Out[690]=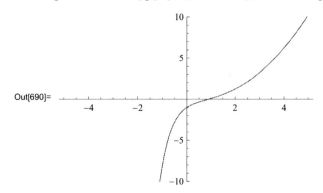

In[691]:= **Show[plot1, plot2, Graphics[{PointSize[Large], Point[{0, -1}]}], ImageSize → 250]**

Out[691]=

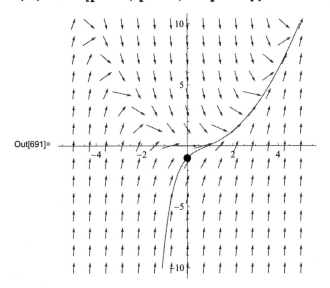

d) We can show several graphs of solution curves (called integral curves) together with the corresponding slope field. Here is an example of how this can be done.

In[692]:= **Clear[y, x, h, a, b]**
sola = DSolve[{y'[x] == f[x, y[x]], y[a] == b}, y[x], x];
h[x_, a_, b_] = Simplify[sola[[1, 1, 2]]]

Out[694]= $\frac{1}{4} e^{-2x} \left(\left(-1 + 2a - 2a^2 + 4b \right) e^{2a} + e^{2x} \left(1 - 2x + 2x^2 \right) \right)$

In[695]:= **plot3 = Plot[Evaluate[Table[h[x, a, b], {a, -3, 3, 2}, {b, -3, 3, 2}]],**
{x, -5, 5}, PlotRange → {-10, 10}];
Show[plot1, plot3, ImageSize → 250]

Out[696]=

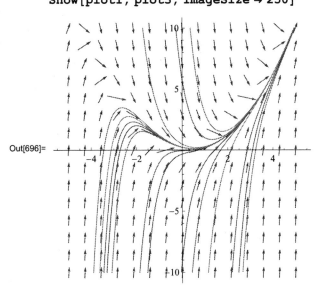

◾ 9.3.2. Euler's Method

The simplest numerical method for solving a first order differential equation is *Euler's Method.* This method approximates the solution by moving along tangent lines described by the slope field of the differential equation. Here is a brief description.

Let $y = \phi(x)$ be the solution of the differential equation

$$y' = f(x, y), \ \ y(x_0) = y_0$$

Then the equation of the line tangent to the graph of $y = \varphi(x)$ at $x = x_0$ is given by

$$y = \varphi'(x_0)(x - x_0) + \varphi(x_0)$$

But when $x = x_0$, we have $\varphi(t_0) = y_0$ and $\varphi'(x_0) = f(x_0, y_0)$. Thus, when x is close to x_0, $\varphi(x)$ can be approximated by

$$y \approx f(x_0, y_0)(x - x_0) + y_0$$

We now choose $h > 0$ to be a small positive number, called the step size, and define $x_1 = x_0 + h$. Then $\varphi(x_1)$ is approximately equal to

$$y_1 = y_0 + f(x_0, y_0)(x_1 - x_0)$$

or

$$y_1 = y_0 + h f(x_0, y_0)$$

We repeat the above argument at the point (x_1, y_1) to get an approximation of $\varphi(x_2)$, where $x_2 = x_1 + h = x_0 + 2h$:

$$y_2 = y_1 + h f(x_1, y_1)$$

Proceeding in this manner, we obtain Euler's Method:

$$y_{n+1} = y_n + h f(x_n, y_n) \text{ for } n = 0, \ 1, \ 2, \ 3, \ ....$$

where $\varphi(x_n) \approx y_n$.

If the approximated solution is calculated over an interval $[a, b]$ and the step size h is specified, then the number of iterations (or steps) required is given by $m = (b - a)/h$, where $x_0 = a$ and $x_n = x_0 + nh$.

Here is a *Mathematica* program called **Euler** for evaluating Euler's Method in m steps (the option **SetPrecision** sets the precision of our calculations to 10 digits).

```
In[697]:= Clear[f, x, y, x0, y0, h, m]
       Euler[f_, h_, m_] := Module[{n},
         Do[
          y[n + 1] = SetPrecision[N[y[n] + h * f[x[n], y[n]]], 10];
          x[n + 1] = x[n] + h,
          {n, 0, m}]]
```

Example 9.7. Use the **Euler** program to construct a table of solution values for the differential equation $y' = x^2 + 2y$, $y(0) = 1$ with a step size of $h = 0.1$ and for $m = 10$ steps.

Solution: Here $f(x, y) = x^2 + 2y$, $x_0 = 0$, $y_0 = 1$.

In[699]:= $f[x\_, y\_] := x^2 + 2 y$
$m = 10;$
$x0 = 0;$
$y0 = 1;$
$h = 0.1;$
$x[0] = x0;$
$y[0] = y0;$
$Euler[f, h, m]$
$TableForm\big[Table[\{n, x[n], y[n]\}, \{n, 1, m\}],$
$\quad TableHeadings \rightarrow \big\{\{\}, \{"n\ ", "x_n", "y_n"\}\big\}\big]$

Out[707]//TableForm=

n	x_n	y_n
1	0.1	1.200000000
2	0.2	1.441000000
3	0.3	1.733200000
4	0.4	2.088840000
5	0.5	2.522608000
6	0.6	3.052129600
7	0.7	3.698555520
8	0.8	4.487266624
9	0.9	5.448719949
10	1.	6.619463939

To see how accurate the above approximation is, we solve the differential equation for the exact solution and plot both the approximate and exact solutions on the same axes.

In[708]:= $Clear[z, t, exact]$
$exact = DSolve[\{z'[t] == f[t, z[t]], z[x0] == y0\}, z[t], t];$
$z[t\_] = z[t] /. exact[[1]]$

Out[710]= $\dfrac{1}{4}\left(-1 + 5\,e^{2\,t} - 2\,t - 2\,t^2\right)$

In[711]:= $Clear[plot1, plot2]$
$plot1 = Plot[z[t], \{t, 0, 1\}];$
$plot2 = ListPlot[Table[\{x[n], y[n]\}, \{n, 0, m\}], PlotStyle \rightarrow PointSize[0.01]];$
$Show[\{plot1, plot2\}, ImageSize \rightarrow 250]$

Out[714]=

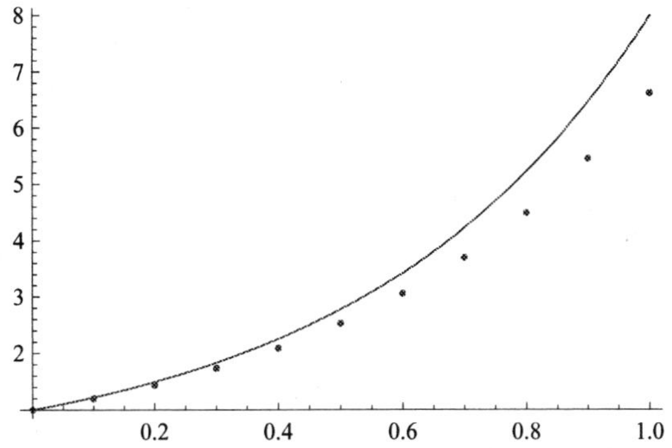

Observe that the approximations become less accurate as we move away from the initial point (0, 1). This is typical of numerical methods such as Euler's Method. However, we can increase the accuracy of our approximation by decreasing the step size. For example, we recompute the solution using $h = 0.05$ (this increases the number of steps to $m = 20$):

In[715]:= ```
h = 0.05;
m = 20;
Euler[f, h, m]
TableForm[Table[{n, x[n], y[n]}, {n, 1, m}],
  TableHeadings → {{}, {"n ", "x_n ", "y_n "}}]
```

Out[718]//TableForm=

| n | $x_n$ | $y_n$ |
|---|-------|-------|
| 1 | 0.05 | 1.100000000 |
| 2 | 0.1 | 1.210125000 |
| 3 | 0.15 | 1.331637500 |
| 4 | 0.2 | 1.465926250 |
| 5 | 0.25 | 1.614518875 |
| 6 | 0.3 | 1.779095763 |
| 7 | 0.35 | 1.961505339 |
| 8 | 0.4 | 2.163780873 |
| 9 | 0.45 | 2.388158960 |
| 10 | 0.5 | 2.637099856 |
| 11 | 0.55 | 2.913309841 |
| 12 | 0.6 | 3.219765826 |
| 13 | 0.65 | 3.559742408 |
| 14 | 0.7 | 3.936841649 |
| 15 | 0.75 | 4.355025814 |
| 16 | 0.8 | 4.818653395 |
| 17 | 0.85 | 5.332518735 |
| 18 | 0.9 | 5.901895608 |
| 19 | 0.95 | 6.532585169 |
| 20 | 1. | 7.230968686 |

The following plot of the two numerical solutions corresponding to $h = 0.1$ (small blue dots) and $h = 0.05$ (large red dots) clearly shows that the latter is more accurate in comparison to the exact solution (curve):

In[719]:= ```
plot3 = ListPlot[Table[{x[n], y[n]}, {n, 0, m}],
    PlotStyle → {PointSize[0.01], Red, PointSize[0.015] }];
Show[{plot1, plot2, plot3}, ImageSize → 250]
```

Out[720]=

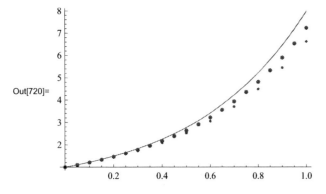

Here is a modification of the **Euler** progam that allows the user to input the endpoints a and b directly (instead of the step size h) and m.

```
In[721]:= Clear[f, x, y, h, a, b, m]

        EulerEndpt[f_, a_, b_, m_] := Module[{n, h}, h = N[(b - a)/m];
          Do[
            y[n + 1] = SetPrecision[N[y[n] + h * f[x[n], y[n]]], 10];
            x[n + 1] = x[n] + h,
            {n, 0, m}]]
```

Example 9.8. For the differential equation $y' = x^2 + 2y$, $y(0) = 1$, approximate its solution over the interval $[0, 2]$ using $m = 10$ steps.

Solution: Again, we have $f(x, y) = x^2 + y$, $x_0 = 0$, $y_0 = 1$. However, we now input the interval $[a, b] = [0, 2]$ into **EulerEndPt**.

```
In[723]:= f[x_, y_] := x^2 + y
        m = 10;
        x0 = 0;
        y0 = 1;
        x[0] = x0;
        y[0] = y0;
        a = 0;
        b = 2;
```

```
In[731]:= EulerEndpt[f, 0, 2, m]
        TableForm[Table[{n, x[n], y[n]}, {n, 1, m}],
          TableHeadings → {{}, {"n ", "x_n", "y_n"}}]
```

Out[732]//TableForm=

n	x_n	y_n
1	0.2	1.200000000
2	0.4	1.448000000
3	0.6	1.769600000
4	0.8	2.195520000
5	1.	2.762624000
6	1.2	3.515148800
7	1.4	4.506178560
8	1.6	5.799414272
9	1.8	7.471297126
10	2.	9.613556552

This time we numerically compare the approximate solution with the exact solution:

In[733]:= `Clear[z, t, exact]`
`exact = DSolve[{z'[t] == f[t, z[t]], z[x0] == y0}, z[t], t];`
`z[t_] = z[t] /. exact[[1]]`
`TableForm[Table[{n, x[n], y[n], N[z[x0 + n (b - a) / m]]}, {n, 1, m}],`
`  TableHeadings → {{}, {"n ", "x`$_n$`", "y`$_n$`", "y(n) "}}]`

Out[735]= $-2 + 3 e^t - 2 t - t^2$

Out[736]//TableForm=

n	x_n	y_n	y(n)
1	0.2	1.200000000	1.22421
2	0.4	1.448000000	1.51547
3	0.6	1.769600000	1.90636
4	0.8	2.195520000	2.43662
5	1.	2.762624000	3.15485
6	1.2	3.515148800	4.12035
7	1.4	4.506178560	5.4056
8	1.6	5.799414272	7.0991
9	1.8	7.471297126	9.30894
10	2.	9.613556552	12.1672

■ Exercises

In Exercises 1 through 4, plot the slope field of the given differential equations:

1. $y' = x^2 + y^2$ 2. $y' = t^2 y$ 3. $y' = \sin(x + y)$ 4. $y' = x e^{-y}$

5. Consider the differential equation $y' = 3 y - 2 y^2$.

a) Draw the slope field for the differential equation.

b) Solve the differential equation.

c) Assume $y(0) = 2$. Plot the graph of the solution for this case and also the slope field on the same axes. Discuss the behavior of the solution as $x \to \infty$.

d) Redo part c) for the same differential equation but with initial condition given by $y(a) = b$ (choose various values for a and b).

In Exercises 6 through 9, use Euler's Method to find a numerical solution to the given initial value problem along the stated interval and using the prescribed number of steps. Also, find their exact solutions and compare the results.

6. $y' = x^2 - y$, $y(0) = 1$; [0, 1]; $m = 10$ 7. $y' = (1 - x^2) \cos y$, $y(1) = 0$; [1, 2]; $m = 20$ 8. $y' - y^2 = x$, $y(0) = 1$; [0, 5]; $m = 50$ 9. $y' = -3 x/2 + \ln(x^2 + y)$, $y(1) = 1$; [1, 2]; $m = 100$

10. *Heun's method* is a numerical method that improves on Euler's method. It uses the approximation from Euler's method as an auxiliary value (called a *predictor*), which we denote by y_{n+1}^*:

$$y_{n+1}^* = y_n + h f(x_n, y_n)$$

The actual approximation (called the *corrector*) is then computed as the mean of y_{n+1}^* (based on the slope of the tangent line at (x_n, y_n)) and $y_{n+1}^{**} = y_n + h f(x_{n+1}, y_{n+1}^*)$ (based on the slope of the tangent line at (x_{n+1}, y_{n+1}^*)):

$$y_{n+1} = \frac{1}{2}[y_{n+1}^* + y_{n+1}^{**}] = y_n + \frac{1}{2}[h f(x_n, y_n) + h f(x_{n+1}, y_{n+1}^*)]$$

a) Apply Heun's method to Exercise 6 and the compare the results obtained by Euler's method with the exact solution. How much more accurate is Heun's method?

b) Redo part a) using $m = 20$. How much more accurate is the solution compared to that for $m = 10$?

■ 9.4 The Logistic Equation

Students should read Section 9.4 of Rogawski's *Calculus* [1] for a detailed discussion of the material presented in this section.

The differential equation

$$\frac{dy}{dt} = k\, y\left(1 - \frac{y}{A}\right)$$

is called the *logistics equation.* Here, $k > 0$ and A is a constant called the *carrying capacity.* This equation is useful for modeling the growth of a population where resources are limited and can only sustain a certain maximum population given by the carrying capacity.

Example 9.5. The population $p(t)$ of mosquito larvae growing in a tree hole increases according to the logistics equation with growth constant $k = 0.3$ per day and carrying capacity $A = 1000$.

a) Assuming that the initial population of the larvae is 50, find the population $p(t)$ at any time t.
b) After how many days will the larvae population exceed 500?
c) When does the larvae population reach 99% of the maximum capacity?

Solution:

a) We use $k = \frac{3}{10}$ and solve the corresponding differential equation in *Mathematica*:

In[737]:= `Clear[y]`

$$\texttt{solde = DSolve}\left[\left\{\texttt{y'[t]} == \frac{3}{10}\,\texttt{y[t]}\left(1 - \frac{\texttt{y[t]}}{1000}\right),\ \texttt{y[0]} == 50\right\},\ \texttt{y[t]},\ \texttt{t}\right]$$

Solve::ifun : Inverse functions are being used by Solve, so
    some solutions may not be found; use Reduce for complete solution information. ≫

Out[738]= $\left\{\left\{\texttt{y[t]} \to \dfrac{1000\ e^{3\,t/10}}{19 + e^{3\,t/10}}\right\}\right\}$

NOTE: Be careful with using a decimal approximation for k. For example, try using $k = 0.3$ and see what happens.

Next, for convenience we write the solution given in the previous output as

In[739]:= `Clear[p, t]`
`p[t_] = solde[[1, 1, 2]]`

Out[740]= $\dfrac{1000\ e^{3\,t/10}}{19 + e^{3\,t/10}}$

Thus, the population of larvae at any time t is given by

$$p(t) = \frac{1000\,e^{3\,t/10}}{19 + e^{3\,t/10}}$$

b) To find how long it takes for the larvae population to reach 500, we solve

In[741]:= `NSolve[p[t] == 500, t]`

NSolve::ifun : Inverse functions are being used by NSolve, so
    some solutions may not be found; use Reduce for complete solution information. ≫

Out[741]= $\{\{t \to 9.8148\},\ \{t \to 9.8148 - 20.944\ i\},\ \{t \to 9.8148 + 20.944\ i\}\}$

Thus, it takes about ten days for the larvae population to exceed 500. Observe that $p(10) \approx 513.887$.

NOTE: We ignored the other two solutions in the previous output since they are complex-valued and not physically relevant.

c) We first plot the graph of $p(t)$ to estimate the number of days required for the larvae population to reach 99% of the maximum capacity, that is, $p(t) = 999$.

In[742]:= **Plot[p[t], {t, 0, 60}, ImageSize → 250]**

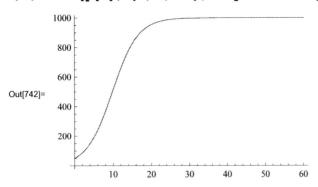

Out[742]=

It appears that the population reaches 999 larvae after $t = 30$. We use the **Table** command to numerically confirm this.

In[743]:= **TableForm[Table[{t, N[p[t], 20]}, {t, 10, 50, 5}],**
     TableHeadings → {{}, {"Days   ", "Larvae Population"}}]

Out[743]//TableForm=

Days	Larvae Population
10	513.88668301168543188
15	825.71546532788782007
20	955.02200538248404316
25	989.60067930023585514
30	997.66069888351031767
35	999.47708104964742173
40	999.88327359193169386
45	999.97395245585093165
50	999.99418788969128789

We can reasonably conclude from the table that the population reaches 999 larvae between 30 and 35 days. To obtain a more precise answer, we use *Mathematica* to solve $p(t) = 999$ for t:

In[744]:= **NSolve[p[t] == 999, t]**

NSolve::ifun : Inverse functions are being used by NSolve, so
     some solutions may not be found; use Reduce for complete solution information. ≫

Out[744]= $\{\{t \to 32.8373\}, \{t \to 32.8373 - 20.944\, i\}, \{t \to 32.8373 + 20.944\, i\}\}$

Thus, the desired time is approximately $t = 33$ days.

■ **Exercises**

1. A population of squirrels live in a forest with a carrying capacity of 3000. Assume logistic growth with growth constant $k = 0.8$ per year.
a) Find the population of the squirrels at any time t assuming an initial population of $P(0) = 800$.
b) How long will it take for the squirrel population to double? Triple?

2. From 1960 to 2000, the world's population doubled from approximately 3 billion to 6 billion people. Assuming that the human population follows logistic growth and that the earth has a carrying capacity of 100 billion people, determine the following:
a) Find the population at any time t. What is the growth constant?
b) What will the population be in the year 2050? How does this answer compare with projections from the United Nations?
c) Find the year in which the human population will reach half its carrying capacity?
d) When will the population grow the fastest, that is, the point on the graph where it changes from concave up to concave down (point of inflection)? What is the growth rate then?

3. In medicine, the logistics equation is used to model the growth of tumors in certain organs. Suppose a patient is diagnosed with a tumor that has doubled in size to 2% of his liver when a year ago it only covered 1% of his liver. How long will it take the tumor to grow to 10% of his liver when a transplant will most like by required to increase his chances of survival.

4. The current population of a herd of bison living inside a national park is 1000. To ensure that the population does not reach more than 1500 bison in 50 years time and 2000 bison in 100 years time, what carrying capacity should the park maintain? Assume that the bison population follows a logistics model.

Chapter 10   Infinite Series

■ 10.1 Sequences

Students should read Section 10.1 of Rogawski's *Calculus* [1] for a detailed discussion of the material presented in this section.

Recall that a sequence is a function whose domain is the set of non-negative integers.

In *Mathematica,* we denote a sequence a_n as a function. Thus, instead of a_n we write $a(n)$. The limit of a sequence is evaluated by using the **Limit** command. When **Limit[a[n], n→∞]** is evaluated, *Mathematica* automatically assumes that **n** is a continuous variable (instead of a discrete variable). It employs various techniques to evaluate limits.

To plot the graph of a sequence, we use the **ListPlot** command. **ListPlot[list]** plots the graph of **list**, where **list** is a list of points (x, y), denoted in *Mathematica* by **{x,y}**. In our case, **list** will be the table of values of the form **{n,a[n]}**. The corresponding plot command in this case would be **ListPlot[Table[{n,a[n]},{n,min,max}]]**.

Example 10.1. Consider the sequence defined by

$$a_n = \frac{4\,n+1}{3\,n+2}$$

a) Find the first few terms of the sequence.

b) Plot the graph of the sequence.

c) Make a conjecture for the limit based on the graph.

d) Find the limit of the sequence.

Solution:

a) We define the sequence as a function of n and use the **Table** command to generate the first ten terms of the sequence.

In[745]:= **Clear[a, n]**

$$\mathbf{a[n\_] := \frac{4\,n+1}{3\,n+2}}$$

In[747]:= **TableForm[Table[{n, a[n]}, {n, 1, 10}],**
    TableHeadings → {{}, {"n", "a$_n$"}}]

Out[747]//TableForm=

n	a_n
1	1
2	$\frac{9}{8}$
3	$\frac{13}{11}$
4	$\frac{17}{14}$
5	$\frac{21}{17}$
6	$\frac{5}{4}$
7	$\frac{29}{23}$
8	$\frac{33}{26}$
9	$\frac{37}{29}$
10	$\frac{41}{32}$

To obtain decimal expressions of these values, we evaluate

In[748]:= **TableForm[N[Table[{n, a[n]}, {n, 1, 10}]],**
    TableHeadings → {{}, {"n", "a$_n$"}}]

Out[748]//TableForm=

n	a_n
1.	1.
2.	1.125
3.	1.18182
4.	1.21429
5.	1.23529
6.	1.25
7.	1.26087
8.	1.26923
9.	1.27586
10.	1.28125

b) To plot the graph of the sequence, we use the **ListPlot** command. Here is a plot of the first 100 terms of the sequence.

In[749]:= **ListPlot[Table[{n, a[n]}, {n, 1, 100}]]**

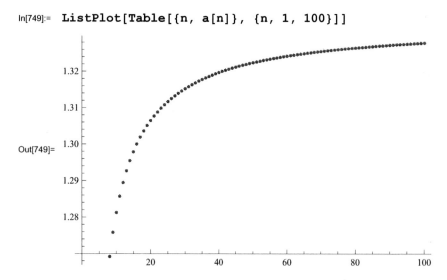

Out[749]=

c) The graph suggests that the limit is 1.333 .... We can use the **Table** command to see this more clearly.

In[750]:= **TableForm[N[Table[{n, a[n]}, {n, 1000, 10 000, 1000}]],**
TableHeadings → {{}, {"n", "a_n"}}]

Out[750]//TableForm=

n	a_n
1000.	1.33278
2000.	1.33306
3000.	1.33315
4000.	1.33319
5000.	1.33322
6000.	1.33324
7000.	1.33325
8000.	1.33326
9000.	1.33327
10 000.	1.33328

Hence, the limit seems to be 1.3333... or 4/3. Here is a plot of $y = 4/3$ and the graph of the sequence for large values of *n*:

```
In[751]:= Clear[plot1, plot2]
          plot1 = ListPlot[Table[{n, a[n]}, {n, 1, 1000, 10}]];
          plot2 = Plot[4 / 3, {x, 1, 1000}];
          Show[plot1, plot2, PlotRange → {1.25, 4 / 3}]
```

Out[754]=

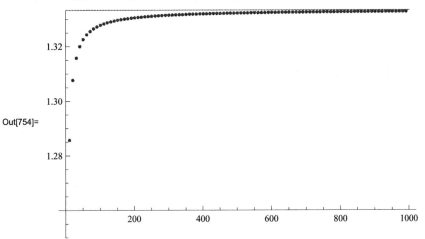

d) Finally, we confirm this in *Mathematica* by evaluating the limit as *n* goes to ∞.

```
In[755]:= Limit[a[n], n -> Infinity]
```

$$\text{Out[755]=} \quad \frac{4}{3}$$

Example 10.2. Consider the sequence defined by

$$a_n = \frac{(-1)^n}{n}$$

a) Plot the graph of the sequence.

b) Does the sequence converge?

Solution:

a) Again, we use **ListPlot** to plot the graph.

```
In[756]:= Clear[a, n]
          a[n_] := (-1)^n / n
```

In[758]:= `ListPlot[Table[{n, a[n]}, {n, 1, 100}]]`

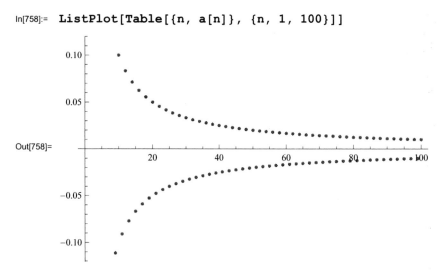

Out[758]=

b) From the graph, it is clear that the sequence approaches 0 in the limit. We confirm this using the **Limit** command.

In[759]:= `Limit[a[n], n -> Infinity]`

Out[759]= 0

NOTE: There are instances where the sequence a_n may not be well-defined if n is treated as a real variable (as opposed to an integer variable). In such cases, *Mathematica* may return the limit unevaluated or else gives an output that indicates the limit may not exist, as the following example illustrates.

Example 10.3. Determine whether or not the sequence defined below converges:

$$a_n = (-1)^n \frac{n}{n+1}$$

Solution: First, we will plot the graph of the sequence.

In[760]:= `Clear[a, n]`

$$a[n\_] := (-1)^n \frac{n}{n+1}$$

In[762]:= `ListPlot[Table[{n, a[n]}, {n, 1, 100}]]`

Out[762]=

The graph clearly indicates the sequence does NOT converge (to a *unique* limiting value). We can see this by investigating the following tables of values. The first one lists the even terms while the second one lists the odd terms of the sequence.

In[763]:= `TableForm[Table[{n, N[a[2 n]]}, {n, 10, 100, 10}],`
   `TableHeadings → {{}, {"n", "a₂ₙ"}}]`

Out[763]//TableForm=

n	a_{2n}
10	0.952381
20	0.97561
30	0.983607
40	0.987654
50	0.990099
60	0.991736
70	0.992908
80	0.993789
90	0.994475
100	0.995025

In[764]:= `TableForm[Table[{n, N[a[2 n - 1]]}, {n, 10, 100, 10}],`
   `TableHeadings → {{}, {"n", "a₂ₙ₋₁"}}]`

Out[764]//TableForm=

n	a_{2n-1}
10	-0.95
20	-0.975
30	-0.983333
40	-0.9875
50	-0.99
60	-0.991667
70	-0.992857
80	-0.99375
90	-0.994444
100	-0.995

Finally, let us evaluate the limit.

In[765]:= `Limit[a[n], n -> Infinity]`

Out[765]= $e^{2 i \, \text{Interval}[\{0, \pi\}]}$

This output, specifically the notation **Interval[{0, π}]**, means that the limit does not exist *uniquely*, but has subsequences whose limits take on the set of complex values e^{2ix} for all $x \in [0, \pi]$. This is because the variable **n** that appears in the **Limit** command is automatically assumed by *Mathematica* to be a complex variable. In our case, for **n** an integer variable, we have two subsequences, a_{2n} and a_{2n+1} (even and odd, respectively), converging to different limits (1 and −1, respectively). Thus, a_n diverges.

Example 10.4. Consider the sequence $\{a_n\}$ defined recursively by $a_1 = 1$ and $a_{n+1} = \sqrt{a_n + 1}$. Generate the first ten terms of this sequence and compute its limit.

Solution: Here is one method of defining a recursive sequence.

In[766]:= `Clear[a, n]`
   `a[1] = 1`
   `a[n_] := a[n] = Sqrt[a[n - 1] + 2]`

Out[767]= 1

NOTE: The second occurrence of **a[n]** in the preceding command tells *Mathematica* to store all intermediate values of the recurrence in evaluating **a[n]**.

Here are the first ten terms of the sequence:

In[769]:= **TableForm$\left[$Table[{n, a[n]}, {n, 1, 10}],**

TableHeadings $\rightarrow \left\{$ {}, {"n", "a$_n$"}$\right\}\right]$

Out[769]//TableForm=

n	a$_n$
1	1
2	$\sqrt{3}$
3	$\sqrt{2+\sqrt{3}}$
4	$\sqrt{2+\sqrt{2+\sqrt{3}}}$
5	$\sqrt{2+\sqrt{2+\sqrt{2+\sqrt{3}}}}$
6	$\sqrt{2+\sqrt{2+\sqrt{2+\sqrt{2+\sqrt{3}}}}}$
7	$\sqrt{2+\sqrt{2+\sqrt{2+\sqrt{2+\sqrt{2+\sqrt{3}}}}}}$
8	$\sqrt{2+\sqrt{2+\sqrt{2+\sqrt{2+\sqrt{2+\sqrt{2+\sqrt{3}}}}}}}$
9	$\sqrt{2+\sqrt{2+\sqrt{2+\sqrt{2+\sqrt{2+\sqrt{2+\sqrt{2+\sqrt{3}}}}}}}}$
10	$\sqrt{2+\sqrt{2+\sqrt{2+\sqrt{2+\sqrt{2+\sqrt{2+\sqrt{2+\sqrt{2+\sqrt{3}}}}}}}}}$

The following table gives decimal expressions of the same first ten terms and reveals the limit to be equal to 2.

In[770]:= **TableForm[Table[{n, N[a[n]]}, {n, 1, 10}],**
      TableHeadings → {{}, {"n", "a$_n$"}}]

Out[770]//TableForm=

n	a$_n$
1	1.
2	1.73205
3	1.93185
4	1.98289
5	1.99572
6	1.99893
7	1.99973
8	1.99993
9	1.99998
10	2.

NOTE: In general, *Mathematica* is not able to directly compute limits of sequences defined recursively. Assuming a_n converges (prove this!), we then compute its limit, called *L,* say, by letting $n \to \infty$ in the recurrence formula for a_n:

$$L = \lim_{n \to \infty} a_n = \lim_{n \to \infty} \sqrt{a_{n-1} + 2} = \sqrt{\lim_{n \to \infty} a_{n-1} + 2} = \sqrt{L + 2}$$

Solving the equation $L = \sqrt{L + 2}$ then yields $L = 2$ as the limit.

In[771]:= **Solve[L == Sqrt[L + 2], L]**

Out[771]= $\{\{L \to 2\}\}$

Example 10.5. Let $a_1 = 1$ and $b_1 = \sqrt{2}$. Define two sequences recursively by

$$a_{n+1} = \sqrt{a_n \, b_n} \quad \text{and} \quad b_{n+1} = \frac{a_n + b_n}{2}$$

a) Choose various values of a_1 and b_1 and calculate the first ten terms of the sequences $\{a_n\}$ and $\{b_n\}$.

b) Show that $a_n \leq b_n$ for every positive integer n.

c) Show that both sequences converge to the same limit. (NOTE: This common limit is called the *arithmetic-geometric mean of* a_1 and b_1.)

Solution:

a) Here is a program that generates the first ten values of a_n and b_n.

In[772]:= **Clear[a, b, n]**
      a[1] = 1
      b[1] = 10

      a[i_] := a[i] = $\sqrt{\text{a[i - 1] * b[i - 1]}}$;

      b[i_] := b[i] = $\dfrac{\text{a[i - 1] + b[i - 1]}}{\text{2}}$;

Out[773]= 1

Out[774]= 10

In[777]:= `TableForm[Table[{k, N[a[ k], 10], N[b[ k], 10]}, {k, 1, 10}],`
    `TableHeadings → {{}, {"n", "a[n]", "b[n]"}}]`

Out[777]//TableForm=

n	a[n]	b[n]
1	1.000000000	10.00000000
2	3.162277660	5.500000000
3	4.170434885	4.331138830
4	4.250027349	4.250786858
5	4.250407086	4.250407103
6	4.250407095	4.250407095
7	4.250407095	4.250407095
8	4.250407095	4.250407095
9	4.250407095	4.250407095
10	4.250407095	4.250407095

b) The following table suggests that $a_n \le b_n$ for at least the first ten terms:

In[778]:= `TableForm[`
    `Table[{k, N[a[ k], 10], N[b[ k], 10], N[b[k], 10] - N[a[k], 10]}, {k, 1, 10}],`
    `TableHeadings → {{}, {"n", "a[n]", "b[n]", "b[n]-a[n]"}}]`

Out[778]//TableForm=

n	a[n]	b[n]	b[n]-a[n]
1	1.000000000	10.00000000	9.00000000
2	3.162277660	5.500000000	2.337722340
3	4.170434885	4.331138830	0.160703945
4	4.250027349	4.250786858	0.000759508
5	4.250407086	4.250407103	1.7×10^{-8}
6	4.250407095	4.250407095	$0. \times 10^{-10}$
7	4.250407095	4.250407095	$0. \times 10^{-10}$
8	4.250407095	4.250407095	$0. \times 10^{-10}$
9	4.250407095	4.250407095	$0. \times 10^{-10}$
10	4.250407095	4.250407095	$0. \times 10^{-10}$

For a better feel on this, let us plot the graphs on the same axes. To this end, we define two lists using the **Table** command and use the **ListPlot** command to plot the graphs.

In[779]:= `plot1 = ListPlot[Table[{k, a[k]}, {k, 1, 10}], PlotStyle → {Blue}];`
    `plot2 = ListPlot[Table[{k, b[k]}, {k, 1, 10}], PlotStyle → {Red}];`
    `Show[plot1, plot2, PlotRange → {0, 10}]`

Out[781]=

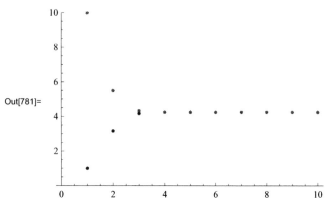

The above graph suggests that the two sequences converge to the same limit. Unfortunately, *Mathematica*'s **Limit** command cannot help us compute the limit of a_n and b_n due to their recursive nature. (Try this!)

NOTE: We encourage the reader to experiment with different initial values for a_1 and b_1 to see if the sequences a_n and b_n always converge to the same limit.

Example 10.6. Consider the sequence

$$a_n = \frac{(n!)^{1/n}}{n}$$

a) Show that if $b_n = \ln a_n$, then $b_n = \frac{\ln(n!) - n \ln n}{n}$.

b) Does b_n converge? If so, find the limit.

c) Does a_n converge? If so, find the limit.

Solution:

a) We define a sequence $c_n = \frac{\ln(n!) - n \ln n}{n}$ and then show that $b_n = c_n$.

In[782]:= `Clear[a, b, c]`

$$a[n\_] := \frac{(n!)^{1/n}}{n}$$

`b[n_] := Log[a[n]]`

$$c[n\_] := \frac{\text{Log}[n!] - n\,\text{Log}[n]}{n}$$

In[786]:= `TableForm[Table[{N[c[n]], N[b[n]], N[c[n], 10] - N[b[n], 10]}, {n, 2, 10}],`
    `TableHeadings → {Automatic, {" `c_n`", " `b_n`", " `c_n`-`b_n`"}}]`

Out[786]//TableForm=

	c_n	b_n	$c_n - b_n$
1	-0.346574	-0.346574	$0. \times 10^{-11}$
2	-0.501359	-0.501359	$0. \times 10^{-10}$
3	-0.591781	-0.591781	$0. \times 10^{-10}$
4	-0.65194	-0.65194	$0. \times 10^{-10}$
5	-0.695218	-0.695218	$0. \times 10^{-10}$
6	-0.72803	-0.72803	$0. \times 10^{-10}$
7	-0.753866	-0.753866	$0. \times 10^{-10}$
8	-0.774799	-0.774799	$0. \times 10^{-10}$
9	-0.792144	-0.792144	$0. \times 10^{-10}$

The preceding table indicates that the two sequences are the same. Here is a plot of both:

In[787]:= `ListPlot[{Table[{n, b[n]}, {n, 1, 100}], Table[{n, c[n]}, {n, 1, 100}]}, PlotRange → {-1, 0.1}, AxesOrigin → {0, 0}]`

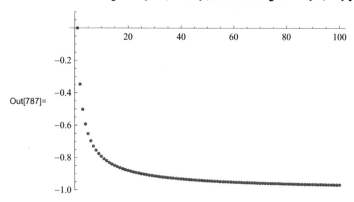

Out[787]=

This plot clearly shows that $b_n = c_n$, that is, $\ln(a_n) = \ln\left(\frac{(n!)^{1/n}}{n}\right) = \frac{\ln(n!)-n\ln n}{n}$. We leave it to the student to establish this equality using properties of the natural logarithmic function.

b) The previous plot indicates that the limit of b_n is -1. To confirm this, we use the **Limit** command.

In[788]:= `Limit[b[n], n → Infinity]`

Out[788]= -1

c) Since $b_n = \ln(a_n)$, it follows that $a_n = e^{b_n}$ and hence $\lim_{n\to\infty} a_n = e^{-1}$. Again, we verify this using the **Limit** command:

In[789]:= `Limit[a[n], n → Infinity]`

Out[789]= $\dfrac{1}{e}$

◾ Exercises

In Exercises 1 though 3, determine the convergence of the given sequence.

1. $a_n = \dfrac{3n^2+n+2}{2n^2+1}$
2. $a_n = \ln\left(\dfrac{2n+3}{n+1}\right)$
3. $a_n = \sqrt[n]{n}$

4. Let $c_n = \dfrac{1}{n+1} + \dfrac{1}{n+2} + \dfrac{1}{n+3} + \dots + \dfrac{1}{2n}$.

a. Find the first ten terms of the sequence.
b. Plot the graph of the sequence.
c. Is the sequence increasing? Bounded? Convergent? Prove each of your assertions.
d. Find $\lim_{n\to\infty} c_n$.

5. The *n*th *harmonic number* is defined to be the sum

$$H_n = 1 + \frac{1}{2} + \frac{1}{3} + \dots + \frac{1}{n}.$$

Let $a_n = H_n - \ln n$ and $b_n = \int_1^{n+1} \frac{1}{x}\, dx$.

a. Show that $H_n \geq b_n$ for $n = 1, 2, 3, \dots, 10$. Prove that this holds for all positive integers n.

b. Show that $a_n \geq 0$ for $n = 1, 2, 3, \dots, 10$. Prove that this holds for all positive integers n.

c. Use the **ListPlot** command to plot the graph of a_n. Does the graph indicate that a_n is decreasing or increasing?

d. Evaluate $\lim_{n \to \infty} a_n$.

e. The limit in part d) is called Euler's Constant and is denoted by γ. Compute γ accurate to 20 digits.

■ 10.2 Infinite Series

Students should read Section 10.2-10.3 of Rogawski's *Calculus* [1] for a detailed discussion of the material presented in this section.

■ 10.2.1 Finite Sums

Sum[a[n], n, n1, n2] evaluates the finite sum of a_n as n goes from n_1 to n_2.
Sum[a[n], n, n1, Infinity] evaluates the infinite series of a_n as n goes from n_1 to ∞.

Using the **BasicMathInput Palette**, we can also enter finite sums or infinite series as $\sum_{n=n1}^{n2} a[n]$ or $\sum_{n=n1}^{\infty} a[n]$, respectively.

Example 10.7. Compute the following finite sums:

a) $\sum_{n=1}^{10} \frac{(-1)^n}{n}$ b) $\sum_{k=1}^{5} (k-1)(k+1)$

c) $\sum_{k=1}^{30} \binom{20}{k} 2^k$ d) $\sum_{i=1}^{n} (3i-2)$ e) $\sum_{k=0}^{10} \frac{k^2+1}{k^3+2k^2+1}$

Solution:

a)

In[790]:= $\displaystyle\sum_{n=1}^{10} \frac{(-1)^n}{n}$

Out[790]= $-\dfrac{1627}{2520}$

b)

In[791]:= **Sum[(k + 1) (k - 1), {k, 1, 5}]**

Out[791]= 50

c) The binomial coefficient $\binom{n}{m} = \frac{n!}{m! \, (n-m)!}$ is expressed in *Mathematica* by the command **Binomial[n, m]**.

In[792]:= $\displaystyle\sum_{k=0}^{30}$ **Binomial[30, k] 2^k**

Out[792]= 205 891 132 094 649

NOTE: The above number is the same as $3^{30} = 205\,891\,132\,094\,649$. Verify this!

d)

In[793]:= $\displaystyle\sum_{j=1}^{n} (3\,j - 2)$

Out[793]= $\dfrac{1}{2}\left(-n + 3\,n^2\right)$

In[794]:= **Simplify[%]**

Out[794]= $\dfrac{1}{2}\,n\,(-1 + 3\,n)$

e)

In[795]:= $\displaystyle\sum_{k=0}^{10} \dfrac{k^2 + 1}{k^3 + 2\,k^2 + 1}$

Out[795]= $\dfrac{361\,278\,549\,115\,758\,513}{126\,627\,880\,430\,636\,728}$

▪ 10.2.2 Partial Sums and Convergence

Example 10.8. Consider the series $\sum_{n=1}^{\infty} \dfrac{1}{4\,n^2-1}$. Let s_n denote its nth partial sum.

a) Find s_{100}.

b) Compute every 10th partial sum up to $n = 100$.

c) Compute every 1000th partial sum up to $n = 10,000$.

d) From the tables of values in parts a) and b) what do you infer about the convergence of the series? Prove your assertion.

Solution:

a) First, we define s_n in *Mathematica* and then evaluate s_{100}.

In[796]:= **Clear[s, n]**

$\quad$ **s[n_] :=** $\displaystyle\sum_{j=1}^{n} \dfrac{1}{4\,j^2 - 1}$

$\quad$ **s[100]**

Out[798]= $\dfrac{100}{201}$

In[799]:= **N[%]**

Out[799]= 0.497512

b) Here, we use the command **Table[s[n],{n,1,J,K}]**, which gives the list of every **K**-th value of s_n, as **n** goes from **1** to **J**. The command **TableForm[N[Table[s[n],{n, 1, J, K }]]]** lists the values in column form.

In[800]:= **Table[s[n], {n, 1, 100, 10}]**

Out[800]= $\left\{\dfrac{1}{3},\ \dfrac{11}{23},\ \dfrac{21}{43},\ \dfrac{31}{63},\ \dfrac{41}{83},\ \dfrac{51}{103},\ \dfrac{61}{123},\ \dfrac{71}{143},\ \dfrac{81}{163},\ \dfrac{91}{183}\right\}$

In[801]:= **N[%]**

Out[801]= {0.333333, 0.478261, 0.488372, 0.492063,

0.493976, 0.495146, 0.495935, 0.496503, 0.496933, 0.497268}

In[802]:= **TableForm[Table[{n, N[s[n]]}, {n, 10, 100, 10}],**

TableHeadings → {{}, {"n", "s_n"}}]

Out[802]//TableForm=

n	s_n
10	0.47619
20	0.487805
30	0.491803
40	0.493827
50	0.49505
60	0.495868
70	0.496454
80	0.496894
90	0.497238
100	0.497512

c)

In[803]:= **TableForm[Table[{n, N[s[n]]}, {n, 1000, 10 000, 1000}],**

TableHeadings → {{}, {"n", " s_n"}}]

Out[803]//TableForm=

n	s_n
1000	0.49975
2000	0.499875
3000	0.499917
4000	0.499938
5000	0.49995
6000	0.499958
7000	0.499964
8000	0.499969
9000	0.499972
10 000	0.499975

d) It seems that the partial sums converge to 0.5. We confirm this by evaluating

In[804]:= **Limit[s[n], n → ∞]**

Out[804]= $\dfrac{1}{2}$

Can you prove this? Hint: Use the method of partial fractions to decompose this series into a *telescoping* series as discussed in your calculus text.

Example 10.9. Let s_n be the nth partial sum of the *harmonic series*

$$\sum_{k=1}^{\infty} \frac{1}{k}.$$

a) Find s_{100}.

b) Compute every 1000th partial sum up to $n = 10,000$

c) Plot the graphs of the partial sums.

d) From the table of values in part (b) what do you infer? Prove your assertion.

Solution: We will follow the method of the preceding example. First, we define the nth partial sum.

In[805]:= **Clear[s, n]**
     s[n_] := Sum[1 / k, {k, 1, n}]

a) Then s_{100} is given by

In[807]:= **s[100]**

Out[807]= 14 466 636 279 520 351 160 221 518 043 104 131 447 711 /
          2 788 815 009 188 499 086 581 352 357 412 492 142 272

In[808]:= **N[%]**

Out[808]= 5.18738

b) Here is a table of values of every 1000th term in the sequence s_n for n less than or equal to 10,000.

In[809]:= **TableForm[Table[{n, N[s[n]]}, {n, 1000, 10 000, 1000}],**
     TableHeadings → {{}, {"n", " s_n"}}]

Out[809]//TableForm=

n	s_n
1000	7.48547
2000	8.17837
3000	8.58375
4000	8.87139
5000	9.09451
6000	9.27681
7000	9.43095
8000	9.56447
9000	9.68225
10 000	9.78761

c) Here is a plot of s_n.

In[810]:= **ListPlot[Table[{n, s[n]}, {n, 1, 300, 20}]]**

Out[810]=

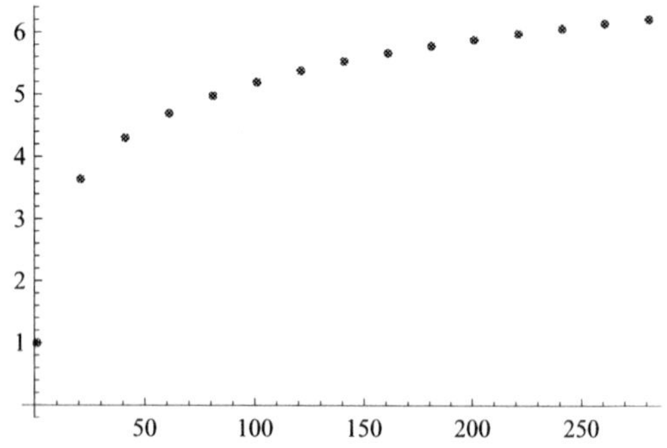

The graph above indicates a slow growth that makes it difficult to reach a definitive conclusion regarding the convergence of the harmonic series.

d) The table in b) and the plot in c) both suggest that the sequence of the partial sums is increasing. To convince ourselves of this, we compare s_{2^n} and $\frac{n}{2}$.

In[811]:= **TableForm$\left[\text{Table}[\{n / 2., N[s[2^n]]\}, \{n, 1, 10\}],\right.$**
$\left.\text{TableHeadings} \rightarrow \left\{\{\}, \left\{"\frac{n}{2}", " s_{2^n}"\right\}\right\}\right]$

Out[811]//TableForm=

$\frac{n}{2}$	s_{2^n}
0.5	1.5
1.	2.08333
1.5	2.71786
2.	3.38073
2.5	4.0585
3.	4.74389
3.5	5.43315
4.	6.12434
4.5	6.81652
5.	7.50918

This table suggests that $s_{2^n} \geq \frac{n}{2}$ for $n \geq 2$. Use this fact (a proof of it can be found in your calculus text) to establish the divergence of the harmonic series.

Example 10.10. Determine whether the following series converges or diverges.

a) $\sum_{n=1}^{\infty} \frac{(-1)^n}{n^2}$ b) $\sum_{j=1}^{\infty} \frac{j-1}{j}$ c) $\sum_{n=1}^{\infty} \left(\frac{1}{\sqrt{n}} - \frac{1}{\sqrt{n+1}} \right)$ d) $\sum_{n=1}^{\infty} (\ln(n+1) - \ln n)$

Solution: In all cases, we let *Mathematica* attempt to evaluate the infinite sum. For those cases where *Mathematica* returns a numeric output, this is understood to mean that the series converges and that the sum of the series is the given value.

a)

In[812]:= $\sum_{n=1}^{\infty} \frac{(-1)^n}{n^2}$

Out[812]= $-\frac{\pi^2}{12}$

Thus, the series converges to $-\frac{\pi^2}{12}$. To see this graphically, we plot the graph of the partial sums of the series using the **ListPlot** command, along with the horizontal line representing its sum $s = -\frac{\pi^2}{12} \approx -0.822467$.

In[813]:= **Clear[s, n]**

$s[n\_] = \sum_{k=1}^{n} \frac{(-1)^k}{k^2};$

In[815]:= `plot1 = ListPlot[Table[{n, s[n]}, {n, 1, 100}]];`

$$plot2 = Plot\left[-\frac{\pi^2}{12}, \{x, 1, 100\}\right];$$

`Show[plot1, plot2]`

Out[817]=

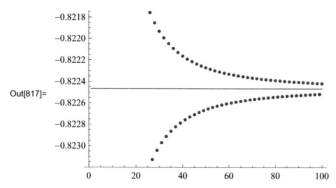

b) Observe that $\lim_{j\to\infty} \frac{j-1}{j} = 1 \neq 0$. Hence, the series does not converge according to the Test for Divergence. This explains the following output message from *Mathematica* if we attempt to evaluate the series.

In[818]:= $\displaystyle\sum_{j=1}^{\infty} \frac{j-1}{j}$

Sum::div : Sum does not converge. ≫

Out[818]= $\displaystyle\sum_{j=1}^{\infty} \frac{-1+j}{j}$

c) Since this is a telescoping series, it can be shown that the *n*th partial sum is given by $s_n = 1 - \frac{1}{\sqrt{n+1}}$. This can be seen in the following output:

In[819]:= $\mathbf{s[n\_]} := \displaystyle\sum_{k=1}^{n} \left(\frac{1}{\sqrt{k}} - \frac{1}{\sqrt{k+1}}\right)$

In[820]:= `TableForm[Table[{n, s[n]}, {n, 1, 10}],`
     `TableHeadings → {{}, {"n", " `s_n`"}}]`

Out[820]//TableForm=

n	s_n
1	$1 - \dfrac{1}{\sqrt{2}}$
2	$1 - \dfrac{1}{\sqrt{3}}$
3	$\dfrac{1}{2}$
4	$1 - \dfrac{1}{\sqrt{5}}$
5	$1 - \dfrac{1}{\sqrt{6}}$
6	$1 - \dfrac{1}{\sqrt{7}}$
7	$1 - \dfrac{1}{2\sqrt{2}}$
8	$\dfrac{2}{3}$
9	$1 - \dfrac{1}{\sqrt{10}}$
10	$1 - \dfrac{1}{\sqrt{11}}$

Hence, the series converges to 1, which we confirm with *Mathematica*.

In[821]:= $\displaystyle\sum_{n=1}^{\infty}\left(\frac{1}{\sqrt{n}} - \frac{1}{\sqrt{n+1}}\right)$

Out[821]= 1

d) This, too, is a telescoping series with the nth partial sum given by $s_n = \ln(n+1)$ (verify this). Hence, the series diverges, as shown by the following output.

In[822]:= $\displaystyle\sum_{n=1}^{\infty}$ `(Log[n + 1] - Log[n])`

    Sum::div : Sum does not converge. ≫

Out[822]= $\displaystyle\sum_{n=1}^{\infty}$ `(-Log[n] + Log[1 + n])`

■ Exercises

1. Consider the series $\sum_{n=1}^{\infty} \frac{1}{n^2+3n+2}$.

a. Use the **Apart** command to decompose the terms of the series, $a_n = \frac{1}{n^2+3n+2}$, into partial fractions.

b. Use part (a) to find a formula for the nth partial sum of the series.

c) Is the series convergent? If so, then find its sum.

In Exercises 2 through 5, determine if the given series is convergent. If it is, then find its sum.

2. $\sum_{n=1}^{\infty} \frac{1}{n(n+1)}$ 　　　　　　3. $\sum_{n=0}^{\infty} \frac{(-1)^n}{n!}$ 　　　　　　4. $\sum_{n=1}^{\infty} (-1)^{n+1}$

5. The sereis $\sum_{n=0}^{\infty} a\, r^n$ is called a *geometric series.*

a. Find the *n*th partial sum of the geometric series.

b. For what values of *r* does the series converge? Diverge?

c. Find the sum of the geometric series for those values where the series converges.

6. Consider the series $\sum_{n=1}^{\infty} \frac{1}{\sqrt[3]{n}}$.

a. Use the **ListPlot** command to plot the first ten partial sums of this series.

b. Show that the series converges.

■ 10.3 Tests for Convergence

Students should read Sections 10.4-10.5 of Rogawski's *Calculus* [1] for a detailed discussion of the material presented in this section.

■ 10.3.1 Comparison and Limit Comparison Tests

The Comparison Test: Suppose $0 \le a_n \le b_n$ for all $n > M$, where M is some positive integer.

a) If $\sum_{n=1}^{\infty} b_n$ is convergent, then $\sum_{n=1}^{\infty} a_n$ is also convergent.

b) If $\sum_{n=1}^{\infty} a_n$ is divergent, then $\sum_{n=1}^{\infty} b_n$ is also divergent.

The Limit Comparison Test: Suppose a_n and b_n are both positive and $\lim_{n \to \infty} \frac{a_n}{b_n} = l$. If $0 < l < \infty$ (i.e.,, if l is a finite positive number), then $\sum_{n=1}^{\infty} a_n$ and $\sum_{n=1}^{\infty} b_n$ both converge or both diverge.

To test convergence of a given series $\sum_{n=1}^{\infty} a_n$ using the Limit Comparison Test, it is important that the series $\sum_{n=1}^{\infty} b_n$ easily be checked for convergence.

Example 10.11. Discuss the convergence of the series

$$\sum_{n=1}^{\infty} \frac{1}{\sqrt{n^2+2}}$$

Solution: Since $\frac{1}{\sqrt{n^2+2}} < \frac{1}{\sqrt{n^2}} = \frac{1}{n}$ and the harmonic series $\sum_{n=1}^{\infty} \frac{1}{n}$ was shown to divergence in Example 10.8 of this text, it

follows by the Comparison Test that our series diverges also. This is verified by *Mathematica*:

In[823]:= $\sum_{n=1}^{\infty} \frac{1}{\sqrt{n^2+2}}$

　　　Sum::div : Sum does not converge. ≫

Out[823]= $\sum_{n=1}^{\infty} \frac{1}{\sqrt{2+n^2}}$

Example 10.12. Discuss the convergence of the series

$$\sum_{n=1}^{\infty} \frac{3\,n^3 + 40\,n^2 + 4}{n^5 + 200\,n^4 + 1}$$

Solution: To find another series to compare ours with, we consider one with terms $b_n = \frac{3}{n^2}$. This comes from considering lower powers of n in both the numerator and denominator of a_n.

In[824]:= **Clear[a, b, n]**

$$a[n\_] := \frac{3\,n^3 + 40\,n^2 + 4}{n^5 + 200\,n^4 + 1}$$

$$b[n\_] := \frac{3}{n^2}$$

In[827]:= **Limit$\left[\frac{a[n]}{b[n]}, n \to Infinity\right]$**

Out[827]= 1

Since the series $\sum_{n=1}^{\infty} \frac{3}{n^2}$ is convergent (*p*-series) and $\lim_{n\to\infty} \frac{a_n}{b_n} = 1$, we conclude from the Limit Comparison Test that our series $\sum_{n=1}^{\infty} \frac{3\,n^3 + 40\,n^2 + 4}{n^5 + 200\,n^4 + 1}$ is also convergent.

Example 10.13. Discuss the convergence of the series $\sum_{n=1}^{\infty}\left[1 - \cos\left(\frac{1}{n}\right)\right]$.

Solution: We note that $\lim_{n\to\infty}\left[1 - \cos\left(\frac{1}{n}\right)\right] = 0$. This is confirmed by *Mathematica*.

In[828]:= **Limit[1 - Cos[1 / n], n → ∞]**

Out[828]= 0

Thus, the necessary condition for convergence is satisfied. But this does not guarantee convergence. We will use the **ListPlot** command to plot the graph of the partial sums to see if the series converges.

In[829]:= **Clear[s]**
        s[n_] := Sum[1 - Cos[1 / k], {k, 1, n}]

In[831]:= **ListPlot[Table[{n, s[n]}, {n, 1, 100}], PlotRange → {0, 1}]**

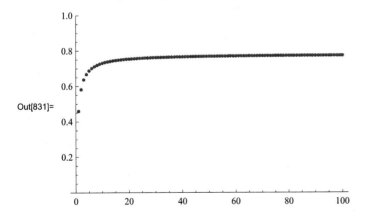

Out[831]=

The graph above clearly indicates convergence. To see that this is indeed true, we compare it with a series that is known to converge: $\sum_{n=1}^{\infty} \frac{1}{n^2}$. To this end, let us define a_n and b_n as follows.

In[832]:= `Clear[a, b, n]`

$$a[n\_] := 1 - Cos\left[\frac{1}{n}\right]$$

$$b[n\_] := \frac{1}{n^2}$$

Observe that both a_n and b_n are positive terms for all n. Hence, we can apply Limit Comparison Test:

In[835]:= `Limit`$\left[\dfrac{a[n]}{b[n]}, \ n \to Infinity\right]$

Out[835]= $\dfrac{1}{2}$

Therefore, the given series, $\sum_{n=1}^{\infty}\left[1 - \cos\left(\frac{1}{n}\right)\right]$, converges.

■ **10.3.2 The Integral Test**

The Integral Test. Given an infinite series

$$\sum_{n=1}^{\infty} a_n$$

we define $f(x)$ so that $f(n) = a_n$. If $f(x)$ is positive on the interval $[1, \infty)$, decreasing on this interval, and if $\lim_{x \to \infty} f(x) = 0$, then

$$\int_1^{\infty} f(x)\,dx \quad \text{and} \quad \sum_{n=1}^{\infty} a_n$$

both converge or both diverge.

Example 10.14. Use the integral test to determine the convergence of the following series.

a) $\sum_{n=1}^{\infty} \dfrac{1}{\sqrt{n}}$ 　　　c) $\sum_{j=1}^{\infty} j\,e^{-j^2}$ 　　　c) $\sum_{n=1}^{\infty} \dfrac{1}{\sqrt{n}\,\ln n}$

Solution:

a) Here, $a_n = \dfrac{1}{\sqrt{n}}$ and so we define $f(n)$ in *Mathematica*:

In[836]:= `Clear[f, x]`

$$f[x\_] := \frac{1}{\sqrt{x}}$$

In[838]:= `f'[x]`

Out[838]= $-\dfrac{1}{2\,x^{3/2}}$

Since $f'(x) < 0$ for all $x \in [1, \infty)$, it follows that f is decreasing. Clearly f is positive in value and $\lim_{x \to \infty} f(x) = 0$. Thus we can apply the Integral Test by evaluating $\int_1^{\infty} f(x)\,dx$:

In[839]:= **Integrate[f[x], {x, 1, Infinity}]**

Integrate::idiv : Integral of $\dfrac{1}{\sqrt{x}}$ does not converge on $\{1, \infty\}$. $\gg$

Out[839]= $\displaystyle\int_{1}^{\infty} \dfrac{1}{\sqrt{x}}\, dx$

To confirm this, we evaluate this improper integral according to its limit definition:

In[840]:= **Clear[F, b]**
F[b_] := Integrate[f[x], {x, 1, b}]

In[842]:= **Limit[F[b], b → ∞]**

Out[842]= ∞

b) Here, we define *f* as

In[843]:= **Clear[f, x]**
f[x_] = x E$^{-x^2}$

Out[844]= $e^{-x^2}\, x$

In[845]:= **Plot[f[x], {x, 0, 5}, PlotRange → {0, 1}]**

Out[845]=

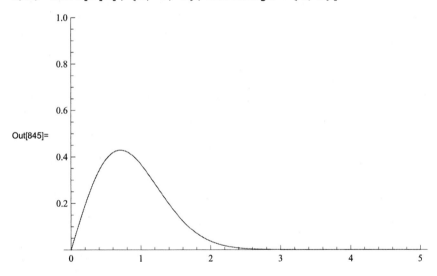

The graph clearly shows that the function is decreasing. We can confirm this by solving

In[846]:= **f'[x]**
Solve[f'[x] == 0]

Out[846]= $e^{-x^2} - 2\, e^{-x^2}\, x^2$

Out[847]= $\left\{ \left\{ x \to -\dfrac{1}{\sqrt{2}} \right\}, \left\{ x \to \dfrac{1}{\sqrt{2}} \right\} \right\}$

In[848]:= **f'[1]**

Out[848]= $-\dfrac{1}{e}$

In[849]:= **N[1 / Sqrt[2]]**

Out[849]= 0.707107

Thus, f has critical points at $\pm\frac{1}{\sqrt{2}} \approx 0.707$. Since $f'(1) < 0$, we conclude that f is decreasing on $(1, \infty)$.

The graph also shows that $\lim_{x\to\infty} f(x) = 0$. Again, we can confirm this by evaluating

In[850]:= **Limit[f[x], x → Infinity]**

Out[850]= 0

Hence, the Integral Test can be used to determine if the series is convergent. That the series $\sum_{j=1}^{\infty} j\, e^{-j^2}$ is convergent follows from the fact that

In[851]:= $\int_1^\infty$ **f[x] dx**

Out[851]= $\dfrac{1}{2\,e}$

Since the corresponding integral is convergent, it follows that the series $\sum_{j=1}^{\infty} j\, e^{-j^2}$ is also convergent.

c) In this case, we define f as

In[852]:= **Clear[f, x]**

f[x_] = $\dfrac{1}{\sqrt{x}\ \textbf{Log[x]}}$

Out[853]= $\dfrac{1}{\sqrt{x}\ \text{Log}[x]}$

In[854]:= **Plot[f[x], {x, 2, 100}]**

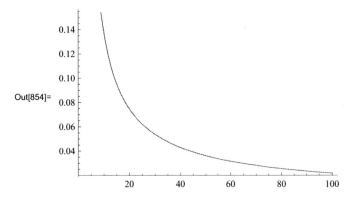

We leave it for the reader to check that f satisfies all the conditions of the Integral Test, which we now apply.

In[855]:= $\int_2^\infty \mathbf{f[x]} \, \mathbf{dx}$

Integrate::idiv : Integral of $\dfrac{1}{\sqrt{x}\ \text{Log}[x]}$ does not converge on $\{2, \infty\}$. ≫

Out[855]= $\int_2^\infty \dfrac{1}{\sqrt{x}\ \text{Log}[x]} \, dx$

Since the preceding output states that the integral is divergent, we conclude that the corresponding series is divergent also.

Example 10.15. For what values of p does the series $\sum_{n=2}^\infty \frac{1}{n(\ln n)^p}$ converge?

Solution: We apply the Integral Test. Toward this end, we define $f(x)$ so that $f(n) = \frac{1}{n(\ln n)^p}$ and then verify that $f(x)$ is positive and decreasing on the interval $[a, \infty)$, and that $\lim_{x \to \infty} f(x) = 0$:

In[856]:= $\mathbf{Clear[f, x, p]}$

$\mathbf{f[x\_]} := \dfrac{1}{\mathbf{x\ (Log[x])^P}}$

In[858]:= $\mathbf{Limit[f[x], x \to Infinity]}$

Out[858]= 0

To confirm this limit, we will plot graphs of $f(x)$ for some values of p

In[859]:= $\mathbf{Plot[Evaluate[Table[f[x], \{p, -4, 2, .5\}]], \{x, 2, 100\}, PlotRange \to \{0, 5\}]}$

Out[859]=

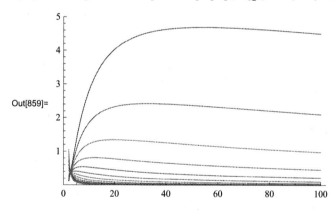

In the plot above, observe that some of the graphs are initially increasing, but then begin to decrease at a certain point. Let us then find the interval over which the function $f(x)$ is decreasing for each p. To this end, we compute the derivative $f'(x)$ and solve $f'(x) < 0$ for x.

In[860]:= $\mathbf{f'[x]}$

Out[860]= $-\dfrac{p\ \text{Log}[x]^{-1-p}}{x^2} - \dfrac{\text{Log}[x]^{-p}}{x^2}$

In[861]:= $\mathbf{Simplify[\%]}$

Out[861]= $-\dfrac{\text{Log}[x]^{-1-p}\ (p + \text{Log}[x])}{x^2}$

In[862]:= **Solve[f'[x] == 0, x]**

Out[862]= $\{\{x \to e^{-p}\}\}$

Since $(\ln x)^{-1-p} > 0$ for all $x > 1$, we see that $f'(x) < 0$ if $\ln x > -p$, or equivalently, $x = e^{-p}$. Thus, $f(x)$ is decreasing on $[2, \infty)$ where a is the maximum of 2 and e^{-p}.

To apply the Integral Test, we integrate f over the interval $[2, \infty)$. This is easier than integrating over the interval $[a, \infty)$, and permissible since the integrals $\int_2^\infty f(x)\,dx$ and $\int_a^\infty f(x)\,dx$ either converge or diverge together.

In[863]:= **Integrate[f[x], {x, 2, ∞}]**

Out[863]= $\text{ConditionalExpression}\left[\dfrac{\text{Log}[2]^{1-p}}{-1+p}, \text{Re}[p] > 1\right]$

The preceding output shows that $\int_2^\infty f(x)\,dx$ is convergent for $p > 1$. However, the case $p \le 1$ remains unsolved. To evaluate the integral in this situation, we define its anti-derivative $F(b) = \int_2^b f(x)\,dx$ and find the limit of $F(b)$ as $b \to \infty$.

In[864]:= **Clear[F, b]**
F[b_] = Integrate[f[x], {x, 2, b}]

Out[865]= $\text{ConditionalExpression}\left[\dfrac{\text{Log}[2]^{1-p} - \text{Log}[b]^{1-p}}{-1+p}, \text{Re}[b] \ge 1 \,||\, b \notin \text{Reals}\right]$

Since b is a real number and $b > 2$, the solution to our integral is the first one, that is, $F(b) = \frac{(\ln 2)^{1-p} - \ln(b)^{1-p}}{1-p}$, provided $p \ne 1$. But then for $p < 1$, we see that $\lim_{b\to\infty} F(b) = \infty$ since $\lim_{b\to\infty} \ln(b)^{1-p} = \infty$. For $p > 1$, we have $\lim_{b\to\infty} F(b) = \frac{(\ln 2)^{1-p}}{1-p}$, which we already knew from the second previous *Mathematica* output. The following tables might be helpful to convince you about this.

In[866]:= **Table[Limit[F[b], b → Infinity], {p, -3, .9, .5}]**

Out[866]= $\{\infty, \infty, \infty, \infty, \infty, \infty, \infty, \infty\}$

In[867]:= **Table[Limit[F[b], b → Infinity], {p, 1.1, 9, .5}]**

Out[867]= {10.3733, 2.0766, 1.3605, 1.12346, 1.02813, 0.997425, 1.0048, 1.03926,
1.09605, 1.1734, 1.27122, 1.39056, 1.53333, 1.70219, 1.90056, 2.13262}

For $p = 1$, we make this substitution inside the integral and evaluate it directly:

In[868]:= **p = 1;**
Integrate[f[x], {x, 2, ∞}]

Integrate::idiv : Integral of $\dfrac{1}{x \, \text{Log}[x]}$ does not converge on $\{2, \infty\}$. »

Out[869]= $\displaystyle\int_2^\infty \dfrac{1}{x \, \text{Log}[x]}\,dx$

Therefore, the infinite series $\sum_{n=2}^\infty \frac{1}{n(\ln n)^p}$ is convergent for $p > 1$ and divergent for $p \le 1$.

NOTE: To see how slow the growth of this series is for the value of $p = 1$, we consider the following table of partial sums. Recall that $f(n)$ is the nth term of the series and hence the nth partial sum is given by

In[870]:= `Clear[p, s, n]`
`s[n_] = Sum[f[k], {k, 2, n}]`

Out[871]= $\sum_{k=2}^{n} \frac{\text{Log}[k]^{-p}}{k}$

The following output shows that the sum of the first ten thousand terms is only about 3.01501088.

In[872]:= `p = 1;`
`N[s[10 000]]`

Out[873]= `3.01501`

Here is a plot of the graph of the first ten thousand partial sums in steps of 1,000.

In[874]:= `ListPlot[Table[{n, s[n]}, {n, 1000, 10 000, 1000}]]`

Out[874]=

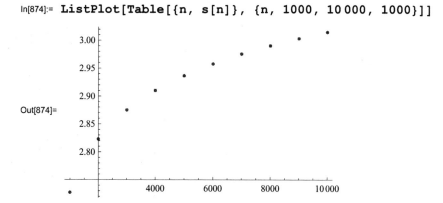

■ 10.3.3 Absolute and Conditional Convergence

Suppose $a_n > 0$ for all n. The infinite series

$$\sum_{n=1}^{\infty} (-1)^n a_n$$

is called an *alternating series*. If the series $\sum_{n=1}^{\infty} (-1)^n a_n$ is convergent but the series $\sum_{n=1}^{\infty} a_n$ is divergent, then the alternating series is called *conditionally convergent*. If $\sum_{n=1}^{\infty} a_n$ is convergent, then the alternating series $\sum_{n=1}^{\infty} (-1)^n a_n$ is called *absolutely convergent*.

Alternating Series Test: If a_n is decreasing and $\lim_{n \to \infty} a_n = 0$, then the series $\sum_{n=1}^{\infty} (-1)^n a_n$ is convergent.

Example 10.16. Determine if the given series is conditionally or absolutely convergent.

a) $\sum_{n=1}^{\infty} \frac{(-1)^n}{n^2+1}$ c) $\sum_{n=2}^{\infty} \frac{(-1)^n}{n \ln n}$

Solution:

a) We define $a_n = \frac{1}{n^2+1}$ in *Mathematica* and check that a_n satisfies the conditions of the Alternating Series Test.

In[875]:= `Clear[a, n]`
$a[n\_] := \frac{1}{n^2 + 1}$

In[877]:= **Limit[a[n], n -> ∞]**

Out[877]= 0

In[878]:= **f[x_] = a[x];**
f'[x]

Out[879]= $-\dfrac{2x}{\left(1+x^2\right)^2}$

Thus, a_n is decreasing since $f'(x) > 0$, where $f(n) = a_n$. Moreover, a_n converges to 0. Hence, the series $\sum_{n=1}^{\infty} \frac{(-1)^n}{n^2+1}$ is convergent by the Alternating Series Test.

To check absolute convergence, we use the Limit Comparison Test with $b_n = \frac{1}{n^2}$.

In[880]:= **Limit$\left[\dfrac{a[n]}{1/n^2}, \ n \to Infinity\right]$**

Out[880]= 1

Since the series $\sum_{n=1}^{\infty} \frac{1}{n^2}$ is convergent and the previous output shows $\lim_{n\to\infty} \frac{a_n}{b_n} = 1$, we conclude that the series $\sum_{n=1}^{\infty} a_n = \sum_{n=1}^{\infty} \frac{1}{n^2+1}$ is also convergent. Therefore, the alternating series $\sum_{n=1}^{\infty} \frac{(-1)^n}{n^2+1}$ is absolutely convergent.

b) We procced as in part a).

In[881]:= **Clear[a, n]**

a[n_] := $\dfrac{1}{n \ Log[n]}$

In[883]:= **Limit[a[n], n -> ∞]**

Out[883]= 0

In[884]:= **f[x_] = a[x];**
f'[x]

Out[885]= $-\dfrac{1}{x^2 \ Log[x]^2} - \dfrac{1}{x^2 \ Log[x]}$

For the same reasons we conclude that a_n is decreasing and converges to 0. Hence, the series $\sum_{n=2}^{\infty} \frac{(-1)^n}{n \ln n}$ is convergent by the Alternating Series Test.

To check absolute convergence, we apply the Intgeral Test to $f(x)$:

In[886]:= **Clear[m]**

Limit$\left[\displaystyle\int_2^m f[x] \, dx, \ m \to Infinity\right]$

Out[887]= ∞

From this, we conclude that the series is conditionally convergent.

Example 10.17. Show that the series

$$\sum_{n=1}^{\infty} \frac{(-1)^n}{\sqrt{n^2+1}}$$

is conditionally convergent. Find a value of n for which the partial sum s_n approximates the series by an error less than 10^{-5}. Also, find the corresponding value for s_n.

Solution: We leave it for the reader to check that the series converges conditionally as in the preceding example. For the second part of the problem, we proceed by first defining the partial sums of the series.

In[888]:= **Clear[s, a, n]**

$$a[n\_] := \frac{1}{\sqrt{n^2+1}}$$

$$s[n\_] := Sum\big[(-1)^k a[k], \{k, 1, n\}\big]$$

If S denotes the sum of the alternating series, it can be shown that $|S - s_n| < a_{n+1}$ (refer to your calculus text for a proof of this fact). The following table of values gives some numerical evidence of this fact:

$$\sum_{n=1}^{\infty} \frac{(-1)^n}{\sqrt{1+n^2}}$$

In[891]:= $\mathbf{Table\Big[\Big\{N\Big[Abs\Big[\sum_{n=1}^{\infty} \frac{(-1)^n}{\sqrt{n^2+1}} - s[m]\Big]\Big], N[a[m]]\Big\}, \{m, 1, 10\}\Big]}$

Out[891]= {{0.266189, 0.707107}, {0.181024, 0.447214},
     {0.135203, 0.316228}, {0.107332, 0.242536}, {0.088784, 0.196116},
     {0.075615, 0.164399}, {0.0658064, 0.141421}, {0.0582284, 0.124035},
     {0.0522031, 0.110432}, {0.0473006, 0.0995037}}

In[892]:= **Clear[S, n]**

$$S = \sum_{n=1}^{\infty} \frac{(-1)^n}{\sqrt{n^2+1}}$$

Out[893]= $\displaystyle\sum_{n=1}^{\infty} \frac{(-1)^n}{\sqrt{1+n^2}}$

The table below gives the values of a_n for large values of n.

In[894]:= **Table[N[a[10^n]], {n, 1, 10}]**

Out[894]= $\big\{0.0995037, 0.0099995, 0.001, 0.0001,$
     $0.00001, 1. \times 10^{-6}, 1. \times 10^{-7}, 1. \times 10^{-8}, 1. \times 10^{-9}, 1. \times 10^{-10}\big\}$

Thus, $n = 10^6$ is a possible value. But solving $a_n = 10^{-5}$ can give us a more accurate value.

In[895]:= $\mathbf{NSolve\big[a[x] == 10^{-5}, x\big]}$

Out[895]= $\{\{x \to -100\,000.\}, \{x \to 100\,000.\}\}$

Thus, if $n = 100\,001$, we have $|S - s_n| < 10^{-5}$. We confirm this with *Mathematica*:

In[896]:= **N[S − s[100 001]]**

Out[896]= 4.99993×10^{-6}

Can you find a smaller value of *n* for which $\left| S - s_n \right| < 10^{-5}$?

■ 10.3.4 Ratio Test

The Ratio Test: Suppose $a_n > 0$ and let

$$r = \lim_{n \to \infty} \frac{a_{n+1}}{a_n}.$$

a) If $r < 1$, the series $\sum_{n=1}^{\infty} a_n$ converges.

b) If $r > 1$, the series $\sum_{n=1}^{\infty} a_n$ diverges.

c) If $r = 1$, no conclusion can be drawn about the convergence of the series $\sum_{n=1}^{\infty} a_n$. In other words, if $r = 1$, then we must use another test to determine the convergence.

Example 10.18. Use the Ratio Test to determine the convergence of the following series.

a) $\sum_{n=1}^{\infty} \frac{n^n}{n!}$ c) $\sum_{j=2}^{\infty} \frac{1}{j (\ln j)^3}$ c) $\sum_{n=1}^{\infty} \frac{3 n^3 + 40 n^2 + 4}{n^5 + 200 n^4 + 1}$

Solution: For each series, we define a_n to be its *n*th term and evaluate $\lim_{n \to \infty} \frac{a_{n+1}}{a_n}$.

a)

In[897]:= **Clear[a, n]**

a[n_] := $\frac{n^n}{n!}$

In[899]:= **Limit[a[n + 1] / a[n], n -> ∞]**

Out[899]= e

Since $e > 1$, the series $\sum_{n=1}^{\infty} \frac{n^n}{n!}$ converges by the Ratio Test.

b)

In[900]:= **Clear[a, j]**

a[j_] := $\frac{1}{j (Log[j])^3}$

Limit[a[j + 1] / a[j], j -> ∞]

Out[902]= 1

This output means that we must use a different test. However, this is an instance of Example 11.12 in this text with $p = 3$. Hence, the series converges by the Integral Test.

c)

In[903]:= **Clear[a, n]**

a[n_] := $\frac{3 n^3 + 40 n^2 + 1}{n^5 + 200 n^4 + 1}$

In[905]:= **Limit[a[n + 1] / a[n], n -> ∞]**

Out[905]= 1

Again, this output means we are forced to use a different test. Therefore, we shall use the Limit Comparison Test instead. To this end, we define $b_n = \frac{3}{n^2}$:

In[906]:= **Clear[b, n]**

   b[n_] := $\frac{3}{n^2}$

In[908]:= **Limit$\left[\frac{a[n]}{b[n]}, n \to \text{Infinity}\right]$**

Out[908]= 1

Since the series $\sum_{n=1}^{\infty} \frac{1}{n^2}$ is convergent, we conclude that the series $\sum_{n=1}^{\infty} \frac{3 n^3 + 40 n^2 + 4}{n^5 + 200 n^4 + 1}$ is also convergent.

■ 10.3.5 Root Test

The Root Test: Suppose $a_n > 0$ and let

$$r = \lim_{n \to \infty} (a_n)^{1/n}.$$

a) If $r < 1$, the series $\sum_{n=1}^{\infty} a_n$ converges.

b) If $r > 1$, the series $\sum_{n=1}^{\infty} a_n$ diverges.

c) If $r = 1$, no conclusion can be drawn about the convergence of the series $\sum_{n=1}^{\infty} a_n$. In other words, if $r = 1$, then we must use another test to determine the convergence.

Example 10.19. Use the Root Test to determine the convergence of the following series:

a) $\sum_{n=1}^{\infty} \left(\frac{n}{2n+1}\right)^n$ b) $\sum_{n=1}^{\infty} \frac{1}{n \, 3^n + n^2}$ c) $\sum_{n=1}^{\infty} \frac{3n+1}{n^2+n+1}$

Solution: For each series we define a_n to be its nth term and evaluate $\lim_{n \to \infty} (a_n)^{1/n}$.

a)

In[909]:= **Clear[a, n]**

   a[n_] := $\left(\frac{n}{2n+1}\right)^n$

In[911]:= **Limit$\left[(a[n])^{1/n}, n \to \infty \right]$**

Out[911]= $\frac{1}{2}$

Thus, the series $\sum_{n=1}^{\infty} \left(\frac{n}{2n+1}\right)^n$ converges by Root Test.

b)

In[912]:= **Clear[a, n]**

   a[n_] := $\frac{1}{n \, 3^n + n^2}$

In[914]:= $\text{Limit}\left[(\text{a}[\text{n}])^{1/n}, \text{n} \to \infty\right]$

Out[914]= $\dfrac{1}{3}$

Even though the preceding **Limit** command is returned as unevaluated, the **N** command reveals that it is approximately 1/3.

In[915]:= **N[%]**

Out[915]= 0.333333

To verify this, we use the Squeeze Theorem (discussed in your calculus text) with $b_n = \dfrac{1}{2 n 3^n}$ and $c_n = \dfrac{1}{n 3^n}$. First, note that $b_n \le a_n \le c_n$. We can verify this using the following plot:

In[916]:= $\text{Plot}\left[\left\{\dfrac{3^{-x}}{2 x}, \text{a}[\text{x}], \dfrac{3^{-x}}{x}\right\}, \{\text{x}, 1, 10\}, \text{PlotStyle} \to \{\text{Green}, \text{Red}, \text{Blue}\}\right]$

Out[916]=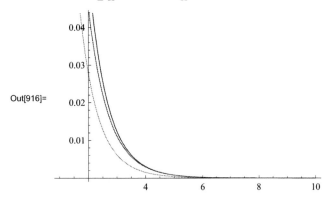

We now define b_n and c_n as and evaluate $\lim_{n \to \infty} (c_n)^{1/n}$ and $\lim_{n \to \infty} (b_n)^{1/n}$.

In[917]:= **Clear[b, c, n]**

$\text{b}[\text{n\_}] := \dfrac{1}{2 n 3^n}$

$\text{c}[\text{n\_}] := \dfrac{1}{n 3^n}$

In[920]:= $\text{Limit}\left[(\text{b}[\text{n}])^{1/n}, \text{n} \to \text{Infinity}\right]$

$\text{Limit}\left[(\text{c}[\text{n}])^{1/n}, \text{n} \to \text{Infinity}\right]$

Out[920]= $\dfrac{1}{3}$

Out[921]= $\dfrac{1}{3}$

Thus, we also have $\lim_{n \to \infty} (a_n)^{1/n} = \dfrac{1}{3}$ and hence the series converges by the Root Test.

c)

In[922]:= **Clear[a, n]**

$\text{a}[\text{n\_}] := \dfrac{3 n + 2}{n^2 - n + 1}$

In[924]:= **Limit$\left[\,(\mathbf{a[n]})^{1/n},\ \mathbf{n} \to \infty\,\right]$**

Out[924]= 1

The Root Test fails. Let us try the Ratio Test:

In[925]:= **Limit$\left[\dfrac{\mathbf{a[n+1]}}{\mathbf{a[n]}},\ \mathbf{n} \to \textbf{Infinity}\right]$**

Out[925]= 1

The Ratio Test fails as well. We can easily verify that the Integral Test is applicable. We will evaluate the integral

In[926]:= $\displaystyle\int_{1}^{\infty} \mathbf{a[x]}\ d\mathbf{x}$

Integrate::idiv : Integral of $\dfrac{2}{1-x+x^2} + \dfrac{3x}{1-x+x^2}$ does not converge on $\{1, \infty\}$. $\gg$

Out[926]= $\displaystyle\int_{1}^{\infty} \dfrac{2+3\,x}{1-x+x^2}\ dx$

To confirm the divergence of the improper integral, we leave it to the reader to evalaute the function $F(x)$ defined below for large values of x.

In[927]:= **Clear[F, b]**

$\mathbf{F[b\_]} := \displaystyle\int_{1}^{b} \mathbf{a[x]}\ d\mathbf{x}$

■ Exercises

In Exercises 1 through 6, use the Comparison Test or the Limit Comparison Test to determine if the given series is convergent. If it is convergent, then find its sum.

1. $\sum_{n=1}^{\infty} \dfrac{n}{\sqrt{n^3+1}}$

2. $\sum_{n=2}^{\infty} \dfrac{\ln n}{n^2 + 3\ln n}$

3. $\sum_{n=1}^{\infty} \dfrac{n^4 + 200\,n^2 + 1000\,n + 2222}{n^6 + 5\,n^4 + n + 1}$

4. $\sum_{n=1}^{\infty} \dfrac{\ln n}{n^2}$

5. $\sum_{n=2}^{\infty} \dfrac{1}{n^{\ln n}}$

6. $\sum_{n=1}^{\infty} \left(1 - 2^{-1/n}\right)$

In Exercises 7 through 9, use the Integral Test to determine if the given series is convergent. If it converges, then find its sum.

7. $\sum_{n=1}^{\infty} \dfrac{n}{n^2+1}$

8. $\sum_{n=2}^{\infty} \dfrac{n}{2^n}$

9. $\sum_{n=1}^{\infty} \dfrac{(\ln n)^3}{n^2}$

10. For what values of p does the series $\sum_{n=1}^{\infty} \dfrac{1}{n^p \ln n}$ converge?

11. Consider the series $\sum_{n=2}^{\infty} \dfrac{(\ln n)^k}{n^p}$.

a. Fix a value of p (say, $p = 2$ or $p = 1/2$) and find all values of k for which the series converges.

b. Fix a value of k (say, $k = 2$ or $k = -2$) and find all values of p for which the series converges.

c. Generalize the results of a) and b) to all values of p and k.

12. Let f be a positive valued function that decreases on $[1, \infty)$ and let $a_n = f(n)$. It can be shown that

$$\int_1^\infty f(x)\,dx \le \sum_{n=1}^\infty a_n \le a_1 + \int_1^\infty f(x)\,dx .$$

a. Use $f(x) = \dfrac{1}{x^{1.1}}$ to verify this.

b. Approximate $\sum_{n=1}^\infty \dfrac{1}{n^{1.1}}$ using its nth partial sums with $n = 10,\ 100,\ 1000,\ 10000$.

In Exercises 13 through 16, determine if each of the infinite series is absolutely convergent, conditionally convergent, or divergent. Justify your conclusions!

13. $\sum_{n=1}^\infty \dfrac{(-1)^n (n^2-1)}{n^2+1}$

14. $\sum_{n=1}^\infty \dfrac{20\,n^2-n-1}{n^3+n^2+33}$

15. $\sum_{n=1}^\infty \dfrac{(-2)^n}{n!}$

16. $\sum_{n=1}^\infty (-1)^{n+1}\left[\sqrt{n+1} - \sqrt{n}\ \right]$

17. Discovery Exercise:

a. Determine the convergence or divergence of $\sum_{n=2}^\infty \dfrac{1}{n \ln (\ln \ln n)^{0.5}}$, $\sum_{n=2}^\infty \dfrac{1}{n \ln (\ln \ln n)}$, and $\sum_{n=2}^\infty \dfrac{1}{n \ln (\ln \ln n)^2}$.

b. Generalize your work in part a) by determining for which real numbers p the series $\sum_{n=2}^\infty \dfrac{1}{n \ln (\ln \ln n)^p}$ converges.

In Exercises 18 through 25, determine the convergence or divergence of the given infinite series using any of the convergence tests discussed in this section.

18. $\sum_{n=1}^\infty \dfrac{3\,n+1}{4\,n+5}$

19. $\sum_{n=1}^\infty \dfrac{n}{2\,n^2+1}$

20. $\sum_{n=1}^\infty \dfrac{n+3}{4\,n^3+5}$

21. $\sum_{n=1}^\infty n\left(\dfrac{2}{3}\right)^n$

22. $\sum_{n=1}^\infty n\left(\dfrac{3}{2}\right)^n$

23. $\sum_{n=1}^\infty \dfrac{n^n}{n!}$

24. $\sum_{n=1}^\infty \dfrac{(n!)^2}{(3\,n)!}$

25. $\sum_{n=0}^\infty (-1)^n \left(1+\dfrac{1}{n}\right)^n$

26. The Ratio Test proved to be inconclusive for some of the series in the previous exercise. Can you conjecture for what type of series the Ratio Test will fail in general? Use other tests to rework the problems in the first exercise where the Ratio Test failed.

27. Of the following four conditions, one guarantees that a series will diverge, two conditions guarantee that a series will converge, and one has no guarantee (the series can either converge or diverge). Identify each one and explain your reasoning.

$$\lim_{n\to\infty} \left|\dfrac{a_{n+1}}{a_n}\right| = 0$$

$$\lim_{n\to\infty} \left|\dfrac{a_{n+1}}{a_n}\right| = \dfrac{1}{2}$$

$$\lim_{n\to\infty} \left|\dfrac{a_{n+1}}{a_n}\right| = 1$$

$$\lim_{n\to\infty} \left|\dfrac{a_{n+1}}{a_n}\right| = 2$$

28. Identify the two series that are the same:

a. $\sum_{n=1}^\infty n\left(\dfrac{3}{4}\right)^n$

b. $\sum_{n=0}^\infty (n+1)\left(\dfrac{3}{4}\right)^n$

c. $\sum_{n=1}^\infty n\left(\dfrac{3}{4}\right)^{n-1}$

In Exercises 29 through 32, determine the convergence or divergence of the series:

29. $\sum_{n=1}^\infty \left(2\sqrt[n]{n}+1\right)^n$

30. $\sum_{n=0}^\infty e^{-n}$

31. $\sum_{n=1}^\infty \left(\dfrac{-2\,n}{3\,n+1}\right)^{3\,n}$

32. $\sum_{n=1}^\infty \left(\dfrac{n}{2\,n+1}\right)^n$

33. Construct two examples of infinite series, the first convergent and the second divergent, for which the Root Test generates inconclusive information.

34. Use the Root Test to test for convergence or divergence of the series:

a. $\dfrac{1}{(\ln 3)^3} + \dfrac{1}{(\ln 4)^4} + \dfrac{1}{(\ln 5)^5} + \dfrac{1}{(\ln 6)^6} + \dots$

b. $1 + \dfrac{2}{3} + \dfrac{3}{3^2} + \dfrac{4}{3^3} + \dfrac{5}{3^4} + \dfrac{6}{3^5} + \dots$

Hint: Write a formula for the general nth term in each case.

■ 10.4 Power Series

Students should read Sections 10.6-10.7 of Rogawski's *Calculus* [1] for a detailed discussion of the material presented in this section.

■ 10.4.1 Taylor Polynomials

The Taylor polynomial of a given function f at a point $x = a$ is given by

$$T_n(x) = f(a) + f'(a)(x-a) + \frac{f''(a)}{2!}(x-a)^2 + \frac{f'''(a)}{3!}(x-a)^3 + \dots + \frac{f^{(n)}(a)}{n!}(x-a)^n.$$

The *Mathematica* **Series[f,{x, a, n}]** generates the nth Taylor polynomial $T_n(x)$ plus a term of the form $O[x]^{n+1}$. To obtain the Taylor polynomial without this term, we use the command **Normal[Series[f,{x, a, n}]]**.

The nth remainder $R_n(x)$ of $f(x)$ at $x = a$ is defined by

$$R_n(x) = f(x) - T_n(x).$$

Taylor's Theorem states that

$$R_n(x) = \frac{1}{n!} \int_a^x f^{(n+1)}(u)(x-u)^n \, du.$$

Here is a way to define the Taylor polynomial of f at $x = a$ by defining $T_n(x)$ and the nth remainder $R_n(x)$ (using Taylor's Theorem for R_n) without referring to *Mathematica*'s built-in command **Series**.

In[929]:= **Clear[a, x, f, T, R]**

$$\mathbf{T[x\_, a\_, n\_]} := \sum_{k=0}^{n} \frac{D[f[x], \{x, k\}] \, / . \, x \to a}{k!} \, (x - a)^k$$

$$\mathbf{R[x\_, a\_, n\_]} := \frac{1}{n!} \int_a^x D[f[u], \{u, n+1\}] * (x - u)^n \, du$$

Example 10.20. Let $f(x) = e^x$. Find its 5th Taylor polynomial at $x = 0$.

Solution: We use the **Series** command to obtain the answer:

In[932]:= **Normal[Series[E^x, {x, 0, 5}]]**

Out[932]= $1 + x + \dfrac{x^2}{2} + \dfrac{x^3}{6} + \dfrac{x^4}{24} + \dfrac{x^5}{120}$

Using the polynomial $T[x, a, n]$, we defined above we get

In[933]:= `Clear[f]`

`f[x_] := Eˣ`

`T[x, 0, 5]`

Out[935]= $1 + x + \dfrac{x^2}{2} + \dfrac{x^3}{6} + \dfrac{x^4}{24} + \dfrac{x^5}{120}$

In[936]:= `R[x, 0, 5]`

Out[936]= $\dfrac{1}{120} \left(-120 + 120\, e^x - 120\, x - 60\, x^2 - 20\, x^3 - 5\, x^4 - x^5 \right)$

Example 10.21. Find the *n*th Taylor polynomial of $f(x)$ at $x = a$ for various values of *a* and *n*.

a) $f(x) = \sqrt{x}$ b) $f(x) = \cos x$

Solution: a) We shall use the same function **T[x,a,n]** defined in the previous example (make sure you evaluate this function before you evaluate the table below).

In[937]:= `Clear[a, x, f]`

$$T[x\_, a\_, n\_] := \sum_{k=0}^{n} \frac{D[f[x], \{x, k\}] \,/.\, x \to a}{k!} \,(x - a)^k$$

$$R[x\_, a\_, n\_] := \frac{1}{n!} \int_{a}^{x} D[f[u], \{u, n+1\}] * (x - u)^n \, du$$

In[940]:= `Clear[f]`

`f[x_] = √x`

`TableForm[Table[ T[x, a, n] , {a, 1, 5}, {n, 1, 3}] ,`

`  TableHeadings →`

`    {{"at a=1", "at a=2", "at a=3", "at a=4", "at a=5"}, {"n=1", "n=2", "n=3"}}]`

Out[941]= $\sqrt{x}$

Out[942]//TableForm=

	n=1	n=2	n=3
at a=1	$1 + \frac{1}{2}(-1+x)$	$1 + \frac{1}{2}(-1+x) - \frac{1}{8}(-1+x)^2$	$1 + \frac{1}{2}(-1+x) - \frac{1}{8}(-1+x)^2 + \frac{1}{16}(-1+$
at a=2	$\sqrt{2} + \frac{-2+x}{2\sqrt{2}}$	$\sqrt{2} + \frac{-2+x}{2\sqrt{2}} - \frac{(-2+x)^2}{16\sqrt{2}}$	$\sqrt{2} + \frac{-2+x}{2\sqrt{2}} - \frac{(-2+x)^2}{16\sqrt{2}} + \frac{(-2+x)^3}{64\sqrt{2}}$
at a=3	$\sqrt{3} + \frac{-3+x}{2\sqrt{3}}$	$\sqrt{3} + \frac{-3+x}{2\sqrt{3}} - \frac{(-3+x)^2}{24\sqrt{3}}$	$\sqrt{3} + \frac{-3+x}{2\sqrt{3}} - \frac{(-3+x)^2}{24\sqrt{3}} + \frac{(-3+x)^3}{144\sqrt{3}}$
at a=4	$2 + \frac{1}{4}(-4+x)$	$2 + \frac{1}{4}(-4+x) - \frac{1}{64}(-4+x)^2$	$2 + \frac{1}{4}(-4+x) - \frac{1}{64}(-4+x)^2 + \frac{1}{512}(-4$
at a=5	$\sqrt{5} + \frac{-5+x}{2\sqrt{5}}$	$\sqrt{5} + \frac{-5+x}{2\sqrt{5}} - \frac{(-5+x)^2}{40\sqrt{5}}$	$\sqrt{5} + \frac{-5+x}{2\sqrt{5}} - \frac{(-5+x)^2}{40\sqrt{5}} + \frac{(-5+x)^3}{400\sqrt{5}}$

b) We proceed as in part a):

In[943]:= **Clear[f]**
f[x_] = Cos[x]
TableForm[Table[T[x, a, n] , {a, 0, 2 Pi, Pi / 2}, {n, 1, 4}] ,
  TableHeadings → {{"at a=0", "at a=π/2", "at a=π", "at a=3π/2", "at a=2π"},
    {"n=1", "n=2", "n=3", "n=4"}}]

Out[944]= $\cos[x]$

Out[945]//TableForm=

	n=1	n=2	n=3	n=4
at a=0	1	$1 - \frac{x^2}{2}$	$1 - \frac{x^2}{2}$	$1 - \frac{x^2}{2} + \frac{x^4}{24}$
at a=π/2	$\frac{\pi}{2} - x$	$\frac{\pi}{2} - x$	$\frac{\pi}{2} - x + \frac{1}{6}\left(-\frac{\pi}{2} + x\right)^3$	$\frac{\pi}{2} - x + \frac{1}{6}\left(-\frac{\pi}{2} + x\right)^3$
at a=π	-1	$-1 + \frac{1}{2}(-\pi + x)^2$	$-1 + \frac{1}{2}(-\pi + x)^2$	$-1 + \frac{1}{2}(-\pi + x)^2 - \frac{1}{24}(-\pi$
at a=3π/2	$-\frac{3\pi}{2} + x$	$-\frac{3\pi}{2} + x$	$-\frac{3\pi}{2} + x - \frac{1}{6}\left(-\frac{3\pi}{2} + x\right)^3$	$-\frac{3\pi}{2} + x - \frac{1}{6}\left(-\frac{3\pi}{2} + x\right)^3$
at a=2π	1	$1 - \frac{1}{2}(-2\pi + x)^2$	$1 - \frac{1}{2}(-2\pi + x)^2$	$1 - \frac{1}{2}(-2\pi + x)^2 + \frac{1}{24}(-2$

Example 10.22. Let $f(x) = \frac{1}{2+3x^2}$.

a) Find the Taylor polynomials $T_n(x)$ of f at $x = 0$ for $n = 1, 2, ..., 6$.
b) Draw the graphs of the function f and its Taylor polynomials found in part a).
c) Over which interval does the nth Taylor polynomial gives a close approximation to $f(x)$ if $n = 4$, $n = 10$, and $n = 20$?

Solution:

a) Here are the Taylor polynomials up to order $n = 6$.

In[946]:= **Clear[f]**
f[x_] = $\frac{1}{2 + 3 x^2}$
TableForm[Table[{n, T[x, 0, n]} , {n, 1, 6}] ,
  TableHeadings → {{}, {"n", "T_n at a=0"}}]

Out[947]= $\frac{1}{2 + 3 x^2}$

Out[948]//TableForm=

n	T_n at a=0
1	$\frac{1}{2}$
2	$\frac{1}{2} - \frac{3 x^2}{4}$
3	$\frac{1}{2} - \frac{3 x^2}{4}$
4	$\frac{1}{2} - \frac{3 x^2}{4} + \frac{9 x^4}{8}$
5	$\frac{1}{2} - \frac{3 x^2}{4} + \frac{9 x^4}{8}$
6	$\frac{1}{2} - \frac{3 x^2}{4} + \frac{9 x^4}{8} - \frac{27 x^6}{16}$

b) We first use the **Plot** command to plot the graphs of f and its Taylor polynomial at $x = 0$ for the desired values of n. We then use the **Show** command to plot both graphs on the same axes.

In[949]:= `Clear[plot1, plot2]`
`plot1 = Plot[f[x], {x, -3, 3}, PlotStyle → Red];`
`plot2 = Plot[Evaluate[Table[T[x, 0, n], {n, 1, 6}]], {x, -3, 3}] ;`
`Show[plot1, plot2]`

Out[952]=

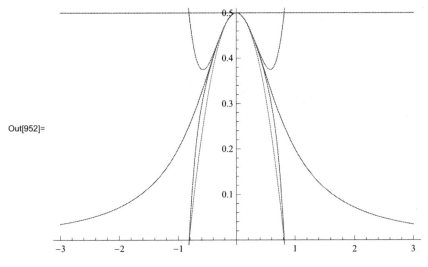

c) We use the same commands as in part b) except that we do not use the **Table** command. The first one is for the case $n = 4$.

In[953]:= `Clear[plot1, plot2]`
`plot1 = Plot[f[x], {x, -3, 3}, PlotStyle → Red];`
`plot2 = Plot[Evaluate[T[x, 0, 4]], {x, -3, 3}] ;`
`Show[plot1, plot2]`

Out[956]=

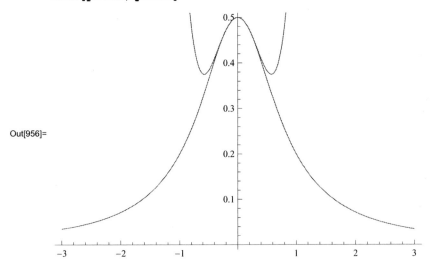

It seems that the two graphs are close to each other if x is in the interval $(-0.5, 0.5)$. To see this close up, we recommend that you change the range of values for x in both plots (plot1 and plot2) to the interval $[-1, 1]$. We can confirm this by plotting the 4th remainder of $f(x)$ at $x = 0$.

In[957]:= `Plot[Evaluate[R[x, 0, 4]], {x, -1, 1}, PlotRange → {-1, 1}]`

Out[957]=

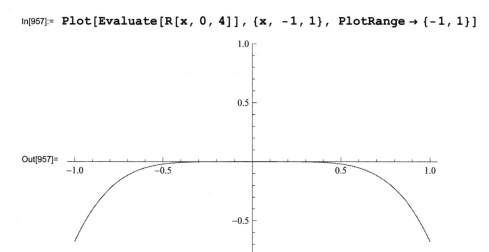

We repeat the above with $n = 10$.

In[958]:= `Clear[plot1, plot2]`
`plot1 = Plot[f[x], {x, -3, 3}, PlotStyle → Red];`
`plot2 = Plot[Evaluate[T[x, 0, 100]], {x, -3, 3}] ;`
`Show[plot1, plot2]`

Out[961]=

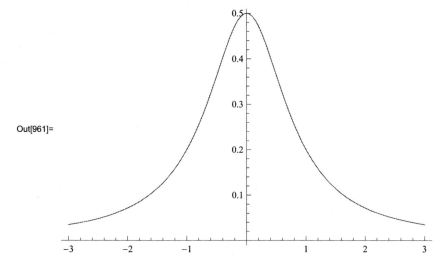

The graph above clearly indicates the 10th Taylor polynomial gives a close approximation for f in the interval $[-.6, .6]$. Again, plotting R_n will confirm this.

In[962]:= **Plot[Evaluate[R[x, 0, 10]], {x, -1, 1}, PlotRange → {-1, 1}]**

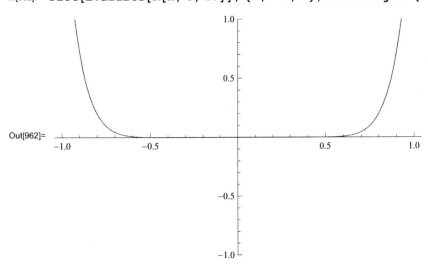

If we continue in this manner, we see that the Taylor polynomial P_n for large values of n gives a better approximation of f in the interval $[-1, 1]$. In fact, for $n = 20$, we see that $R_n(x)$ is almost zero in the interval $[-0.7, 0.7]$, which is an improvement over the previous interval $[-0.6, 0.6]$ obtained for $n = 10$.

In[963]:= **Plot[Evaluate[R[x, 0, 20]], {x, -1, 1}, PlotRange → {-1, 1}]**

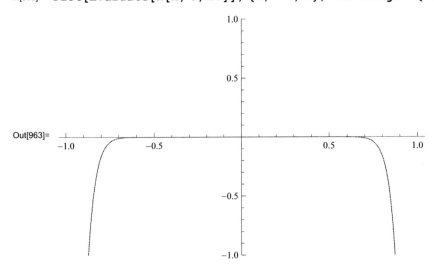

■ 10.4.2 Convergence of Power Series

A series of the form

$$\sum_{n=0}^{\infty} a_n(x - x_0)^n = a_0 + a_1(x - x_0) + a_2(x - x_0)^2 + a_3(x - x_0)^3 + \ldots.$$

is called a power series.

The set of all x for which the series converges is called the *interval of convergence*.

If the series converges for $x = x_0$ only, we say is *radius of interval* is $R = 0$. In this case, its interval of convergence is $\{x_0\}$.

If the series converges for all real numbers x, we say its *radius of convergence is $R = \infty$*. In this case, its interval of convergence is $(-\infty, \infty)$.

If the series converges for some $x \neq x_0$ and diverges for some y, then it can be shown that there exists $R > 0$ such that the power series converges for all x for which $|x - x_0| < R$ and diverges for all x for which $|x - x_0| > R$. The convergence at $x = x_0 - R$ and $x = x_0 + R$ needs to be checked.

When the radius of convergence R is a positive real number, there are four possiblities for the interval of convergence:

$$(x_0 - R, \ x_0 + R) \text{ or } [x_0 - R, \ x_0 + R) \text{ or } (x_0 - R, \ x_0 + R] \text{ or } [x_0 - R, \ x_0 + R]$$

depending on the convergence at the end points of the intervals.

The radius of convergence R of the power series $\sum_{n=0}^{\infty} a_n (x - x_0)^n$ can be found by using the Ratio or Root Test. Let

$$r = \lim_{n \to \infty} \left| \frac{a_{n+1}}{a_n} \right| \quad \text{or} \quad r = \lim_{n \to \infty} \sqrt[n]{|a_n|}$$

a) If $r = 0$, then $R = \infty$.
b) If $r = \infty$, then $R = 0$.
c) If $0 < r < \infty$, then $R = \frac{1}{r}$.

Example 10.23. Find the radius and interval of convergence for the given power series.

a) $\sum_{n=0}^{\infty} \frac{n}{2n+1} x^n$
b) $\sum_{n=1}^{\infty} \frac{(x-3)^n}{n \, 3^n}$
c) $\sum_{n=0}^{\infty} \frac{(x+2)^n}{n^2+n+1}$

d) $\sum_{n=0}^{\infty} n^n x^n$
e) $\sum_{n=0}^{\infty} \frac{1}{n!} (x - 1)^n$

Solution:

a) Let us define $s_m(x)$ to be the mth partial sum of the series and plot the graph of some of these partial sums. We will plot every 100th partial sum up to 10,000 terms.

In[964]:= **Clear[s, n, m]**

$$s[x\_, m\_] := \sum_{n=0}^{m} \frac{n}{2\,n+1}\,x^n$$

In[966]:= **Plot[Evaluate[Table[s[x, m], {m, 1, 1000, 100}]], {x, -2, 2}]**

Out[966]=

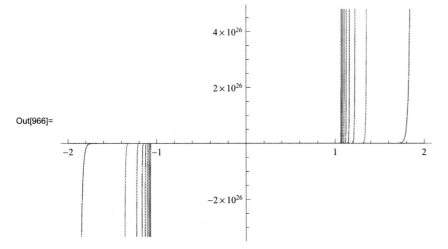

This clearly indicates that the partial sums diverge outside $(-1, 1)$. Here is the plot over the interval $(-1, 1)$.

In[967]:= **Plot[Evaluate[Table[s[x, m], {m, 1, 1000, 100}]], {x, -1, 1}]**

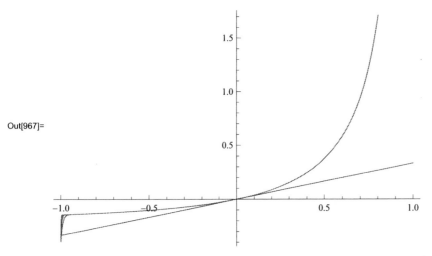

Out[967]=

We now use calculus. Here, note that $a_n = \frac{n}{2n+1}$ and $x_0 = 0$. We first define a_n in *Mathematica* and find the radius of convergence. We recall $|a|$ (absolute value of a) is entered as **Abs[a]**.

In[968]:= **Clear[a, n, r]**

$$a[n\_] := \frac{n}{2\,n+1}$$

In[970]:= $r = \text{Limit}\left[\text{Abs}\left[\frac{a[n+1]}{a[n]}\right], n \to \text{Infinity}\right]$

Out[970]= 1

Thus, the radius of convergence is $R = \frac{1}{r} = \frac{1}{1} = 1$. The power series convrges on $(-1,\ 1)$. To check convergence at the endpoints $x = -1$ and $x = 1$, we note that the power series becomes $\sum_{n=0}^{\infty} \frac{n}{2n+1}(-1)^n$ and $\sum_{n=0}^{\infty} \frac{n}{2n+1}(1)^n$, both of which are divergent, since their nth terms do not converge to 0. Here, *Mathematica* confirms the divergence at the endpoints.

In[971]:= $\sum_{n=0}^{\infty} \frac{n}{2\,n+1}\,(-1)^n$

Sum::div : Sum does not converge. ≫

Out[971]= $\sum_{n=0}^{\infty} \frac{(-1)^n\,n}{1+2\,n}$

In[972]:= $\sum_{n=0}^{\infty} \frac{n}{2\,n+1}\,(1)^n$

Sum::div : Sum does not converge. ≫

Out[972]= $\sum_{n=0}^{\infty} \frac{n}{1+2\,n}$

Therefore, the interval of convergence is $(-1,\ 1)$.

b) $\sum_{n=1}^{\infty} \frac{(x-3)^n}{n\,3^n}$

In[973]:= **Clear[a, r, n]**

$$a[n\_] := \frac{1}{n \, 3^n}$$

In[975]:= $r = \text{Limit}\left[\frac{a[n+1]}{a[n]}, n \to \text{Infinity}\right]$

Out[975]= $\frac{1}{3}$

Thus the radius of convergence is $R = \frac{1}{r} = \frac{1}{1/3} = 3$.

Since $x_0 = 3$, the power series converges on $(x_0 - R, \ x_0 + R) = (3 - 3, \ 3 + 3) = (0, 6)$. We need to check the endpoints $x = 0$ and $x = 6$. We substitute these in the power series and evaluate

In[976]:= $\displaystyle\sum_{n=1}^{\infty} \frac{(x-3)^n}{n \, 3^n} \ /. \ x \to \{0, 6\}$

Out[976]= $\{-\text{Log}[2], \infty\}$

Thus, the interval of convergence is $[0, 6)$.

c) $\sum_{n=1}^{\infty} \frac{(x+2)^n}{n^2+n+1}$

In[977]:= **Clear[a, r, n]**

$$a[n\_] := \frac{1}{n^2 + n + 1}$$

In[979]:= $r = \text{Limit}\left[\text{Abs}\left[\frac{a[n+1]}{a[n]}\right], n \to \infty\right]$

Out[979]= 1

Hence, the radius of convergence is $R = \frac{1}{1} = 1$. Since $x_0 = -2$, we see that the power series converges at least on the open interval $(-2 - 1, -2 + 1) = (-3, -1)$. To determine the actual interval of convergence we need to check the endpoints. As in part c), we evaluate

In[980]:= $\displaystyle\sum_{n=0}^{\infty} \frac{(x+2)^n}{n^2 + n + 1} \ /. \ x \to \{-3, -1\}$

Out[980]= $\left\{\text{HypergeometricPFQ}\left[\{1, (-1)^{1/3}, -(-1)^{2/3}\}, \left\{\frac{3}{2} - \frac{i\sqrt{3}}{2}, \frac{3}{2} + \frac{i\sqrt{3}}{2}\right\}, -1\right],\right.$

$\left.\text{HypergeometricPFQ}\left[\{1, (-1)^{1/3}, -(-1)^{2/3}\}, \left\{\frac{3}{2} - \frac{i\sqrt{3}}{2}, \frac{3}{2} + \frac{i\sqrt{3}}{2}\right\}, 1\right]\right\}$

In[981]:= **N[%]**

Out[981]= $\{0.76131 + 4.70246 \times 10^{-16} \, i, \ 1.79815 - 4.96787 \times 10^{-16} \, i\}$

Since this is not clear, we examine the series by plugging in by hand $x = -3$ and $x = -1$. When $x = -3$ the series becomes $\sum_{n=1}^{\infty} \frac{(-3+2)^n}{n^2+n+1} = \sum_{n=1}^{\infty} \frac{(-1)^n}{n^2+n+1}$, which is an alternating series. We leave it to the reader to verify that the Alternating Series Test applies in this case. Thus, we have a convergent series.

Next, we substitute $x = -1$ to obtain the series $\sum_{n=1}^{\infty} \frac{(-1+2)^n}{n^2+n+1} = \sum_{n=1}^{\infty} \frac{1}{n^2+n+1}$ to which we apply the Integral Test (verify that the conditions of the Integral Test are satisfied):

In[982]:= **Integrate$\left[\dfrac{1}{x^2 + x + 1}, \{x, 0, \text{Infinity}\}\right]$**

Out[982]= $\dfrac{2\pi}{3\sqrt{3}}$

Thus, the series converges in this case as well. Therefore, the interval of convergence for the power series is $[-3, -1]$.

d) $\sum_{n=0}^{\infty} n^n x^n$

In[983]:= **Clear[a, r, n]**
a[n_] := n^n

In[985]:= **r = Limit$\left[\text{Abs}\left[\dfrac{a[n+1]}{a[n]}\right], n \to \infty\right]$**

Out[985]= ∞

Thus, the radius of convergence is $R = 0$ and the series converges for $x = 0$ only.

e) $\sum_{n=0}^{\infty} \frac{1}{n!} (x-1)^n$

In[986]:= **Clear[a, r, n]**
a[n_] := $\dfrac{1}{n!}$

In[988]:= **r = Limit$\left[\text{Abs}\left[\dfrac{a[n+1]}{a[n]}\right], n \to \infty\right]$**

Out[988]= 0

Thus, the radius of convergence is $R = \infty$ and the series converges for all real x. Hence, the interval of convergence is $(-\infty, \infty)$.

■ **10.4.3 Taylor Series**

The *Taylor series* for $f(x)$ at $x = a$ is given by the power series

$$\sum_{n=0}^{\infty} \frac{f^{(n)}(a)}{n!} (x-a)^n = f(a) + f'(a)(x-a) + \frac{f''(a)}{2}(x-a)^2 + \frac{f'''(a)}{6}(x-a)^3 + \ldots..$$

The *Mathematica* command **Series[f,{x, a, n}]** generates the power series of f at $x = a$ to the order $(x-a)^n$. It is not possible to write all the terms explicitly since there are infinitely many.

Example 10.24. Let $f(x) = \frac{1+x}{1+x^2}$.

a) Find the first ten terms of the Taylor series of f at $x = 0$.
b) Estimate the radius and interval of convergence of the Taylor series of f at $x = 0$.

Solution:

a) We use the **Series** command to obtain the Taylor series as follows:

In[989]:= **Clear[f, x]**

$$f[x\_] := \frac{1-x}{2+x}$$

In[991]:= **Series[f[x], {x, 0, 10}]**

Out[991]= $\frac{1}{2} - \frac{3x}{4} + \frac{3x^2}{8} - \frac{3x^3}{16} + \frac{3x^4}{32} - \frac{3x^5}{64} + \frac{3x^6}{128} - \frac{3x^7}{256} + \frac{3x^8}{512} - \frac{3x^9}{1024} + \frac{3x^{10}}{2048} + O[x]^{11}$

This output gives the Taylor series to order $n = 10$.

b) To first gain intuition for the radius of convergence of the Taylor series, we define the nth Taylor polynomial of $f(x)$ as a function of n (note our use of the **Normal** command to truncate the remainder term from the Taylor series).

In[992]:= **Clear[T, x, n]**

T[x_, n_] := Normal[Series[f[x], {x, 0, n}]]

Here is a list of the first 20 of these polynomials.

In[994]:= **Table[T[x, n], {n, 0, 10}]**

Out[994]= $\{\frac{1}{2}, \frac{1}{2} - \frac{3x}{4}, \frac{1}{2} - \frac{3x}{4} + \frac{3x^2}{8}, \frac{1}{2} - \frac{3x}{4} + \frac{3x^2}{8} - \frac{3x^3}{16},$

$\frac{1}{2} - \frac{3x}{4} + \frac{3x^2}{8} - \frac{3x^3}{16} + \frac{3x^4}{32}, \frac{1}{2} - \frac{3x}{4} + \frac{3x^2}{8} - \frac{3x^3}{16} + \frac{3x^4}{32} - \frac{3x^5}{64},$

$\frac{1}{2} - \frac{3x}{4} + \frac{3x^2}{8} - \frac{3x^3}{16} + \frac{3x^4}{32} - \frac{3x^5}{64} + \frac{3x^6}{128}, \frac{1}{2} - \frac{3x}{4} + \frac{3x^2}{8} - \frac{3x^3}{16} + \frac{3x^4}{32} - \frac{3x^5}{64} + \frac{3x^6}{128} - \frac{3x^7}{256},$

$\frac{1}{2} - \frac{3x}{4} + \frac{3x^2}{8} - \frac{3x^3}{16} + \frac{3x^4}{32} - \frac{3x^5}{64} + \frac{3x^6}{128} - \frac{3x^7}{256} + \frac{3x^8}{512},$

$\frac{1}{2} - \frac{3x}{4} + \frac{3x^2}{8} - \frac{3x^3}{16} + \frac{3x^4}{32} - \frac{3x^5}{64} + \frac{3x^6}{128} - \frac{3x^7}{256} + \frac{3x^8}{512} - \frac{3x^9}{1024},$

$\frac{1}{2} - \frac{3x}{4} + \frac{3x^2}{8} - \frac{3x^3}{16} + \frac{3x^4}{32} - \frac{3x^5}{64} + \frac{3x^6}{128} - \frac{3x^7}{256} + \frac{3x^8}{512} - \frac{3x^9}{1024} + \frac{3x^{10}}{2048}\}$

Observe that each polynomial appears twice, that is, $T_{2n} = T_{2n+1}$, since f is an even function. Next, we plot the graphs of some of these polynomials:

In[995]:= **Clear[plot1]**
plot1 =
Plot[Evaluate[Table[T[x, n], {n, 1, 20}]], {x, -5, 3}, PlotRange → {-10, 10}]

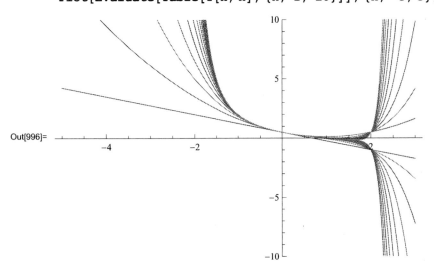

Out[996]=

To compare the graph of these polynomials, we plot the graph of *f* and use the **Show** command.

In[997]:= **Clear[plot2]**
plot2 = Plot[f[x], {x, -5, 3}, PlotRange → {-10, 10}, PlotStyle → Red]

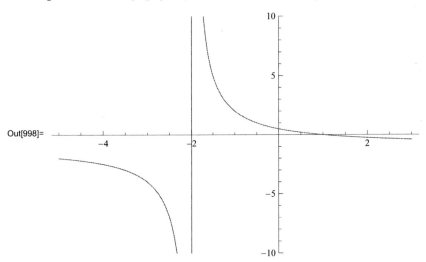

Out[998]=

In[999]:= `Show[{plot1, plot2}, PlotRange → {-10, 10}]`

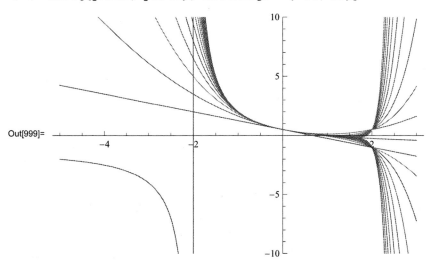

Out[999]=

Observe that the graphs of the Taylor polynomials in the preceding plot seem to give a good approximation to f only inside the interval $(-2, 2)$. This suggests that the radius of convergence is 2. This becomes more evident as we plot the graph of T_n for large values of n as shown in the following plot, where $n = 30, 35, 40, 45, 50$.

In[1000]:= `Clear[plot3]`
`plot3 = Plot[Evaluate[Table[T[x, n], {n, 30, 50, 5}]], {x, -3, 3}];`
`plot4 = Plot[f[x], {x, -5, 3}, PlotStyle → {Red, Thickness[0.002]}];`
`Show[{plot3, plot4}, PlotRange → {-10, 10}]`

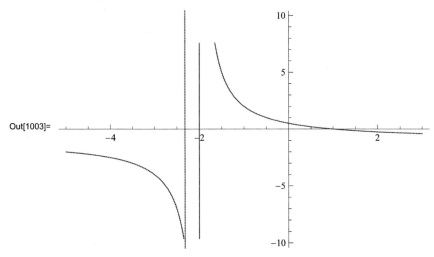

Out[1003]=

To prove that the radius of convergence is indeed $R = 2$, we first find a formula for the Taylor coefficients. Based on the following table, it is clear that $a_0 = 1/2$ and $a_n = (-1)^n \, 3 \big/ 2^{n+1}$ (prove this for all n).

In[1004]:= `a[n_] := D[f[x], {x, n}] / n! /. x → 0`
`Table[a[n], {n, 0, 10}]`

Out[1005]= $\left\{ \dfrac{1}{2}, \ -\dfrac{3}{4}, \ \dfrac{3}{8}, \ -\dfrac{3}{16}, \ \dfrac{3}{32}, \ -\dfrac{3}{64}, \ \dfrac{3}{128}, \ -\dfrac{3}{256}, \ \dfrac{3}{512}, \ -\dfrac{3}{1024}, \ \dfrac{3}{2048} \right\}$

We now apply the Ratio Test on $\sum_{n=0}^{\infty} a_n \, x^n$.

In[1006]:= **Clear[a]**

a[n_] = (-1)^n * 3 / 2^(n + 1)

$$r = \text{Limit}\left[\text{Abs}\left[\frac{a[n+1]}{a[n]}\right], n \to \infty\right]$$

Out[1007]= $3 \, (-1)^n \, 2^{-1-n}$

Out[1008]= $\dfrac{1}{2}$

Hence, the radius of convergence is $R = 1/r = 2$.

Next, we determine whether the endpoints should be included in the interval of convergence. For this, we evaluate our Taylor series at $x = -2$ and $x = 2$.

In[1009]:= $\displaystyle\sum_{n=1}^{\infty} \mathbf{a[n] \, (-2)\char94 n}$

$\displaystyle\sum_{n=1}^{\infty} \mathbf{a[n] \, (2)\char94 n}$

Sum::div : Sum does not converge. ≫

Out[1009]= $\displaystyle\sum_{n=1}^{\infty} \frac{3}{2} \, (-1)^{2\,n}$

Sum::div : Sum does not converge. ≫

Out[1010]= $\displaystyle\sum_{n=1}^{\infty} \frac{3 \, (-1)^n}{2}$

This shows that the Taylor series diverges at both endpoints. Thus, the interval of convergence is $(-2, 2)$.

Example 10.25. Let $f(x) = \sin x$.

a) Find the Taylor series of f at $x = 0$.
b) Find the radius and interval of convergence of the Taylor series.

Solution:

a) We repeat the steps in the previous example.

In[1011]:= **Clear[f]**

f[x_] := Sin[x]

In[1013]:= **Clear[T]**

T[x_, n_] := Normal[Series[f[x], {x, 0, n}]]

In[1015]:= **Table[T[x, n], {n, 0, 10}]**

Out[1015]= $\left\{0, \; x, \; x, \; x - \dfrac{x^3}{6}, \; x - \dfrac{x^3}{6}, \; x - \dfrac{x^3}{6} + \dfrac{x^5}{120}, \; x - \dfrac{x^3}{6} + \dfrac{x^5}{120}, \; x - \dfrac{x^3}{6} + \dfrac{x^5}{120} - \dfrac{x^7}{5040}, \right.$

$\left. x - \dfrac{x^3}{6} + \dfrac{x^5}{120} - \dfrac{x^7}{5040}, \; x - \dfrac{x^3}{6} + \dfrac{x^5}{120} - \dfrac{x^7}{5040} + \dfrac{x^9}{362\,880}, \; x - \dfrac{x^3}{6} + \dfrac{x^5}{120} - \dfrac{x^7}{5040} + \dfrac{x^9}{362\,880}\right\}$

Observe that all terms of the Taylor polynomials are odd powers of x. Can you explain why?

Here is a plot of the graphs of the first ten of these polynomials and the function f.

```
In[1016]:= Clear[plot1, pl0t2]
        plot1 = Plot[Evaluate[Table[T[x, n], {n, 0, 10}]], {x, -3 Pi, 3 Pi}];
        plot2 = Plot[f[x], {x, -3 Pi, 3 Pi}, PlotStyle → Red];
        Show[{plot1, plot2}, PlotRange → {-10, 10}]
```

Out[1019]=

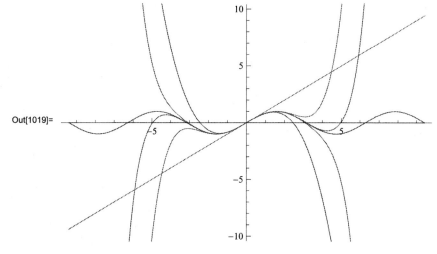

b) Observe that the higher the order of the Taylor polynomial the better it approximates f over a wider interval. To see this more clearly, we plot T_n for $n = 20, 40, 60$.

```
In[1020]:= Clear[plot1, plot2]
        plot1 = Plot[f[x], {x, -40, 40}, PlotStyle → Red, PlotRange → {-5, 5}];
        plot2 =
          Plot[ Evaluate[T[x, 20]] , {x, -40, 40 }, PlotStyle → Blue, PlotRange → {-5, 5}];
        plot3 = Plot[ Evaluate[T[x, 40]] , {x, -40, 40 },
            PlotStyle → Blue, PlotRange → {-5, 5}];
        plot4 = Plot[ Evaluate[T[x, 60]] , {x, -40, 40 },
            PlotStyle → Blue, PlotRange → {-5, 5}];
        Show[{plot1, plot2}]
```

Out[1025]=

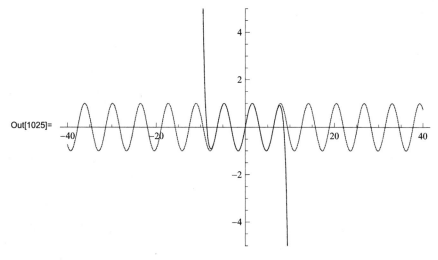

In[1026]:= **Show[{plot1, plot3}]**

Out[1026]=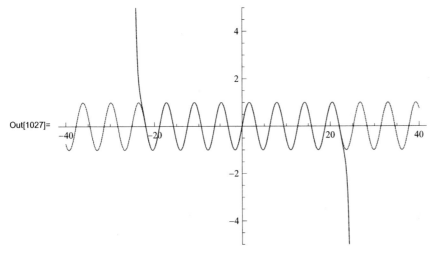

In[1027]:= **Show[{plot1, plot4}]**

Out[1027]=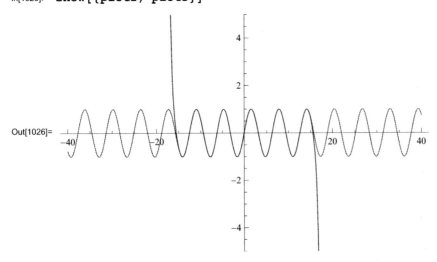

The preceding plots suggest that the radius of convergence for the Taylor series of $\sin x$ is $R = \infty$. To prove this, we first find a formula for the Taylor coefficients $\{a_n\}$. Again, based on the following table, it is clear that $a_n = \sin(\pi n/2)/n!$ (prove this for all n).

In[1028]:= **a[n_] := D[f[x], {x, n}] / n! /. x → 0**
Table[a[n], {n, 0, 10}]

Out[1029]= $\left\{0,\ 1,\ 0,\ -\dfrac{1}{6},\ 0,\ \dfrac{1}{120},\ 0,\ -\dfrac{1}{5040},\ 0,\ \dfrac{1}{362\,880},\ 0\right\}$

We now apply the Root Test on $\sum_{n=0}^{\infty} a_n x^n$.

```
In[1030]:= Clear[a, n, r]
        a[n_] = Sin[Pi * n / 2] / n!
        Table[a[n], {n, 0, 10}]
        r = Limit[Abs[a[n]] ^ (1 / n), n → ∞]
```

$$Out[1031]= \frac{\operatorname{Sin}\left[\frac{n\,\pi}{2}\right]}{n!}$$

$$Out[1032]= \left\{0,\ 1,\ 0,\ -\frac{1}{6},\ 0,\ \frac{1}{120},\ 0,\ -\frac{1}{5040},\ 0,\ \frac{1}{362\,880},\ 0\right\}$$

Out[1033]= 0

Hence, the radius of convergence is $R = \infty$.

■ **Exercises**

In Exercises 1 through 6, determine the radius and interval of convergence for the given power series.

1. $\sum_{n=1}^{\infty} \frac{(-1)^{n+1} x^n}{4^n}$

2. $\sum_{n=0}^{\infty} (2\,n)! \left(\frac{x}{2}\right)^n$

3. $\sum_{n=1}^{\infty} \frac{n! \, x^n}{(2\,n)!}$

4. $\sum_{n=0}^{\infty} (-1)^n \frac{x^n}{n+1}$

5. $\sum_{n=0}^{\infty} (4\,x)^n$

6. $\sum_{n=0}^{\infty} \frac{(2\,x)^n}{n!}$

7. Give examples of power series that have an infinite radius of convergence, a radius of convergence containing only the center, and a radius of convergence of one.

8. Find the Taylor series for $f(x) = e^{2\,x}$ centered about $c = 0$.

9. Find the Taylor series for $f(x) = \ln x$ centered about the point $c = 1$.

In Exercises 10 through 12, find the MacLaurin series for each of the given function.

10. $f(x) = \sin 2\,x$

11. $g(x) = \sinh x$

12. $h(x) = (\arc \sin x)/x$

13. Consider the function $f(x) = \begin{cases} e^{-1/x^2} & \text{if } x \neq 0 \\ 0 & \text{if } x = 0 \end{cases}$.

a. Plot the graph of this function using *Mathematica*.
b. Use the limit definition of the derivative and L'Hopital's Rule to show that every higher-order derivative of f at $x = 0$ vanishes.
c. Find the MacLaurin series for f. Does the series converge to f?

14. Use Taylor series to evalaute the following definite integral, which cannot be integrated via elementary means:

$$\int_0^1 \frac{\sin x}{x}\, d\,x.$$

15. Find the following limit using the theory of Taylor series.

$$\lim_{x \to 0} \frac{1 - \cos x}{x}$$

Chapter 11   Parametric Equations, Polar Curves, and Conic Sections

■ 11.1 Parametric Equations

Students should read Sections 11.1-11.2 of Rogawski's *Calculus* [1] for a detailed discussion of the material presented in this section.

Parametric equations are useful for describing curves not modeled by functions or motions parametrized by quantities such as time. The standard form for a set of parametric equations is

$$x(t) = f(t)$$
$$y(t) = g(t)$$

where *t* is called the *parameter*.

■ 11.1.1. Plotting Parametric Equations

The *Mathematica* command for plotting a curve defined by parametric equations $x = f(t)$ and $y = g(t)$ for $a \le t \le b$ is **Parametric-Plot[{f(t),g(t)},{t,a,b}]**.

Here are some examples:

Example 11.1. Plot the curve described by the parametric equations $x = \cos t$ and $y = \sin t$ for $0 \le t \le 2\pi$.

Solution:

In[1034]:= **ParametricPlot[{Cos[t], Sin[t]}, {t, 0, 2 π}, ImageSize → 200]**

Out[1034]=

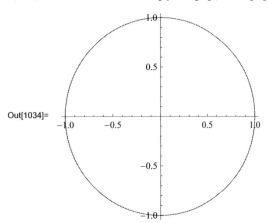

NOTE: Recall that the above parametric equations represent the unit circle. However, *Mathematica* may produce a graph that, depending on its default settings, looks visually like an ellipse due to different scalings of the *x*- and *y*-axes. In that case, the plot option **AspectRatio** can be used to specify the ratio of the height to the width for a plot. For example, to stretch the plot above so that the circle becomes elliptical where the height is twice as long as the width, we can set **AspectRatio** equal to 2.

In[1035]:= **ParametricPlot[{Cos[t], Sin[t]}, {t, 0, 2 π}, AspectRatio → 2, ImageSize → 200]**

Out[1035]=

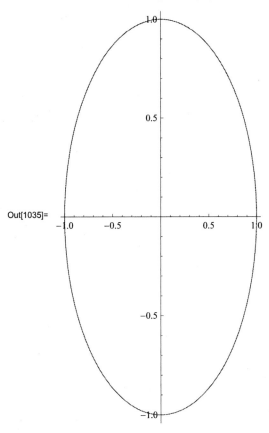

Example 11.2. Plot the curve described by the parametric equations $x = t^2 - 4$ and $y = t/2$ for $-2 \le t \le 3$.

Solution: Here is a plot of the curve:

In[1036]:= **ParametricPlot[{t^2 - 4, t / 2}, {t, -2, 3}]**

Out[1036]=

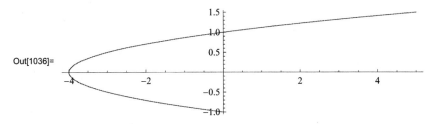

Example 11.3. Plot the curve (*prolate cycloid*) described by the parametric equations $x = 2\theta - 4\sin\theta$ and $y = 2 - 4\cos\theta$ for $0 \le t \le 2\pi$ and determine its y-intercepts.

Solution: We first plot the curve:

In[1037]:= **Clear[f, g, θ]**
f[θ_] = 2 θ - 4 Sin[θ];
g[θ_] = 2 - 4 Cos[θ];
ParametricPlot[{f[θ], g[θ]}, {θ, -4 Pi, 4 Pi},
PlotLabel -> "Prolate cycloid"]

Out[1040]=

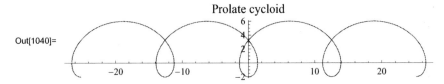

To find the *y*-intercepts (there appears to be two based on the graph), we solve $f(\theta) = 0$ for θ:

In[1041]:= **Solve[f[θ] == 0, θ]**

Solve::nsmet : This system cannot be solved with the methods available to Solve. ≫

Out[1041]= Solve[2 θ - 4 Sin[θ] == 0, θ]

Observe that the **Solve** command here fails to give us an answer since the equation is non-algebraic. However, note that the negative *y*-intercept is trivially located at $y = -2$ corresponding to $\theta = 0$. The other (positive) *y*-intercept must be solved numerically using the **FindRoot** command (even the **NSolve** command fails in this case), where we provide a nearby location ($\theta = \pi/2$) for our desired solution.

In[1042]:= **root = FindRoot[f[θ] == 0, {θ, Pi / 2}]**

Out[1042]= {θ → 1.89549}

In[1043]:= **g[root[[1, 2]]]**

Out[1043]= 3.27609

Thus, the second *y*-intercept is located approximately at $y \approx f(1.89549) = 3.27609$.

NOTE: Observe that we used of the option **PlotLabel** to print the label "Prolate cycloid" in the plot above. In general, the inside **PlotLabel** →**"text"** inside a plot command prints the title **text** for the given plot.

■ 11.1.2. Parametric Derivatives

Recall that for a curve described by parametric equations $x = f(t)$ and $y = g(t)$, its derivative dy/dx can be expressed as a ratio between the parametric derivatives dy/dt and dx/dt (application of the Chain Rule):

$$\frac{dy}{dx} = \frac{\frac{dy}{dt}}{\frac{dx}{dt}} = \frac{g'(t)}{f'(t)}$$

where it is assumed that $f'(t) \neq 0$.

Example 11.4. Consider the following parametric equations (*folium of Descartes*):

$$x = \frac{4t}{1+t^3} \text{ and } y = \frac{4t^2}{1+t^3}$$

a) Plot the curve described by the parametric equations above (select an appropriate interval for *t* that captures all the salient features of the graph).
b) Find all points of horizontal tangency on the curve.

c) Find the derivative at the tip of the folium.

Solution:

a) Here is a plot of the folium of Descartes on the interval [0, 20]:

In[1044]:= `Clear[f, g, t]`
`f[t_] = 3 t / (1 + t^3);`
`g[t_] = 3 t^2 / (1 + t^3);`
`ParametricPlot[{f[t], g[t]}, {t, 0, 20}, PlotRange → All, AspectRatio → 1,`
`PlotLabel -> "Folium of Descartes", ImageSize → 200]`

Out[1047]=
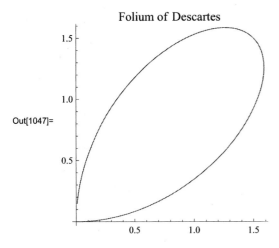

NOTE: The plot above does not reveal the full graph of the folium. A more complete graph is shown in the following plot. The dashed line indicates an asymptote. Can you generate a *Mathematica* plot of it? Can you find an equation of the asymptote (see Exercise 7)? Hint: Beware of the discontinuity at $t = -1$.

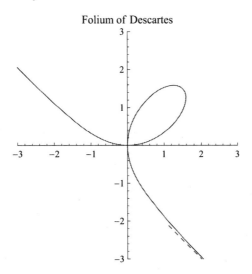

b) In order to find points of horizontal tangency, that is, points where the slope of the tangent line is equal to zero, it suffices to solve $\frac{dy}{dx} = 0$, or equivalently, $\frac{dy}{dt} = 0$ (assuming $\frac{dx}{dt} \neq 0$). Hence, we evaluate

In[1048]:= `Solve[D[g[t], t] == 0, t]`

Out[1048]= $\left\{ \{t \to 0\}, \left\{t \to -(-2)^{1/3}\right\}, \left\{t \to 2^{1/3}\right\}, \left\{t \to (-1)^{2/3} \, 2^{1/3}\right\} \right\}$

Since $\frac{dx}{dt}$ does not vanish at $t = 0$ and $t = 2^{1/3}$ (we ignore the imaginary solutions), we conclude that there are two points corresponding to these values at which the tangent lines are horizontal, namely at $(0, 0)$ and $\left(2^{1/3}, 2^{2/3}\right)$:

In[1049]:= `{f[t], g[t]} /. t → 0`
`{f[t], g[t]} /. t → 2^(1/3)`

Out[1049]= $\{0, 0\}$

Out[1050]= $\left\{2^{1/3}, 2^{2/3}\right\}$

c) To locate the tip of the folium, we take advantage of the folium's symmetry to argue that the slope of the tangent at the tip must equal -1 (parallel to the asymptote of the folium). Thus, we solve $\frac{dy}{dx} = -1$, or equivalently, $g'(t) = -f'(t)$, for t:

In[1051]:= `sol = Solve[g'[t] == -f'[t], t]`

Out[1051]= $\{\{t \to -1\}, \{t \to 1\}\}$

In[1052]:= `f[sol[[1, 1, 2]]]`
`g[sol[[1, 1, 2]]]`

Power::infy : Infinite expression $\frac{1}{0}$ encountered. ≫

Out[1052]= ComplexInfinity

Power::infy : Infinite expression $\frac{1}{0}$ encountered. ≫

Out[1053]= ComplexInfinity

Thus, the tip is located at $(3/2, 3/2)$.

■ 11.1.3. Arclength and Speed

The arc length of a curve described by parametric equations $x = f(t)$ and $y = g(t)$, $a \leq t \leq b$, is given by

$$s = \int_a^b \sqrt{\left(\frac{dx}{dt}\right)^2 + \left(\frac{dy}{dt}\right)^2} \, dt$$

Suppose $(x(t), y(t))$ now represent the position of a particle moving along a path at time t. The distance traveled by the particle over the interval $[t_0, t]$ is given by

$$s(t) = \int_{t_0}^t \sqrt{\left(\frac{dx}{du}\right)^2 + \left(\frac{dy}{du}\right)^2} \, du$$

and

$$\frac{ds}{dt} = \sqrt{\left(\frac{dx}{dt}\right)^2 + \left(\frac{dy}{dt}\right)^2}$$

represents its speed (length of the velocity vector $(x'(t), y'(t))$).

Example 11.5. Find the arc length of the curve $x = e^{-t} \cos t$, $y = e^{-t} \sin t$ for $0 \leq t \leq \pi/2$.

Solution: Here is a plot of the curve:

In[1054]:= **Clear[x, y, t]**
x[t_] = E^(-t) * Cos[t];
y[t_] = E^(-t) * Sin[t];
ParametricPlot[{x[t], y[t]}, {t, 0, Pi / 2}, ImageSize → 250]

Out[1057]=

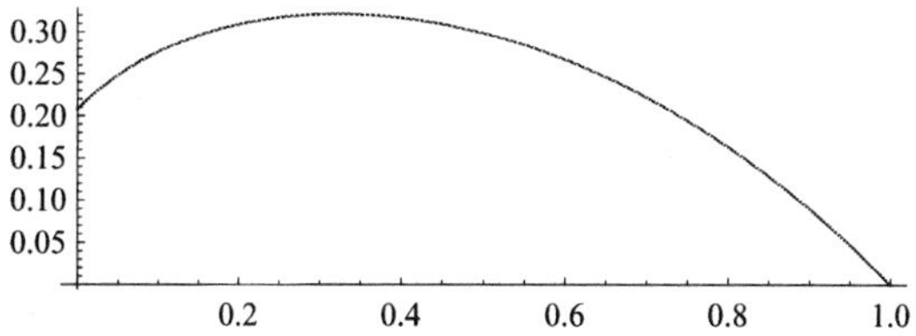

To find its arc length, we compute

In[1058]:= $\int_0^{\pi/2} \sqrt{((D[x[t], t])^2 + (D[y[t], t])^2)} \, dt$

Out[1058]= $\sqrt{2} \left(1 - e^{-\pi/2}\right)$

In[1059]:= **N[%]**

Out[1059]= 1.12023

This answer makes sense based on the graph.

Example 11.5. A particle moves along a path described by $x = t^2 - 4$, $y = t/2$.
a) Find the distance traveled by the particle over the interval $[-3, 3]$.
b) What is the particle's minimum speed over the same interval? When does this occur?

Solution:
a) The distance traveled is given by

In[1060]:= **Clear[x, y, t]**
x[t_] = t^2 - 4;
y[t_] = t / 2;
$\int_{-3}^{3} \sqrt{((D[x[t], t])^2 + (D[y[t], t])^2)} \, dt$

Out[1063]= $\frac{1}{8} \left(12 \sqrt{145} + \text{ArcSinh}[12]\right)$

In[1064]:= **N[%]**

Out[1064]= 18.4599

a) We make a plot of the particle's speed:

In[1065]:= **speed = $\sqrt{\,((D[x[t], t])\char94 2 + (D[y[t], t])\char94 2)}$**
    Plot[speed, {t, -3, 3}, ImageSize → 250]

Out[1065]= $\sqrt{\dfrac{1}{4} + 4\,t^2}$

Out[1066]=

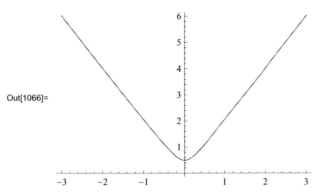

This shows that the minimum speed is 1/2 and occurs at $t = 0$. Can you verify this using calculus techniques?

■ **Exercises**

In Exercises 1 through 3, sketch the curve represented by the given parametric equations. Be sure to select an appropriate interval for the parameter that captures all the salient features of the curve.

1. $x = t^3$, $y = t^2/2$ 2. $x = 2\,(\theta - \sin\theta)$, $y = 1 - \cos\theta$ 3. $x = 3\cos^3\theta$, $y = 3\sin^3\theta$

4. Find all points of horizontal and vertical tangency to the curve $x = \cos\theta + \theta\sin\theta$, $y = \sin\theta - \theta\cos\theta$, $0 \le \theta \le 2\pi$.

5. Consider parametric equations given by $x = 3\cos(t/3) - \cos t$ and $y = 3\sin(t/3) - \sin t$.
a) Graph the curve represented by the parametric equations above.
b) Find the slope of the line tangent to the curve at the point where $t = \pi/4$.
c) Find the arc length of the curve from $t = 0$ to $t = 3\pi/2$.

6. Consider a particle moving along a curve described by $x = t - \cos t$ and $y = t - \sin t$ with respect to time t.
a) Approximate the distance traveled by the particle over the interval $[0, 2\pi]$. Hint: Use the **NIntegrate** command.
b) Find the minimum and maximum speeds of the particle over the same interval. At what times do they occur?

7. *Cornu's spiral* (also known as Euler's spiral) is a curve defined by the following Fresnel integrals:

$$x(t) = \int_0^t \cos(u^2)\,du, \; y(t) = \int_0^t \sin(u^2)\,du$$

a) Plot Cornu's spiral for $-10 \le t \le 10$.
b) Compute the length of Cornu's spiral over the same interval. Then find a formula for the length of Cornu's spiral over the interval $a \le t \le b$.
c) Determine the coordinates of the center of the two "eyes" that form Cornu's spiral.

8. Find the asymptote corresponding to the folium of Descartes (see Example 11.4) and plot the asymptote together with the folium of Descartes.

■ 11.2 Polar Coordinates and Curves

Students should read Sections 11.3-11.4 of Rogawski's *Calculus* [1] for a detailed discussion of the material presented in

this section.

Polar coordinates, expressed as (r, θ), represent the location of a point on the Cartesian plane in terms of distance r from the origin and angle θ with respect to the positive x-axis.

■ 11.2.1. Conversion Formulas

Conversion between Cartesian (rectangular) coordinates (x, y) and polar coordinates (r, θ) can be achieved by the following formulas:

$$r^2 = x^2 + y^2 \qquad\qquad x = r \cos \theta$$
$$\theta = \tan^{-1} y/x \qquad\qquad y = r \sin \theta$$

Example 11.6. Perform the following conversions:
a) Convert the rectangular coordinates $(3, 4)$ into polar coordinates.
b) Convert the polar coordinates $(7, \pi/3)$ into Cartesian coordinates.

Solution:

a) Using the first set of conversion formulas above, we find that

In[1067]:= **r = $\sqrt{3^2 + 4^2}$**
      θ = N[ArcTan[4 / 3]]

Out[1067]= 5

Out[1068]= 0.927295

b) This time, we use the second set of conversion formulas:

In[1069]:= **x = 7 * Cos[Pi / 3]**
      y = 7 * Sin[Pi / 3]

Out[1069]= $\dfrac{7}{2}$

Out[1070]= $\dfrac{7\sqrt{3}}{2}$

■ 11.2.2. Polar Curves

The *Mathematica* command for plotting a curve described by a polar equation in the form $r = f(\theta)$ for $\alpha \le \theta \le \beta$ is **PolarPlot**[f(θ),{θ, α, β}].

Example 11.7. Plot the graph of the limacon $r = 3 - 4 \cos \theta$.

Solution: Here is a plot of the limacon:

In[1071]:= `PolarPlot[3 - 4 Cos[θ], {θ, -4 Pi, 4 Pi},`
`AspectRatio -> Automatic, ImageSize → 200]`

Out[1071]=

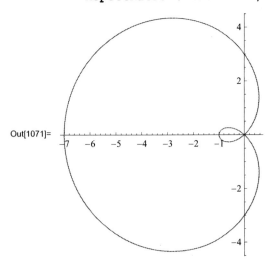

Example 11.8. Plot the graph of the six-leaf rose $r = 2 \cos(3\,\theta/2)$.

Solution: Here is a plot of the six-leaf rose:

In[1072]:= `PolarPlot[2 Cos[3 θ / 2], {θ, -4 Pi, 4 Pi},`
`PlotLabel -> "A Six-Leaf Rose", AspectRatio -> Automatic, ImageSize → 200]`

Out[1072]=

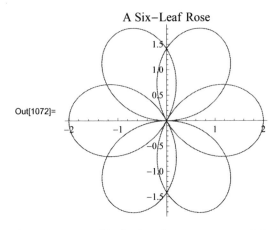

Can you can modify the function to generate a 12-leaf rose?

■ 11.2.3. Calculus of Polar Curves

Recall that the derivative of a polar equation in the form $r = f(\theta)$ for $\alpha \le \theta \le \beta$ is given by

$$\frac{dy}{dx} = \frac{f'(\theta) \sin\theta + f(\theta) \cos\theta}{f'(\theta) \cos\theta - f(\theta) \sin\theta}$$

Moreover, the area A of the region bounded by a polar equation in the form $r = f(\theta)$ between $\alpha \le \theta \le \beta$ is given by

$$A = \frac{1}{2} \int_{\alpha}^{\beta} f^2(\theta) \, d\theta$$

Example 11.9. Locate all horizontal and vertical tangents of the limacon $r = 2 - \sin\theta$.

Solution: We first plot the limacon to anticipate our solution points:

In[1073]:= **PolarPlot[1 + Cos[θ], {θ, -2 Pi, 2 Pi}, ImageSize → 200]**

Out[1073]=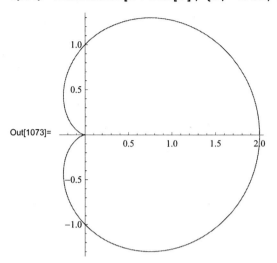

From the plot above, we should expect to find two horizontal tangents and three vertical tangents.

Next, we compute the derivative of the limacon:

In[1074]:= **Clear[f, θ]**
f[θ_] = 1 + Cos[θ]

Out[1075]= $1 + \text{Cos}[\theta]$

In[1076]:= **dydx = Simplify[(f'[θ] * Sin[θ] + f[θ] * Cos[θ]) / (f'[θ] * Cos[θ] - f[θ] * Sin[θ])]**

Out[1076]= $-\dfrac{\text{Cos}\left[\frac{3\theta}{2}\right]\,\text{Csc}\left[\frac{\theta}{2}\right]}{1 + 2\,\text{Cos}[\theta]}$

To obtain horizonal tangents, we solve $dy/dx = 0$ for θ.

In[1077]:= **dydx == 0**
Solve[dydx == 0, θ]

Out[1077]= $-\dfrac{\text{Cos}\left[\frac{3\theta}{2}\right]\,\text{Csc}\left[\frac{\theta}{2}\right]}{1 + 2\,\text{Cos}[\theta]} == 0$

Solve::ifun : Inverse functions are being used by Solve, so
some solutions may not be found; use Reduce for complete solution information. ≫

Out[1078]= $\left\{\left\{\theta \to -\dfrac{5\pi}{3}\right\}, \{\theta \to -\pi\}, \left\{\theta \to -\dfrac{\pi}{3}\right\}, \left\{\theta \to \dfrac{\pi}{3}\right\}, \{\theta \to \pi\}, \left\{\theta \to \dfrac{5\pi}{3}\right\}\right\}$

Therefore, our two horizontal tangents are located at $\theta = \pm\pi/3$.

As for vertical tangents, we solve for where the reciprocal of the derivative is zero, that is, $1/(dy/dx) = 0$ for θ.

In[1079]:= **1 / dydx**
Solve[1 / dydx == 0, θ]

Out[1079]= $-\left(1 + 2\,\text{Cos}[\theta]\right)\,\text{Sec}\left[\dfrac{3\,\theta}{2}\right]\,\text{Sin}\left[\dfrac{\theta}{2}\right]$

Solve::ifun : Inverse functions are being used by Solve, so
   some solutions may not be found; use Reduce for complete solution information. ≫

Out[1080]= $\left\{\{\theta \to 0\},\ \left\{\theta \to -\dfrac{4\,\pi}{3}\right\},\ \left\{\theta \to -\dfrac{2\,\pi}{3}\right\},\ \left\{\theta \to \dfrac{2\,\pi}{3}\right\},\ \left\{\theta \to \dfrac{4\,\pi}{3}\right\}\right\}$

Since the solution above only gives us the principal solution $\theta = 0$ of $-\tan(3\,\theta/2) = 0$, we need to additionally solve $3\,\theta/2 = \pm\pi$ for θ, which yields our two other solutions, $\theta = \pm 2\,\pi/3$.

NOTE: What is the derivative at $\theta = \pi$?

Example 11.10. Find the area of the region contained inside the circle $r = 3 \sin\theta$ and outside the convex limacon $r = 2 - \sin\theta$.

Solution: We first plot the two polar curves on the same set of axes.

In[1081]:= **PolarPlot[{3 Sin[θ], 2 - Sin[θ]}, {θ, 0, 2 π},**
AspectRatio -> Automatic, ImageSize → 200]

Out[1081]=

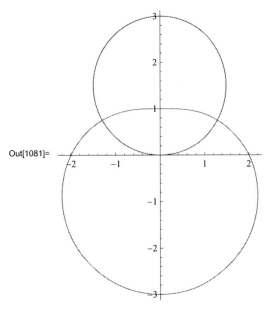

Next, we find their points of intersection by equating them and solving for θ:

In[1082]:= **Solve[3 Sin[θ] == 2 - Sin[θ], θ]**

Solve::ifun : Inverse functions are being used by Solve, so
   some solutions may not be found; use Reduce for complete solution information. ≫

Out[1082]= $\left\{\left\{\theta \to \dfrac{\pi}{6}\right\}\right\}$

Observe that *Mathematica* gives only the solution $\theta = \pi/6$, which lies in the first quadrant since trigonometric inverse functions are involved. We can see from the above graph that the other point of intersection must be at $\theta = 5\,\pi/6$ due to symmetry. Thus, the area of the enclosed region is given by the difference in areas enclosed by the circle and limacon between $\theta = \pi/6$ and

$\theta = 5\pi/6$:

In[1083]:= **(1 / 2) (Integrate[(3 Sin[θ])^2, {θ, Pi / 6, 5 Pi / 6}] -**
**   Integrate[(2 - Sin[θ])^2, {θ, Pi / 6, 5 Pi / 6}])**

Out[1083]= $3\sqrt{3}$

In[1084]:= **N[%]**

Out[1084]= 5.19615

NOTE: Using even symmetry of our region, it would have been enough to integrate between $\theta = \pi/6$ and $\theta = \pi/2$ and double the result.

■ Exercises

In Exercises 1 and 2, use *Mathematica* to perform the following conversions.

1. Convert the rectangular coordinates $\left(-1, \sqrt{3}\right)$ into polar coordinates.

2. Convert the polar coordinates $(5, 3\pi/4)$ into Cartesian coordinates. What if we replace $(5, 3\pi/4)$ with $(-5, 3\pi/4)$?

In Exercises 3 through 6, plot the graph of each of the given polar equations and find an interval for θ over which each graph is traced only once.
3. $r = 3 - 4\cos\theta$ 4. $r = 2 + \sin\theta$ 5. $r = 3\cos(3\theta/2)$ 6. $r = 5\sin 2\theta$

7. Generate the butterfly curve $r = e^{\cos\theta} - 2\cos(4\theta) + \sin^5(\theta/12)$.

8. Find all horizontal and vertical tangents of the lemniscate $r^2 = \cos(2\theta)$. Plot its graph to confirm your answers.

9. Consider the rose curve $r = \cos(2\theta)$ for $-2\pi \le \theta \le 2\pi$.
a) Plot its graph.
b) Find the area of one petal of the curve.

In Exercises 10 through 12, graph and find the area of each of the given regions.
10. The common interior of $r = 3 - 2\sin\theta$ and $r = -3 + 2\sin\theta$.
11. Inside $r = 2(1 + \cos\theta)$ and outside $r = 2\cos\theta$.
12. Inner loop of $r = 3 + 4\sin\theta$.

In Exercises 13 and 14, find the length of the given curve over the specified interval.
13. $r = 1 + \sin\theta, 0 \le \theta \le 2\pi$ 14. $r = 6(1 + \cos\theta),\ 0 \le \theta \le 2\pi$

15. Consider the polar equations $r = 4\sin\theta$ and $r = 2\left(2 - \sin^2\theta\right)$.
a) Graph the polar equations on the same axes.
b) Find the points of intersection of the curves.
c) Find the circumference of each curve.

■ 11.3 Conic Sections

Students should read Section 11.5 of Rogawski's *Calculus* [1] for a detailed discussion of the material presented in this section.

Conic sections refer to the three families of curves (ellipses, hyperbolas, parabolas) generated by intersecting a plane with a cone. Recall the equations for describing each family of curves in standard position:

I. Ellipse

$$\left(\frac{x}{a}\right)^2 + \left(\frac{y}{b}\right)^2 = 1$$

If $b > a > 0$, then the ellipse has two foci located at $(0, \pm c)$, where $c = \sqrt{b^2 - a^2}$.

II. Hyperbola

$$\left(\frac{x}{a}\right)^2 - \left(\frac{y}{b}\right)^2 = 1$$

III. Parabola

$$y = \frac{1}{4\,c^2}\,x^2$$

NOTE: These formulas assume that the "center" of the conic section is at the origin. To translate the center to a different point, say (x_0, y_0), we replace x and y by $x - x_0$ and $y - y_0$, respectively.

The most useful command for plotting conic sections is **ContourPlot[eqn,{x,a,b},{y,c,d}]**, where **eqn** is the equation of the conic.

Example 11.10. Determine the family that each conic section below belongs to and then make a plot of each.

a) $\frac{x^2}{9} + \frac{y^2}{16} = 1$

b) $y = \frac{9}{4}\,x^2$

c) $\frac{x^2}{4} - \frac{y^2}{9} = 1$

Solution:

a) This conic is an ellipse. To plot it, we evaluate

In[1085]:= **ContourPlot[x^2 / 9 + y^2 / 16 == 1, {x, -4, 4},**
     {y, -4, 4}, Axes → True, Frame → False, ImageSize → 200]

Out[1085]=

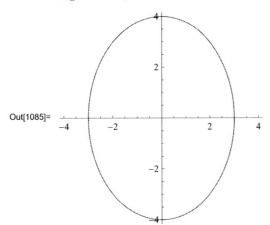

Observe that the length of semi-major and semi-minor axes are 4 and 3, respectively. How would this change if we happen to switch the coefficients 9 and 16?

b) This conic is a parabola. Since the equation here is solved for y, we merely use the **Plot** command:

In[1086]:= `Plot[ (9 / 4) x^2, {x, -2, 2}, ImageSize → 200]`

Out[1086]=

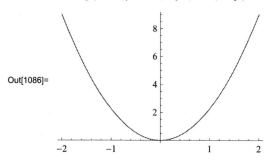

c) This conic is a hyperbola. Here is its plot:

In[1087]:= `ContourPlot[x^2 / 4 - y^2 / 9 == 1, {x, -6, 6},`
`{y, -6, 6}, Axes → True, Frame → False, ImageSize → 200]`

Out[1087]=

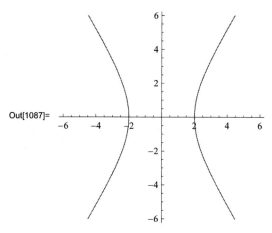

Example 11.11. Find an equation of an ellipse with center at $(-1, 3)$ and having semi-major and semi-minor axes of lengths $\sqrt{5}$ and $1/2$, respectively.

Solution: From the given data, we see that $(x_0, y_0) = (-1, 3)$, $a = \sqrt{5}$, and $b = 1/2$. The equation of our ellipse is therefore:

$$\frac{(x+1)^2}{5} + 4 (y - 3)^2 = 1$$

To plot it, we evaluate

In[1088]:= `ContourPlot[ (x + 1) ^2 / 5 + 4 (y - 3) ^2 == 1, {x, -4, 2}, {y, 2, 4},`
`AspectRatio → 2 / 3, Axes → True, Frame → False, ImageSize → 200]`

Out[1088]=

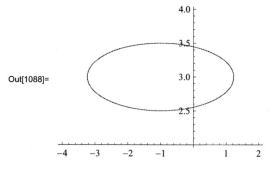

■ **Exercises**

In Exercises 1 through 4, plot each of the given conic sections. Can you determine the family that each conic section belongs to before plotting? Also, what are the values of the parameters a and b (or c) in each conic section?

1. $\frac{x^2}{25} + \frac{y^2}{4} = 1$ 2. $\frac{y^2}{36} - \frac{x^2}{16} = 1$ 3. $y = 3\,x^2$ 4. $\frac{(y-2)^2}{25} - \frac{(x+1)^2}{49} = 1$

5. Consider the ellipse $\frac{x^2}{9} + 4\,y^2 = 1$.

a) Make a plot of the ellipse.
b) What are the lengths of the semi-major and semi-minor axes?
c) Where are the foci located?
d) Compute the sum of the distances from the two foci to any point on the ellipse. Do you recognize the answer?

6. Find an equation of an ellipse with center $(1/2, -5)$ and having semi-major and semi-minor axes of lengths $3/4$ and $\sqrt{7}$, respectively.

7. Find all points on the hyperbola $\frac{x^2}{25} - \frac{y^2}{9} = 1$ where its slope equals 1.

8. Consider a polar curve of the form $r = \frac{d\,e}{1 + e\cos\theta}$, where d and e are non-negative constants.

a) Plot this curve for $d = 3$, and $e = 1/2$. Do you recognize this curve as a conic section? Of which type? Hint: Use the command **PolarPlot**.

b) Repeat part a) but this time use $e = 2$ instead. Do you recognize this curve as a conic section? Of which type?

c) Repeat part a) but this time use $e = 1$ instead. Do you recognize this curve as a conic section? Of which type?

d) Describe how the graph changes as we vary the values d and e. What happens to the graph when $e = 0$? NOTE: The value e is called the *eccentricity* of the conic section.

e) Assume $0 < e < 1$. Convert the polar equation $r = \frac{d\,e}{1 + e\cos\theta}$ to that in standard form for an ellipse, $\left(\frac{x - x_0}{a}\right)^2 + \left(\frac{y - y_0}{b}\right)^2 = 1$, and determine formulas for its center, semi-major, and semi-minor axes. Verify these formulas for the ellipse in part a).

Chapter 12   Vector Geometry

Useful Tip: If you are reading the electronic version of this publication formatted as a *Mathematica* Notebook, then it is possible to view 3-D plots generated by *Mathematica* from different perspectives. First, place your screen cursor over the plot. Then drag the mouse while pressing down on the left mouse button to rotate the plot.

■ 12.1 Vectors

Students should read Sections 12.1 - 12.3 of Rogawski's *Calculus* [1] for a detailed discussion of the material presented in this section.

A vector is an object that has magnitude and direction. In physics, these vectors are denoted by arrows, where the magnitude of the vector is represented by the length of the vector, and the way in which the arrow points indicates its direction. In mathematics, these vectors are represented by points in two or three dimensions, where the vector is the arrow that starts at the origin and ends at the point. For example, the point (2, 1, 3) could be considered both as a point in 3-D space and as a vector from (0, 0, 0) to (2, 1, 3). To distinguish a point from a vector, we will use the angled brackets $\langle$ and $\rangle$ instead of parentheses. Thus, the point (2, 1, 3) is denoted (2, 1, 3) as usual, but the vector from the origin to that point is denoted $\langle 2, 1, 3 \rangle$.

The length or magnitude of a vector **v** is denoted $\|\mathbf{v}\|$, and is read as "norm **v**." If **v** = $\langle$a, b, c$\rangle$, then $\|\mathbf{v}\| = \sqrt{a^2 + b^2 + c^2}$. In two dimensions, if **v** = $\langle$a, b$\rangle$, then $\|\mathbf{v}\| = \sqrt{a^2 + b^2}$.

Vectors and matrices, in *Mathematica*, are simply lists. A vector is a list of numbers within braces, with commas between numbers, while a matrix is a list of lists (vectors), with each vector list being a row of the matrix (for a complete description of lists in *Mathematica*, see Section 1.2.3 of this text). Of course, all rows must be the same size. For example, consider the vector **a** below:

In[1089]:= **a = {1, 3 , 5}**

Out[1089]= {1, 3, 5}

The *i*th component of the vector a is denoted by a_i, or in *Mathematica*, by **a[[i]]**. For instance the second component of **a**, which is 3, would be obtained by:

In[1090]:= **a[[2]]**

Out[1090]= 3

All of the usual vector algebra operations are available to us:

Dot Product

The Dot Product of two vectors **u** = $\langle u_1, u_2, u_3 \rangle$ and **v** = $\langle v_1, v_2, v_3 \rangle$ is defined by **u · v** = $u_1 v_1 + u_2 v_2 + u_3 v_3$. For example:

In[1091]:= **a = {1, 3, 5}**
        b = {1, -2, 3}
        a.b

Out[1091]= {1, 3, 5}

Out[1092]= {1, -2, 3}

Out[1093]= 10

or

In[1094]:= **Dot[a, b]**

Out[1094]= 10

NOTE: We use the ordinary period symbol on the keyboard for the dot product.

Cross Product

The cross product of two vectors $\mathbf{u} = \langle u_1, u_2, u_3 \rangle$ and $\mathbf{v} = \langle v_1, v_2, v_3 \rangle$, is defined as a vector perpendicular to both $\mathbf{u}$ and $\mathbf{v}$, and calculated by the following "right-hand" rule:

$$\mathbf{u} \times \mathbf{v} = \langle u_2 v_3 - u_3 v_2, u_3 v_1 - u_1 v_3, u_1 v_2 - u_2 v_1 \rangle$$

This calculation can be done in *Mathematica* in two ways. The first is to use the **Cross** command:

In[1095]:= **Cross[a, b]**

Out[1095]= {19, 2, -5}

The second is by using the multiplication symbol "×". This special symbol can be entered on the **Basic Math Input Palette** or by pushing the escape key, followed by typing the word "cross" and hitting the escape key again: [**esc**]cross[**esc**]

In[1096]:= **a × b**

Out[1096]= {19, 2, -5}

Recall that the cross product of 2 vectors, **a** and **b** creates a vector perpendicular to the plane of the vectors **a** and **b**. In your Calculus text, the cross product is also defined as the determinant of a special matrix. We will look at this a little later.

Norm (Length) of a Vector

The norm or length of a vector can be calculated in *Mathematica* by the **Norm** command

In[1097]:= **Clear[x, y, z]**

In[1098]:= **Norm[{x, y, z}]**

Out[1098]= $\sqrt{\text{Abs}[x]^2 + \text{Abs}[y]^2 + \text{Abs}[z]^2}$

In[1099]:= **Norm[a]**

Out[1099]= $\sqrt{35}$

In[1100]:= **Norm[2 a]**

Out[1100]= $2\sqrt{35}$

In[1101]:=

Vector Addition

The sum of two vectors $\mathbf{u} = \langle u_1, u_2, u_3 \rangle$ and $\mathbf{v} = \langle v_1, v_2, v_3 \rangle$ is defined to be $\mathbf{u} + \mathbf{v} = u_1 v_1 + u_2 v_2 + u_3 v_3$.

In[1102]:= **2 a - 3 b + {1, 1, 1}**

Out[1102]= $\{0, 13, 2\}$

Example 12.1. Let $\mathbf{a} = \langle 1, 2, 3 \rangle$. Show that $\frac{\mathbf{a}}{\|\mathbf{a}\|}$ is a unit vector.

In[1103]:=

Solution:

In[1104]:= **Norm[a / Norm[a]]**

Out[1104]= 1

Example 12.2. Find the equation of a line in 3-space passing through $P_0 = (3,-1,4)$ in the direction of $\mathbf{v} = \langle 2,7,1 \rangle$ and graph it.

Solution: The line through $P_0 = (x_0, y_0, z_0)$ in the direction of $\mathbf{v} = \langle a, b, c \rangle$ is described in vector or parametric form by:

Vector form: $\mathbf{r}(t) = \langle x_0, y_0, z_0 \rangle + t \langle a, b, c \rangle$

Parametric Form: $x = x_0 + a t, \; y = y_0 + b t, \; z = z_0 + c t$

Thus, the vector description of the line is

In[1105]:= **Clear[r, t];**
r[t_] = {3, -1, 4} + t {2, 7, 1}

Out[1106]= $\{3 + 2 t, -1 + 7 t, 4 + t\}$

To graph this line we use the **ParametricPlot3D** command:

ParametricPlot3D$\left[\left\{ f_x, \; f_y, \; f_z \right\}, \; \{u, \; u_{min}, \; u_{max}\} \right]$

produces a three-dimensional space curve parametrized by a variable u which runs from u_{min} to u_{max}.

In[1107]:= **ParametricPlot3D[r[t], {t, -3, 3},**
ImageSize → {250}, ImagePadding → {{15, 15}, {15, 15}}]

Out[1107]=

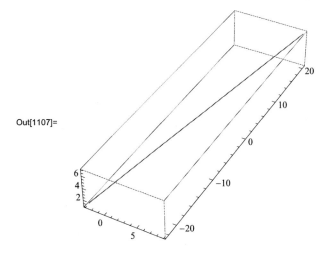

NOTE: This plot command uses the option **ImageSize** to specify the size of graphics output. Settings include **Tiny**, **Small**, **Medium**, **Large**, or **{pt}**, where **pt** is the number of points.

Example 12.3. Give the description in vector form of the line that passes through the points $P = (1, 0, 4)$ and $Q = (3, 2, 1)$, then find the midpoint of the line segment $\overrightarrow{PQ}$ and plot this line segment.

Solution: The line through points $P = (a_1, b_1, c_1)$ and $Q = (a_2, b_2, c_2)$ has vector form $\mathbf{r}(t) = (1 - t) \langle a_1, b_1, c_1 \rangle + t \langle a_2, b_2, c_2 \rangle$. In this parametrization, $\mathbf{r}(0) = P$ and $\mathbf{r}(1) = Q$. Thus,

In[1108]:= **r[t_] = (1 - t) {1, 0, 4} + t {3, 2, 1}**

Out[1108]= {1 + 2 t, 2 t, 4 (1 - t) + t}

The midpoint of the line segment $\overrightarrow{PQ}$ is

In[1109]:= $\mathbf{r}\left[\dfrac{1}{2}\right]$

Out[1109]= $\left\{2, 1, \dfrac{5}{2}\right\}$

The plot of the line segment is

In[1110]:= **ParametricPlot3D[r[t], {t, -0.1, 1.1},
      ImageSize → {250}, ImagePadding → {{15, 15}, {15, 15}}]**

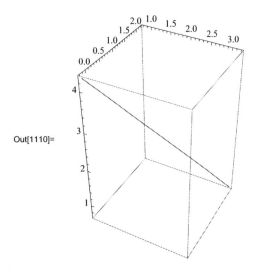

Out[1110]=

Example 12.4. Find the angle between the vectors $\mathbf{v} = \langle 3,6,2 \rangle$ and $\mathbf{w} = \langle 6,3,6 \rangle$.

Solution: Remember that the angle between two vectors, $\mathbf{v}$ and $\mathbf{w}$, is given by θ, which is defined by $\theta = \cos^{-1}\left(\dfrac{\mathbf{v}.\mathbf{w}}{\|\mathbf{v}\| \|\mathbf{w}\|}\right)$. Therefore,

In[1111]:= **v = {3, 6, 2}
      w = {6, 3, 6}**

Out[1111]= {3, 6, 2}

Out[1112]= {6, 3, 6}

In[1113]:= θ = **ArcCos** $\left[\dfrac{\textbf{v.w}}{\textbf{Norm[v] Norm[w]}}\right]$

Out[1113]= $\text{ArcCos}\left[\dfrac{16}{21}\right]$

In[1114]:= **N[%]**

Out[1114]= 0.704547

Therefore, $\theta = .7045$ radians.

■ **Exercises**

1. Calculate the length of the vector $\mathbf{v} = \langle 1, 3, 4 \rangle$.

In Exerices 2 and 3, calculate the linear combinations.

2. $5\langle 2, -2, 5 \rangle + 6\langle 1, 3, 8 \rangle$ 3. $6\langle 2, 0, -1 \rangle - 3\langle 8, 6, 9 \rangle$

4. Find a vector parametrization for the line that passes through $P = (1, 2, -6)$ with direction vector $\mathbf{v} = \langle 2, 1, 5 \rangle$.

In Exercises 5 and 6, determine whether the two given vectors are orthogonal ($\mathbf{v} \perp \mathbf{w}$ iff $\mathbf{v.w} = 0$):

5. $\langle 1, 1, 1 \rangle$, $\langle 1, -2, 3 \rangle$ 6. $\langle 1, 1, 1 \rangle$, $\langle -3, 2, 1 \rangle$

In Exercises 7 and 8, find the angle between the vectors:

7. $\langle 1, 2 \rangle$, $\langle 5, 7 \rangle$ 8. $\langle 2, 4, 1 \rangle$, $\langle 1, -3, 5 \rangle$

■ 12.2 Matrices and the Cross Product

Students should read Section 12.4 of Rogawski's *Calculus* [1] for a detailed discussion of the material presented in this section.

In order to understand the alternate approach to the cross product alluded to above, we need to define the terms matrix and determinant.

Matrices

A *matrix* is a rectangular array of numbers consisting of n rows and m columns (denoted $n \times m$). We are especially interested in square matrices where $m = n$ and, in particular, $m = 2$ or $m = 3$. For example: A 3×3 matrix would be

$$\begin{pmatrix} a_{11} & a_{12} & a_{13} \\ a_{21} & a_{22} & a_{23} \\ a_{31} & a_{32} & a_{33} \end{pmatrix}$$

but *Mathematica* would show this matrix as:

In[1115]:= **A = Table[10 i + j, {i, 3}, {j, 3}]**

Out[1115]= $\{\{11, 12, 13\}, \{21, 22, 23\}, \{31, 32, 33\}\}$

In[1116]:= **B = Table[i + j, {i, 2}, {j, 2}]**

Out[1116]= $\{\{2, 3\}, \{3, 4\}\}$

To have *Mathematica* display a matrix in the traditional way, use the **MatrixForm** command:

In[1117]:= **MatrixForm[A]**
MatrixForm[B]

Out[1117]//MatrixForm=
$$\begin{pmatrix} 11 & 12 & 13 \\ 21 & 22 & 23 \\ 31 & 32 & 33 \end{pmatrix}$$

Out[1118]//MatrixForm=
$$\begin{pmatrix} 2 & 3 \\ 3 & 4 \end{pmatrix}$$

Note that in the definition of the matrices **A** and **B**, *Mathematica* treats them as lists and when we use the command **Matrix-Form**, we can see the matrices presented in the traditional way.

Determinants

The *determinant* is a function, **Det**, which assigns to each square matrix a number which is defined for 2×2 and 3×3 matrices as follows:

In[1119]:= **Clear[a, b];**
F = {{a, b}, {c, d}}
MatrixForm[F]

Out[1120]= $\{\{a, b\}, \{c, d\}\}$

Out[1121]//MatrixForm=
$$\begin{pmatrix} a & b \\ c & d \end{pmatrix}$$

In[1122]:= **Det[F]**

Out[1122]= $-b\,c + a\,d$

In[1123]:= **G = {{a1, a2, a3}, {b1, b2, b3}, {c1, c2, c3}}**
MatrixForm[G]

Out[1123]= $\{\{1, a2, a3\}, \{b1, b2, b3\}, \{c1, c2, c3\}\}$

Out[1124]//MatrixForm=
$$\begin{pmatrix} 1 & a2 & a3 \\ b1 & b2 & b3 \\ c1 & c2 & c3 \end{pmatrix}$$

In[1125]:= **Det[G]**

Out[1125]= $-a3\,b2\,c1 + a2\,b3\,c1 + a3\,b1\,c2 - b3\,c2 - a2\,b1\,c3 + b2\,c3$

Using these definitions, we can now define the cross product of two vectors by the formula

$$\langle b_1, b_2, b_3 \rangle \times \langle c_1, c_2, c_3 \rangle = \mathrm{Det}\begin{pmatrix} \mathbf{i} & \mathbf{j} & \mathbf{k} \\ b_1 & b_2 & b_3 \\ c_1 & c_2 & c_3 \end{pmatrix}$$

where $\mathbf{i} = \langle 1, 0, 0 \rangle$, $\mathbf{j} = \langle 0, 1, 0 \rangle$, and $\mathbf{k} = \langle 0, 0, 1 \rangle$.

Example 12.5. Calculate the cross product of $\mathbf{v} = \langle 1, 3, 6 \rangle$ and $\mathbf{w} = \langle -2, 8, 5 \rangle$.

In[1126]:=

Solution:

```
In[1127]:= Clear[i, j, k]
        g = {i, j, k}
        v = {1, 3, 6}
        w = {-2, 8, 5}
        A = {g, v, w}
```

Out[1128]= {i, j, k}

Out[1129]= {1, 3, 6}

Out[1130]= {-2, 8, 5}

Out[1131]= {{i, j, k}, {1, 3, 6}, {-2, 8, 5}}

In[1132]:= **MatrixForm[A]**

Out[1132]//MatrixForm=
$$\begin{pmatrix} i & j & k \\ 1 & 3 & 6 \\ -2 & 8 & 5 \end{pmatrix}$$

In[1133]:= **v × w**
        Det[A]

Out[1133]= {-33, -17, 14}

Out[1134]= -33 i - 17 j + 14 k

Observe that the two previous outputs are equivalent.

■ **Exercises**

1. Calculate the determinants of $\begin{pmatrix} 0 & 5 & 0 \\ 1 & 3 & 6 \\ 2 & 5 & 5 \end{pmatrix}$ and of $\begin{pmatrix} 3 & 5 \\ 6 & 2 \end{pmatrix}$.

2. Calculate the cross product of $\mathbf{v} = \langle 2, 0, 0 \rangle$ and $\mathbf{w} = \langle -1, 0, 1 \rangle$. Do this using the **Cross** command as well as by the determinant approach.

3. Calculate the area of the parallelogram spanned by the vectors $\mathbf{v}$ and $\mathbf{w}$ above. (Hint: look up the formula for this in your calculus textbook.)

4. Calculate the volumn of the parallelepiped spanned by:
   $\mathbf{u} = \langle 2, 2, 1 \rangle$, $\mathbf{v} = \langle 1, 0, 3 \rangle$, and $\mathbf{w} = \langle 0, -4, 2 \rangle$.

5. Show that $\mathbf{v} \times \mathbf{w} = -\mathbf{w} \times \mathbf{v}$ and that $\mathbf{v} \times \mathbf{v} = 0$.

■ 12.3 Planes in 3-Space

Students should read Section 12.5 of Rogawski's *Calculus* [1] for a detailed discussion of the material presented in this

section.

Note that a plane in 3-D space is defined as all points $P(x, y, z)$ such that the line segment $\overrightarrow{P_0 P}$ is perpendicular to a given vector **n**, called the normal vector, where the initial point of **n** is $P_0 = (x_0, y_0, z_0)$. In vector notation, this is described by the equation $\mathbf{n} \cdot \overrightarrow{P_0 P} = 0$, where $\overrightarrow{P_0 P} = \langle x - x_0, \ y - y_0, z - z_0 \rangle$. Therefore, the equation of the plane through $P_0 = (x_0, y_0, z_0)$ with nonzero normal vector $\mathbf{n} = \langle a, b, c \rangle$ can be denoted by either of the following:

Vector form: $\qquad\qquad\qquad \mathbf{n} \cdot \langle x, y, z \rangle = d$

Scalor form: $\qquad\qquad\qquad a\,x + b\,y + c\,z = d$

Here, $d = a\,x_0 + b\,y_0 + c\,z_0 = \mathbf{n} \cdot \langle x_0, y_0, z_0 \rangle$.

Example 12.6. Find an equation of the plane determined by the points $P = (1, 0, -1)$, $Q = (2, 2, 1)$, and $R = (4, 2, 5)$. Then plot the graph of the plane.

Solution: The vectors $\mathbf{a} = \overrightarrow{PQ}$ and $\mathbf{b} = \overrightarrow{PR}$ lie in the plane, so the cross product $\mathbf{n} = \mathbf{a} \times \mathbf{b}$ is normal to the plane:

In[1135]:= `Clear[a, b, n]`
`a = {2, 2, 1} - {1, 0, -1}`
`b = {4, 2, 5} - {1, 0, -1}`
`n = a × b`
`n . {x, y, z} == d`

Out[1136]= `{1, 2, 2}`

Out[1137]= `{3, 2, 6}`

Out[1138]= `{8, 0, -4}`

Out[1139]= `8 x - 4 z == d`

To compute the value of d, we choose any point on the plane, that is, we can choose either P, Q, or R, and then compute $d = \mathbf{n} \cdot \mathbf{P}$, $d = \mathbf{n} \cdot \mathbf{Q}$, or $d = \mathbf{n} \cdot \mathbf{R}$. Let us choose $\mathbf{P} = \langle 1, 0, -1 \rangle$.

In[1140]:= `d = n . {1, 0, -1}`

Out[1140]= `12`

Therefore, the plane we want has equation $8\,x - 4\,z = 12$ and the graph is obtained by using the **ContourPlot3D** command which has the form:

```
ContourPlot3D[f, {x, xmin, xmax}, {y, ymin, ymax}, {z, zmin, zmax}]
which produces a three-dimensional contour plot of f as a function of x, y and z.
or
        ContourPlot3D[f == g, {x, xmin, xmax}, {y, ymin, ymax}, {z, zmin, zmax}]
        which plots the contour surface for which f = g.
```

In[1141]:= `ContourPlot3D[8 x - 4 z == 12, {x, -2, 2}, {y, -2, 2}, {z, -2, 2}, ImageSize → {250}]`

Out[1141]=

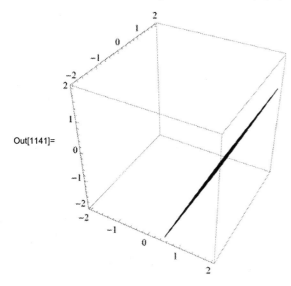

In order to see this plane more clearly from a different perspective, move your cursor over the plot. Then drag the mouse while pressing and holding the left mouse button to rotate the plot.

■ Exercises

1. Let *PL* be the plane with equation $7x - 4y + 2z = 10$. Find an equation of the plane *QL* parallel to *PL* and passing through $Q = (2, 1, 3)$ and graph it.

2. Find the equation of the plane through the points $P = (1, 5, 5)$, $Q = (0, 1, 1)$, and $R = (2, 0, 1)$ and graph it.

3. Find the angle between the two planes: $x + 2y + z = 3$ and $4x + y + 3z = 2$. (Hint: The angle between two planes is the angle between their normal vectors.)

■ 12.4 A Survey of Quadric Surfaces

Students should read Section 12.6 of Rogawski's *Calculus* [1] for a detailed discussion of the material presented in this section.

A quadric surface is the three-dimensional equivalent of a conic section (i.e., ellipses, hyperbolas, and parabolas). The basic types of quadric surfaces are ellipsoids, hyperboloids (of one or two sheets), paraboloids (elliptic or hyperbolic), and cones.

■ 12.4.1 Ellipsoids

The *standard ellipsoid* is described by $(x/a)^2 + (y/b)^2 + (z/c)^2 = 1$. To help us visualize it, we are often interested in the mesh of curves called *traces*, obtained by intersecting our quadric surface with planes parallel to one of the coordinate planes. In the plot below, you can see that mesh, and also see that the traces of an ellipsoid are themselves ellipses.

Example 12.7. Graph the ellipsoid above, with $a = 3$, $b = 4$, and $c = 5$, and describe the traces of this ellipsoid.

Solution: The correct *Mathematica* command to use is **ContourPlot3D**. This is shown following:

In[1142]:= `ContourPlot3D[ (x / 3) ^2 + (y / 4) ^2 + (z / 5) ^2 == 1, {x, -6, 6},`
`{y, -6, 6}, {z, -6, 6}, AxesLabel → {x, y, z}, ImageSize → {250}]`

Out[1142]=

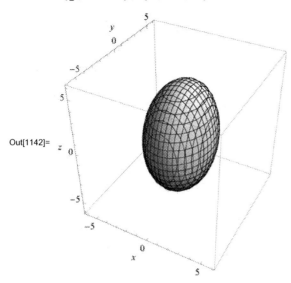

Again, note that the ellipsoid can be manually rotated to look at it from different perspectives. First, place your screen cursor over the plot. Then drag the mouse while pressing down on the left mouse button to rotate the plot. When you do this, you will note that, indeed, all of the traces are ellipses.

■ 12.4.2 Hyperboloids

The three-dimensional hyperbolas are called *hyperboloids*, and come in two types: the hyperboloid of one sheet, with standard form $(x/a)^2 + (y/b)^2 = (z/c)^2 + 1$, and the hyperboloid of two sheets, with standard form $(x/a)^2 + (y/b)^2 = (z/c)^2 - 1$. A limiting case of the hyperboloid is the *elliptic cone*, defined by the equation $(x/a)^2 + (y/b)^2 = (z/c)^2$.

Example 12.8. Describe the traces of the two hyperboloids: $(x/3)^2 + (y/4)^2 = (z/5)^2 + 1$ and $(x/3)^2 + (y/4)^2 = (z/5)^2 - 1$.

Solution: First we graph the hyperboloids:

In[1143]:= `ContourPlot3D[ (x / 3) ^2 + (y / 4) ^2  ==  (z / 5) ^2 + 1, {x, -6, 6},`
`{y, -6, 6}, {z, -6, 6}, AxesLabel → {x, y, z}, ImageSize → {250}]`

Out[1143]=

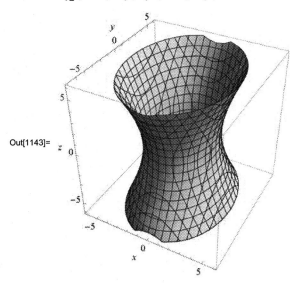

In this case, the traces parallel with the *xy*-axis are all ellipses, and the traces parallel wth the *xz*- and *yz*-axes are hyperbolas.

In[1144]:= `ContourPlot3D[ (x / 3) ^2 + (y / 4) ^2 == (z / 5) ^2 - 1, {x, -30, 30},`
`{y, -30, 30}, {z, -30, 30}, AxesLabel → {x, y, z}, ImageSize → {250}]`

Out[1144]=

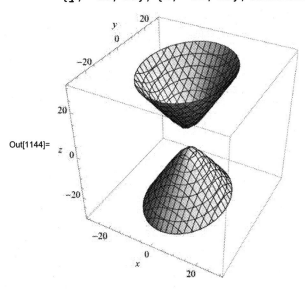

When we look at this plot, we see that the traces are the same as for the previous hyperboloid of one sheet.

Example 12.9. Graph the cone with $a = 3$, $b = 4$, and $c = 5$, and define its relationship to the hyperboloid of one sheet.

Solution: We get the graph by using the **ContourPlot3D** Command:

In[1145]:= `ContourPlot3D[ (x / 3) ^2 + (y / 4) ^2 == (z / 5) ^2, {x, -30, 30},`
`{y, -30, 30}, {z, -30, 30}, AxesLabel → {x, y, z}, ImageSize → {250}]`

Out[1145]=

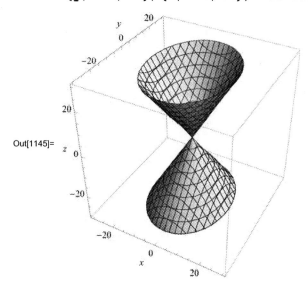

When we compare this plot with that of the hyperboloid of one sheet (see previous example), we can see clearly that this cone can be thought of as a limiting case of the hyperboloid of one sheet in which we pinch the waist down to a point.

■ 12.4.3 Paraboloids

The final family of quadric surfaces that we want to consider are the *paraboloids*, of which there are two types: elliptic and hyperbolic. Their standard equations are $z = (x/a)^2 + (y/b)^2$ (elliptic paraboloid) and $z = (x/a)^2 - (y/b)^2$ (hyperbolic paraboloid).

Example 12.10. Graph the two types of paraboloids for $a = 3$ and $b = 4$ and describe their traces.

Solution: Here is the graph of the elliptic paraboloid:

In[1146]:= `ContourPlot3D[ (x / 3) ^2 + (y / 4) ^2 == z, {x, -30, 30},`
`{y, -30, 30}, {z, -30, 30}, AxesLabel → {x, y, z}, ImageSize → {250}]`

Out[1146]=

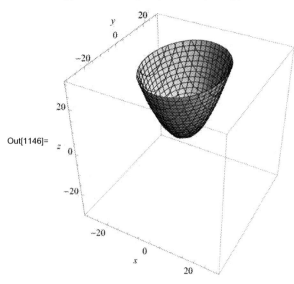

Observe that the traces in the direction of the *xz*- and *yz*-axes are both parabolas while those in the *xy*-direction are ellipses, which can be seen by dragging the plot in the appropriate directions. Similarly, for the hyperbolic paraboloid:

In[1147]:= `ContourPlot3D[ (x / 3) ^2 - (y / 4) ^2 == z, {x, -30, 30},`
`{y, -30, 30}, {z, -30, 30}, AxesLabel → {x, y, z}, ImageSize → {250}]`

Out[1147]=

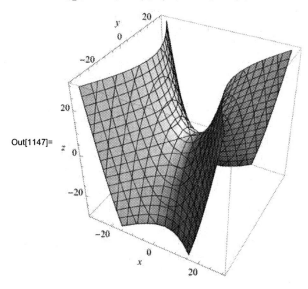

Again, by dragging the plot above, we see that the traces in the *yz*-direction are parabolas while those in the *xz*-direction are hyperbolas.

■ 12.4.4 Quadratic Cylinders

The last group of quadric surfaces we will look at are the quadratic cylinders. These are surfaces formed from a two-dimensional curve (in the *xy*-plane) along with all vertical lines passing through the curve:

Example 12.11. Graph a selection of quadratic cylinders.

Solution:

a) A circular cylinder of radius *r*: $x^2 + y^2 = r^2$. For the graph, we will use $r = 3$.

In[1148]:= **ContourPlot3D[x^2 + y^2 == 3^2, {x, -5, 5}, {y, -5, 5},**
{z, -30, 30}, AxesLabel → {x, y, z}, ImageSize → {250}]

Out[1148]=

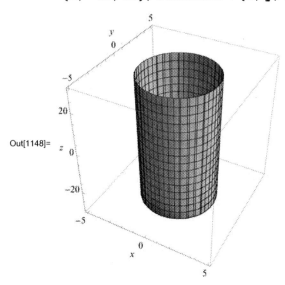

b) An elliptic with equation $(x/a)^2 + (y/b)^2 = 1$. We will use $a = 3$ and $b = 6$.

In[1149]:= **ContourPlot3D[(x / 3)^2 + (y / 6)^2 == 1, {x, -5, 5},**
{y, -8, 8}, {z, -20, 20}, AxesLabel → {x, y, z}, ImageSize → {250}]

Out[1149]=

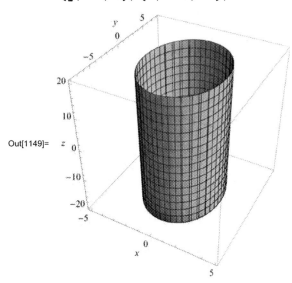

c) A hyperbolic cylinder with equation $(x/a)^2 - (y/b)^2 = 1$. We will use $a = 3$ and $b = 6$.

In[1150]:= `ContourPlot3D[(x / 3) ^2 - (y / 6) ^2 == 1, {x, -10, 10},`
`{y, -10, 10}, {z, -20, 20}, AxesLabel → {x, y, z}, ImageSize → {250}]`

Out[1150]=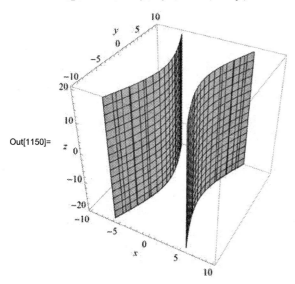

d) A parabolic cylinder with equation $y = a x^2$ with $a = 3$.

In[1151]:= `ContourPlot3D[y == 3 x^2, {x, -3, 3}, {y, -1, 8},`
`{z, -10, 10}, AxesLabel → {x, y, z}, ImageSize → {250}]`

Out[1151]=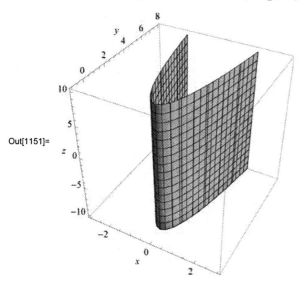

■ Exercises

In Exercises 1 through 5, state whether the given equation defines an ellipsoid, hyperboloid, or paraboloid, and of which type. Then confirm your answer by graphing the quadric surface.

1. $(x/5)^2 + (y/7)^2 + (z/9)^2 = 1$
2. $(x/5)^2 - (y/7)^2 + (z/9)^2 = 1$
3. $x^2 + 5 y^2 - 6 z^2 = 1$
4. $z = (x/5)^2 + (y/7)^2$
5. $z = (x/5)^2 - (y/7)^2$

In Exercises 6 through 8, state the type of the quadric surface and graph it, and then describe the trace obtained by intersecting it with the given plane.

6. $(x/5)^2 + y^2 + (z/9)^2 = 1$, $z = 1/4$

7. $y = 2x^2$, $z = 25$

8. $(x/5)^2 - (y/7)^2 + (z/9)^2 = 1$, $y = 4$

■ 12.5 Cylindrical and Spherical Coordinates

Students should read Section 12.7 of Rogawski's *Calculus* [1] for a detailed discussion of the material presented in this section.

■ 12.5.1 Cylindrical Coordinates

In cylindrical coordinates, the point $P = (x, y, z)$ is expressed as (r, θ, z) where r and θ are the polar coordinates of x and y. The formulas for converting from (x, y, z) to (r, θ, z) are:

Cylindrical to Rectangular

$x = r \cos \theta$

$y = r \sin \theta$

$z = z$

Rectangular to Cylindrical

$r = \sqrt{x^2 + y^2}$

$\tan \theta = y/x$

$z = z$

The commands in *Mathematica* to do these conversions must first be loaded into *Mathematica* from the "Vector Analysis" external package:

In[1152]:= **<< VectorAnalysis`**

Example 12.12. Convert $(r, \theta, z) = (2, 3\pi/4, 5)$ to rectangular coordinates.

Solution: We use the **CoordinatesToCartesian** command to convert from cylindrical to rectangular coordinates:

In[1153]:= **CoordinatesToCartesian[{2, 3 Pi / 4, 5}, Cylindrical]**

Out[1153]= $\left\{ -\sqrt{2}, \sqrt{2}, 5 \right\}$

In[1154]:= **N[%]**

Out[1154]= $\{-1.41421, 1.41421, 5.\}$

Example 12.13. Convert $(x, y, z) = (2, 3, 5)$ to cyclindrical coordinates.

Solution: We use the **CoordinatesFromCartesian** command to convert from rectangular to cylindrical coordinates:

In[1155]:= **CoordinatesFromCartesian[{2, 3, 5}, Cylindrical]**

Out[1155]= $\left\{ \sqrt{13}, \text{ArcTan}\left[\dfrac{3}{2}\right], 5 \right\}$

In[1156]:= **N[%]**

Out[1156]= $\{3.60555, 0.982794, 5.\}$

Of course, one very strong point for *Mathematica* is its graphing ability. It will easily graph functions described in cylindrical coordinates. The command to do this is **RevolutionPlot3D**.

```
RevolutionPlot3D[fz, {t, tmin, tmax}, {θ, θmin, θmax}]
```

takes the azimuthal angle θ to vary between θ_{min} and θ_{max}.

Example 12.14. Graph the cylindrical coordinate function $z = \frac{2 r^2 \sin(5 \theta)}{1+r^2}$.

Solution:

In[1157]:= **Clear[r, θ];**

RevolutionPlot3D$\left[\dfrac{2 \, r^2 \, \text{Sin}[5 \, \theta]}{1 + r^2}\right.$, {r, 0, 5}, {θ, 0, 2 π}, ImageSize → {250}$\left.\right]$

Out[1158]=

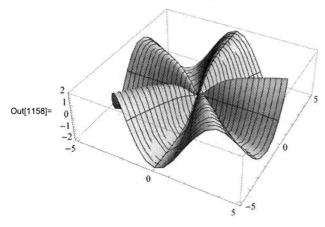

■ 12.5.2 Spherical Coordinates

A point $P = (x, y, z)$ is described in spherical coordinates by a triple (ρ, θ, ϕ) where ρ is the distance of P from the origin, θ is the polar angle of the projection $(x, y, 0)$, and ϕ is the angle between the z-axis and the ray from the origin through P. The formulas for converting between rectangular and spherical coordinates are:

Spherical to Rectangular   **Rectangular to Spherical**

$x = \rho \cos\theta \sin\phi$ $\rho = \sqrt{x^2 + y^2 + z^2}$

$y = \rho \sin\theta \sin\phi$ $\tan\theta = y/x$

$z = \rho \cos\phi$ $\cos\phi = z/\rho$

These conversions are done in *Mathematica* using the same commands as with cylindrical coordinates, but with the word spherical replacing cylindrical.

Example 12.15. Convert $(\rho, \theta, \phi) = (2, 3\pi/4, \pi/5)$ to rectangular coordinates.

Solution:

In[1159]:= **CoordinatesToCartesian[{2, 3 Pi / 4, π / 5}, Spherical]**

Out[1159]= $\left\{\dfrac{1 + \sqrt{5}}{2\sqrt{2}}, \sqrt{2\left(\dfrac{5}{8} - \dfrac{\sqrt{5}}{8}\right)}, -\sqrt{2}\right\}$

In[1160]:= **N[%]**

Out[1160]= {1.14412, 0.831254, -1.41421}

Example 12.16. Convert $(x, y, z) = (2, 3, 5)$ to spherical coordinates.

Solution:

In[1161]:= **CoordinatesFromCartesian[{2, 3, 5}, Spherical]**

Out[1161]= $\left\{ \sqrt{38} , \text{ArcCos}\left[\dfrac{5}{\sqrt{38}} \right], \text{ArcTan}\left[\dfrac{3}{2} \right] \right\}$

In[1162]:= **N[%]**

Out[1162]= $\{6.16441, 0.624754, 0.982794\}$

Again, the main use here of *Mathematica* is its graphing ability. It will easily graph functions described in spherical coordinates. The command to do this is the **SphericalPlot3D** command.

```
SphericalPlot3D[r, {θ, θ_min, θ_max}, {φ, φ_min, φ_max}]
```
generates a 3 D plot with a spherical radius r as a function of spherical coordinates θ and ϕ.

Example 12.17. Graph the spherical coordinate function $\rho = 1 + \sin(6\,\phi)/6$.

Solution:

In[1163]:= **SphericalPlot3D[ρ = 1 + Sin[6 φ] / 6, {θ, 0, Pi}, {φ, 0, 2 Pi}, ImageSize → {250}]**

Out[1163]=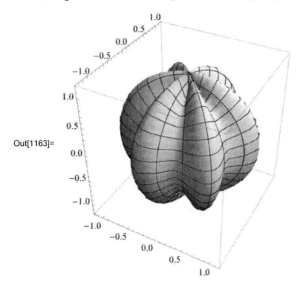

■ **Exercises**

Convert from cylindrical to rectangular:
1. $(2, \pi/3, -4)$ 2. $(1, \pi/2, 3)$

Convert from rectangular to cylindrical:
3. $(2, 2, 5)$ 4. $\left(4, \sqrt{3}, 8\right)$

5. Plot the surface $z^2 + r^2 = 25\,\theta$ and describe it.

Convert from spherical to rectangular:
6. $(2, \pi/5, \pi/3)$ **7.** $(4, \pi/6, 5\,\pi/6)$

Convert from rectangular to spherical:

8. $\left(\sqrt{2}, 2, 3 \right)$ 9. $\left(4, \sqrt{3} \big/ 2, \sqrt{8} \right)$

10. Plot the surface $\rho \sin \phi = 5$ and describe it.

Chapter 13   Calculus of Vector-Valued Functions

Useful Tip: If you are reading the electronic version of this publication formatted as a *Mathematica* Notebook, then it is possible to view 3-D plots generated by *Mathematica* from different perspectives. First, place your screen cursor over the plot. Then drag the mouse while pressing down on the left mouse button to rotate the plot.

■ 13.1. Vector-Valued Functions

Students should read Section 13.1 of Rogawski's *Calculus* [1] for a detailed discussion of the material presented in this section.

A vector-valued function is a vector where the components of the vector are themselves functions of a common parameter (or variable). For example, **r** is a vector-valued function if $\mathbf{r}(t) = \langle x(t), y(t), z(t) \rangle$. If we think of t as the time variable, the $\mathbf{r}(t)$ describes the motion of a particle through three-dimensional space over time. What we want to do is to understand what path is taken. We do this through graphing in three dimensions. Also, sometimes it is helpful to consider the projections of these curves onto the coordinate planes. For example, the projection of $\mathbf{r}(t)$ on the xy-plane is $\langle x(t), y(t), 0 \rangle$.

Example 13.1. Trace the paths of each of the following vector functions and describe its projections onto the xy-, xz-, and yz-planes:

a) $\mathbf{r}(t) = \langle t, \ t^2, \ 2t \rangle$

b) $\mathbf{r}(t) = \langle \cos^3 t, \ \sin^3 t, \ \sin 2t \rangle$

Solution: We use the **ParametricPlot3D** command to trace the path of each curve and to see its projection.

a) First, we look at the plot of $\mathbf{r}(t) = \langle t, \ t^2, \ 2t \rangle$:

In[1164]:= **ParametricPlot3D$\left[\{t, t^2, 2\, t\}, \{t, -3, 3\}, \text{PlotStyle} \rightarrow \text{Red}, \text{ImageSize} \rightarrow \{250\}\right]$**

Out[1164]=

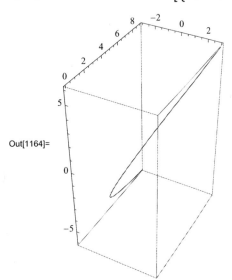

This curve looks very much like a parabola in 3-D space. To see the projections, we look first at:

In[1165]:= **ParametricPlot3D$\left[\left\{t, t^2, 0\right\}, \{t, -3, 3\},\right.$**
PlotRange → {-1, 1}, PlotStyle → Orange, ImageSize → {250}$\left.\right]$

Out[1165]=

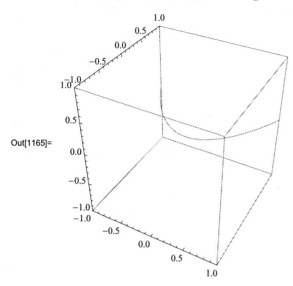

This is clearly a parabola in the *xy*-plane.

In[1166]:= **ParametricPlot3D[{t, 0, 2 t}, {t, -3, 3}, Ticks → {Automatic, {-1, 0, 1}, Automatic},**
PlotStyle → Orange, ImageSize → {250}, ImagePadding → {{15, 15}, {15, 15}}]

Out[1166]=

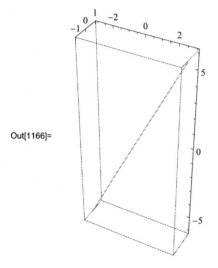

And this clearly a line in the *xz*-plane.

In[1167]:= `ParametricPlot3D[{0, t², 2 t}, {t, -3, 3},`
       `Ticks → {{-1, 0, 1}, Automatic, Automatic}, PlotStyle → Orange, ImageSize → {250}]`

Out[1167]=

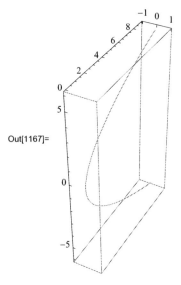

This last plot is also clearly a parabola, but in the *yz*-plane.

b) Next, we look at $\mathbf{r}(t) = \langle \cos^3 t, \sin^3 t, \sin 2 t \rangle$:

In[1168]:= `ParametricPlot3D[{Cos[t]³, Sin[ t]³, Sin[2 t]},`
       `{t, -2 π, 2 π}, PlotStyle → Orange, ImageSize → {250}]`

Out[1168]=

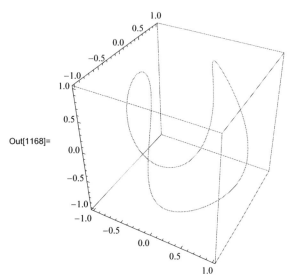

Note that since both sine and cosine are periodic with period 2π, it is not necessary to extend the domain beyond -2π or $+2\pi$. The projection in the *xy*-plane is:

In[1169]:= **ParametricPlot3D$\left[\left\{\text{Cos[t]}^3, \text{Sin[t]}^3, 0\right\},\right.$**
$\left.\{t, -2\pi, 2\pi\}, \text{PlotPoints} \rightarrow 100, \text{ImageSize} \rightarrow \{250\}\right]$

Out[1169]=

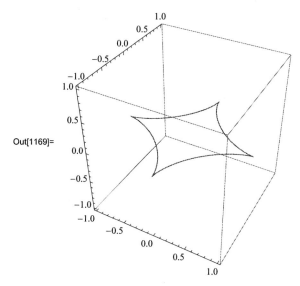

The projection in the *xz*-plane is:

In[1170]:= **ParametricPlot3D$\left[\left\{\text{Cos[t]}^3, 0, \text{Sin[2 t]}\right\}, \{t, -2\pi, 2\pi\}, \text{ImageSize} \rightarrow \{250\}\right]$**

Out[1170]=

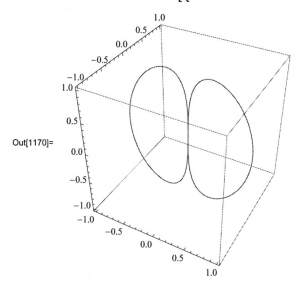

Lastly, the projection in the *yz*-plane is:

In[1171]:= **ParametricPlot3D$\left[\left\{0, \text{Sin}[\ t]^3, \text{Sin}[2\ t]\right\}, \{t, -2\ \pi, 2\ \pi\}, \text{ImageSize} \rightarrow \{250\}\right]$**

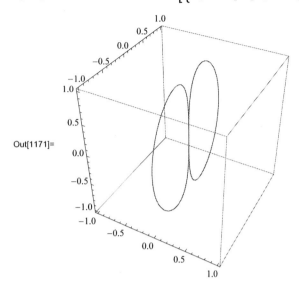

Out[1171]=

Note that the last two projections are almost exactly alike. This is to be expected because the sine and cosine functions have the same graph, but $\pi/2$ radians apart.

■ Exercises

In Exercises 1 through 3, graph **r**(*t*) and its three projections onto the coordinate planes.

1. $\mathbf{r}(t) = \langle \cos(2\,t),\, \cos t,\, \sin t \rangle$ 2. $\mathbf{r}(t) = \langle t + 15,\, e^{0.08\,t}\cos t,\, e^{0.08\,t}\sin t \rangle$

3. $\mathbf{r}(t) = \langle t,\, t,\, 25\,t/(1 + t^2) \rangle$

4. Which of the following curves have the same projection onto the *xz*-plane? Graph the three projections to check your answer.

a. $\mathbf{r}_1(t) = \langle t,\, e^t,\, t^2 \rangle$ b. $\mathbf{r}_2(t) = \langle e^t,\, t,\, t^2 \rangle$ c. $\mathbf{r}_3(t) = \langle t,\, \cos t,\, t^2 \rangle$

■ 13.2. Calculus of Vector-Valued Functions

Students should read Section 13.2 of Rogawski's *Calculus* [1] for a detailed discussion of the material presented in this section.

Since vector-valued functions are differentiated and integrated component by component, *Mathematica* will handle this easily since it treats vectors as lists and automatically performs the indicated operation on each element of the list.

The derivative of a vector valued function $\mathbf{r}(t) = \langle x(t),\, y(t),\, z(t) \rangle$ is defined to be

$$\mathbf{r}'(t) = \langle x'(t),\, y'(t),\, z'(t) \rangle$$

while the integral of **r**(*t*) is

$$\int r(t)\,dt = \left\langle \int x(t)\,dt,\, \int y(t)\,dt,\, \int z(t)\,dt \right\rangle.$$

Similarly, the limit is defined by

$$\lim_{t \to a} \mathbf{r}(t) = \langle \lim_{t \to a} x(t),\, \lim_{t \to a} y(t),\, \lim_{t \to a} z(t) \rangle.$$

Example 13.2. Differentiate and integrate each of the following vector functions:

a) $\mathbf{r}(t) = \langle t, \ t^2, \ 2t \rangle$

b) $\mathbf{s}(t) = \langle \cos^3 t, \ \sin^3 t, \ \sin 2t \rangle$

Solution:

(a)

In[1172]:= **Clear[r, s, t]**

In[1173]:= **r[t_] := {t, t², 2 t}**
s[t_] := {Cos[t]³, Sin[t]³, Sin[2 t]}

In[1175]:= **∂_t r[t]**

Out[1175]= {1, 2 t, 2}

In[1176]:= **∫ r[t] ⅆt**

Out[1176]= $\left\{ \dfrac{t^2}{2}, \ \dfrac{t^3}{3}, \ t^2 \right\}$

(b)

In[1177]:= **∂_t s[t]**

Out[1177]= {- 3 Cos[t]² Sin[t], 3 Cos[t] Sin[t]², 2 Cos[2 t]}

In[1178]:= **∫ s[t] ⅆt**

Out[1178]= $\left\{ \dfrac{3 \sin[t]}{4} + \dfrac{1}{12} \sin[3 t], \ -\dfrac{3 \cos[t]}{4} + \dfrac{1}{12} \cos[3 t], \ -\dfrac{1}{2} \cos[2 t] \right\}$

Limits are handled the same way both in the calculus of vector-valued functions and in *Mathematica*:

Example 13.3. Evaluate $\displaystyle\lim_{h\to0} \dfrac{r(t+h)-r(t)}{h}$ for $\mathbf{r}(t) = \langle t, \ t^2, \ 2t \rangle$.

Solution:

Since $\mathbf{r}(t)$ has been defined in the previous example, we merely evaluate

In[1179]:= **Limit$\left[\dfrac{r[t+h] - r[t]}{h}, h \to 0\right]$**

Out[1179]= {1, 2 t, 2}

As we would expect, this limit gives us the same answer for $\mathbf{r}'(t)$ as in the previous example.

Example 13.4. Evaluate $\displaystyle\lim_{t\to3} \left\langle t^2, 4t, \dfrac{1}{t^3} \right\rangle$.

Solution:

In[1180]:= $\text{Limit}\left[\left\{t^2, \ 4\,t, \ \dfrac{1}{t^3}\right\}, \ t \to 2\right]$

Out[1180]= $\left\{4, \ 8, \ \dfrac{1}{8}\right\}$

Derivatives of Dot and Cross Products

Using the formulas of the derivative of the dot and cross products for vector-valued functions is simple in *Mathematica*. As a reminder, the formulas are:

$$\frac{d}{dt}\,(\mathbf{r}(t)\cdot\mathbf{s}(t)) = \mathbf{r}(t)\cdot\mathbf{s}'(t) + \mathbf{r}'(t)\cdot\mathbf{s}(t) \text{ and } \frac{d}{dt}\,(\mathbf{r}(t)\times\mathbf{s}(t)) = \mathbf{r}(t)\times\mathbf{s}'(t) + \mathbf{r}'(t)\times\mathbf{s}(t)$$

Example 13.5. Evaluate $\frac{d}{dt}\,(\mathbf{r}(t)\cdot\mathbf{s}(t))$ and $\frac{d}{dt}\,(\mathbf{r}(t)\times\mathbf{s}(t))$ for $\mathbf{r}(t) = \langle t, \ t^2, \ 2\,t\rangle$ and $\mathbf{s}(t) = \langle\cos^3 t, \ \sin^3 t, \ \sin 2\,t\rangle$.

Solution:

In[1181]:= $\partial_t\,(\mathbf{r}[t].\mathbf{s}[t])$

Out[1181]= $\text{Cos}[t]^3 + 4\,t\,\text{Cos}[2\,t] - 3\,t\,\text{Cos}[t]^2\,\text{Sin}[t] + 3\,t^2\,\text{Cos}[t]\,\text{Sin}[t]^2 + 2\,t\,\text{Sin}[t]^3 + 2\,\text{Sin}[2\,t]$

In[1182]:= $\partial_t\,(\mathbf{r}[t]\times\mathbf{s}[t])$

Out[1182]= $\{2\,t^2\,\text{Cos}[2\,t] - 6\,t\,\text{Cos}[t]\,\text{Sin}[t]^2 - 2\,\text{Sin}[t]^3 + 2\,t\,\text{Sin}[2\,t],$
$\qquad 2\,\text{Cos}[t]^3 - 2\,t\,\text{Cos}[2\,t] - 6\,t\,\text{Cos}[t]^2\,\text{Sin}[t] - \text{Sin}[2\,t],$
$\qquad -2\,t\,\text{Cos}[t]^3 + 3\,t^2\,\text{Cos}[t]^2\,\text{Sin}[t] + 3\,t\,\text{Cos}[t]\,\text{Sin}[t]^2 + \text{Sin}[t]^3\}$

Tangent Lines

Example 13.6. Find the vector parametrization of the tangent line to $\mathbf{r}(t) = \langle 1 - t^2, \ 5\,t, \ t^3\rangle$ at the point $t = 1$ and plot it along with $\mathbf{r}(t)$.

Solution: Recall that the tangent line at t_0 has vector parametrization $\mathbf{L}(t) = \mathbf{r}(t_0) + t\,\mathbf{r}'(t_0)$:

In[1183]:= $\mathbf{r}[t\_] = \{1 - t^2, \ 5\,t, \ t^3\}$
$\quad\mathbf{r}'[t]$
$\quad\mathbf{L}[t\_] = \mathbf{r}[1] + t*\mathbf{r}'[1]$

Out[1183]= $\{1 - t^2, \ 5\,t, \ t^3\}$

Out[1184]= $\{-2\,t, \ 5, \ 3\,t^2\}$

Out[1185]= $\{-2\,t, \ 5 + 5\,t, \ 1 + 3\,t\}$

Here is a plot of the curve and the tangent line.

In[1186]:= **ParametricPlot3D[{r[t], L[t]}, {t, -2, 4}, ImageSize → Small]**

Out[1186]=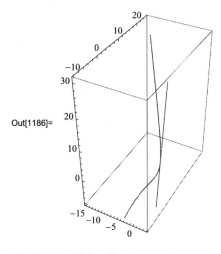

NOTE: Recall that the plot can be rotated to better view it from different perspectives.

■ **Exercises**

In Exercises 1 and 2 evaluate the limits

1. $\lim_{t \to \pi} \langle \sin 2\,t, \cos t, \tan 4\,t \rangle$

2. $\lim_{t \to 0} \left\langle \frac{1}{t+1}, \frac{e^t - 1}{t}, 4\,t \right\rangle$

In Exercises 3 and 4 compute the derivative and integral.

3. $\mathbf{r}(t) = \langle \tan t, 4\,t - 2, \sin t \rangle$

4. $\mathbf{r}(t) = \langle e^t, e^{2\,t} \rangle$

5. Find a parametrization of the tangent line at the point indicated and plot both the vector-valued curve and the tangent line on the same set of axes.

6. Evaluate $\frac{d}{dt}\,\mathbf{r}(g(t))$ for $\mathbf{r}(t) = \langle 4 \sin 2\,t, 2 \cos 2\,t \rangle$ and $g(t) = t^2$.

■ 13.3. Arc Length

Students should read Section 13.3 of Rogawski's *Calculus* [1] for a detailed discussion of the material presented in this section.

The arc length of a path $\mathbf{r}(t) = \langle x(t), y(t), z(t) \rangle$ for $a \le t \le b$ is given by

$$L = \int_a^b \| r'(t) \| \, dt = \int_a^b \sqrt{(x'(t))^2 + (y'(t))^2 + (z'(t))^2} \ dt$$

and like the one-dimensional version is difficult to evaluate by hand. Thus *Mathematica* is the perfect tool for calculating this.

Example 13.7. Compute the arc length of $\mathbf{r}(t) = \langle 1 - t^2, 5\,t, 2\,t^3 \rangle$ over the interval $1 \le t \le 2$.

Solution:

In[1187]:= $\mathbf{r[t\_]} := \{1 - t^2, 5\,t, 2\,t^3\}$

$$L = \int_1^2 \mathbf{Norm[r'[t]]}\, dt$$

Out[1188]= $\left(\dfrac{1}{54} + \dfrac{i}{54}\right)(-1)^{3/4}\left(9\sqrt{130} - 18\sqrt{1234} - \right.$

$(8 - 8\,i)\sqrt{-\dfrac{7}{i + 4\sqrt{14}}}\;\mathrm{EllipticE}\left[i\,\mathrm{ArcSinh}\left[\dfrac{3 + 3\,i}{\sqrt{i - 4\sqrt{14}}}\right], \dfrac{i - 4\sqrt{14}}{i + 4\sqrt{14}}\right] -$

$(1 + i)\sqrt{-\dfrac{2}{i + 4\sqrt{14}}}\;\mathrm{EllipticE}\left[i\,\mathrm{ArcSinh}\left[\dfrac{3 + 3\,i}{\sqrt{i - 4\sqrt{14}}}\right], \dfrac{i - 4\sqrt{14}}{i + 4\sqrt{14}}\right] +$

$(8 - 8\,i)\sqrt{-\dfrac{7}{i + 4\sqrt{14}}}\;\mathrm{EllipticE}\left[i\,\mathrm{ArcSinh}\left[\dfrac{6 + 6\,i}{\sqrt{i - 4\sqrt{14}}}\right], \dfrac{i - 4\sqrt{14}}{i + 4\sqrt{14}}\right] +$

$(1 + i)\sqrt{-\dfrac{2}{i + 4\sqrt{14}}}\;\mathrm{EllipticE}\left[i\,\mathrm{ArcSinh}\left[\dfrac{6 + 6\,i}{\sqrt{i - 4\sqrt{14}}}\right], \dfrac{i - 4\sqrt{14}}{i + 4\sqrt{14}}\right] +$

$(8 - 8\,i)\sqrt{-\dfrac{7}{i + 4\sqrt{14}}}\;\mathrm{EllipticF}\left[i\,\mathrm{ArcSinh}\left[\dfrac{3 + 3\,i}{\sqrt{i - 4\sqrt{14}}}\right], \dfrac{i - 4\sqrt{14}}{i + 4\sqrt{14}}\right] -$

$(224 + 224\,i)\sqrt{-\dfrac{2}{i + 4\sqrt{14}}}\;\mathrm{EllipticF}\left[i\,\mathrm{ArcSinh}\left[\dfrac{3 + 3\,i}{\sqrt{i - 4\sqrt{14}}}\right], \dfrac{i - 4\sqrt{14}}{i + 4\sqrt{14}}\right] -$

$(8 - 8\,i)\sqrt{-\dfrac{7}{i + 4\sqrt{14}}}\;\mathrm{EllipticF}\left[i\,\mathrm{ArcSinh}\left[\dfrac{6 + 6\,i}{\sqrt{i - 4\sqrt{14}}}\right], \dfrac{i - 4\sqrt{14}}{i + 4\sqrt{14}}\right] +$

$\left.(224 + 224\,i)\sqrt{-\dfrac{2}{i + 4\sqrt{14}}}\;\mathrm{EllipticF}\left[i\,\mathrm{ArcSinh}\left[\dfrac{6 + 6\,i}{\sqrt{i - 4\sqrt{14}}}\right], \dfrac{i - 4\sqrt{14}}{i + 4\sqrt{14}}\right]\right)$

Note that the above output indicates that *Mathematica* cannot find an antiderivative for the integrand, and thus we need to find another technique to evaluate this integral. Hence, we next try the numerical integrate command, **NIntegrate**, which does give us our result:

In[1189]:= $\mathbf{L = NIntegrate[Norm[r'[t]], \{t, 1, 2\}]}$

Out[1189]= 15.285

Speed

The vector $\mathbf{r}'(t)$ is also known as the *velocity vector* as it points in the (instantaneous) direction of motion described by $\mathbf{r}(t)$. Its length or *norm*, $\|\mathbf{r}'(t)\|$, gives the speed at time t.

Example 13.8. Compute the speed of $\mathbf{r}(t) = \langle 1 - t^2, 5t, 2t^3 \rangle$ when $t = 1$, 1.5, and 2.

Solution:

The following output gives a list of speeds of $\mathbf{r}'(t)$ at the three given times using the **Norm** command, which calculates the norm of a vector:

In[1190]:= `r[t_] := {1-t², 5 t, 2 t³}`
`Speed = {Norm[r'[1]], Norm[r'[1.5]], Norm[r'[2]]}`

Out[1191]= $\left\{ \sqrt{65}, 14.7054, \sqrt{617} \right\}$

In[1192]:= `N[%]`

Out[1192]= `{8.06226, 14.7054, 24.8395}`

Observe that the speed is increasing as we move along the path of $\mathbf{r}(t)$ from $t = 1$ to $t = 2$. This can be seen graphically by plotting the speed:

In[1193]:= `Norm[r'[t]]`
`Plot[Norm[r'[t]], {t, 1, 2}]`

Out[1193]= $\sqrt{25 + 4\,\mathrm{Abs}[t]^2 + 36\,\mathrm{Abs}[t]^4}$

Out[1194]=

NOTE: Observe how the **Norm** command inserts absolute values around each vector component in the formula for $\|\mathbf{r}'(t)\|$, which seems redundant since each component is squared. This is done because in *Mathematica* vector components are allowed to be complex-valued, in which case absolute values are needed to refer to their magnitudes.

■ Exercises

In Exercises 1 and 2, compute the length of curve over the given interval.

1. $\mathbf{r}(t) = \langle 2 \sin t, 6t, 2 \cos t \rangle$, $-6 \le t \le 6$ 2. $\mathbf{r}(t) = \langle 12t, 8t^{3/2}, 3t^2 \rangle$, $0 \le t \le 1$

In Exercises 3 and 4, find the speed of a particle moving along the curve $\mathbf{r}(t)$ at the given value of t.

3. $\mathbf{r}(t) = \langle e^{t-2}, 15t, 5/t \rangle$, $t = 1$ 4. $\mathbf{r}(t) = \langle \sin 2t, \cos 4t, \sin 6t \rangle$, $t = \pi/2$

5. Compute $s(t) = \int_0^t \| \mathbf{r}'(u) \| \, du$ for $\mathbf{r}(t) = \langle t^2, 2t^2, t^3 \rangle$ and interpret *Mathematica*'s result.

6. For $\mathbf{r}(t) = \langle 4\,t,\ 1 - 3\,t,\ \sqrt{24}\ t \rangle$, compute $s\,(t)$ as in the previous exercise. Then use $s\,(t)$ to find an arc length parametrization of $\mathbf{r}(t)$, that is, find $\varphi(s) = t$, where φ is the inverse of $s\,(t)$, and check to see that $\mathbf{r}(\varphi\,(s))$ has unit speed, that is, $\|\mathbf{r}'\,(\varphi\,(s))\,\| = 1$. Lastly, plot $\mathbf{r}(t)$ and $\mathbf{r}(\varphi\,(s))$ and compare them.

7. Consider the helix $\mathbf{r}(t) = \langle a \sin t,\ a \cos t,\ c\,t \rangle$.
a. Find a formula for the arc length of one revolution of $\mathbf{r}(t)$.
b. Suppose a helix has radius 10, height 5, and makes three revolutions. What is its arc length?

8. The Cornu spiral is defined by $\mathbf{r}(t) = \langle x(t),\ y(t) \rangle$, where $x(t) = \int_0^t \sin\!\left(\frac{u^2}{2}\right) d\,u$ and $y(t) = \int_0^t \cos\!\left(\frac{u^2}{2}\right) d\,u$.
a. Plot the Cornu spiral over various intervals for t.
b. Find a formula for its arc length along the interval $-a \le t \le a$, where a is a positive real number.
c. What is its arc length in the limit as $a \to \infty$?

■ 13.4. Curvature

Students should read Section 13.4 of Rogawski's *Calculus* [1] for a detailed discussion of the material presented in this section.

Vector tools previously studied including arc length enables one to study the idea of curvature, which serves as a measure of how a curve bends, that is, the rate of change in direction of a curve. In arriving at a definition of curvature, consider a path in vector form and parametrized by

$$\mathbf{r}(t) = \langle x\,(t),\ y\,(t),\ z\,(t) \rangle$$

The parametrization is classified as regular if $\mathbf{r}'\,(t) \neq 0$ for all values of t and for which $r\,(t)$ is defined. Assume then that $\mathbf{r}(t)$ is regular and define the *unit tangent vector* in the direction of $\mathbf{r}'\,(t)$, denoted $T\,(t)$, as follows:

$$T(t) = \frac{\mathbf{r}'\,(t)}{\|\mathbf{r}'\,(t)\|}.$$

This unit tangent vector $\mathbf{T}$ at any point enables us to determine the direction of the curve at that point, so one may define the curvature κ (Greek letter kappa) at a point as

$$\kappa = \left\|\frac{d\mathbf{T}}{ds}\right\| = \frac{\|\mathbf{T}'\,(t)\|}{\|\mathbf{r}'\,(t)\|},$$

which represents the magnitude of the rate of change in the unit tangent vector with respect to arc length. One denotes the vector $d\mathbf{T}/ds$ as the curvature vector. Its scalar length therefore measures curvature. For example, a straight line has $\kappa = 0$ (zero curvature) as one would expect. For a circle of radius ρ, we have $\kappa = 1/\rho$ (reciprocal of ρ). This makes sense since a larger circle should have smaller curvature. In general, if we were to secure a circle, called the *osculating circle*, that best fits a curve at a specific point on the curve, then curvature of the curve at such a point should agree with the curvature of the osculating circle, that is,

$$\kappa = \frac{1}{\rho}$$

Moreover, the radius ρ of this circle is called the *radius of curvature*. Note that the equations linking κ and ρ illustrate their inverse relationship:

$$\kappa = \frac{1}{\rho} \text{ and } \rho = \frac{1}{\kappa}$$

Example 13.9. Compute the curvature κ for a circle of radius ρ defined by

$$r(t) = \langle \rho \cos t, \, \rho \sin t \rangle$$

Solution: We first compute the unit tangent vector **T** using the formula $\mathbf{T}(t) = \frac{\mathbf{r}'(t)}{\|\mathbf{r}'(t)\|}$:

In[1195]:= **Clear[r, T, t, ρ]**

In[1196]:= **r[t_] = {ρ Cos[t], ρ Sin[t]}**
r'[t]
T[t_] = r'[t] / Simplify[Norm[r'[t]]]

Out[1196]= {ρ Cos[t], ρ Sin[t]}

Out[1197]= {-ρ Sin[t], ρ Cos[t]}

Out[1198]= $\left\{ - \dfrac{\rho \, \text{Sin}[t]}{\sqrt{\text{Abs}[\rho \, \text{Cos}[t]]^2 + \text{Abs}[\rho \, \text{Sin}[t]]^2}}, \dfrac{\rho \, \text{Cos}[t]}{\sqrt{\text{Abs}[\rho \, \text{Cos}[t]]^2 + \text{Abs}[\rho \, \text{Sin}[t]]^2}} \right\}$

Observe that in this output *Mathematica* is not able to reduce the expression inside the radical, which simplifies to ρ as a result of the fundamental trigonometric identity $\cos^2 x + \sin^2 x = 1$. This is due to the **Norm** command, which employs absolute values. To remedy this, we use the formula $\|\mathbf{r}'(t)\| = \sqrt{\mathbf{r}'(t) \cdot \mathbf{r}'(t)}$ instead of the **Norm** command.

In[1199]:= **T[t_] = r'[t] / Sqrt[Simplify[r'[t].r'[t]]]**

Out[1199]= $\left\{ - \dfrac{\rho \, \text{Sin}[t]}{\sqrt{\rho^2}}, \dfrac{\rho \, \text{Cos}[t]}{\sqrt{\rho^2}} \right\}$

We then compute the curvature using the formula $\kappa = \frac{\|\mathbf{T}'(t)\|}{\|\mathbf{r}'(t)\|}$:

In[1200]:= **κ = Sqrt[Simplify[T'[t].T'[t]] / Simplify[r'[t].r'[t]]]**

Out[1200]= $\sqrt{\dfrac{1}{\rho^2}}$

Since the radius ρ is assumed to be positive, we conclude that $\kappa = \sqrt{\frac{1}{\rho^2}} = \left|\frac{1}{\rho}\right| = \frac{1}{\rho}$ as expected.

Example 13.10. Compute the curvature κ for the curve defined by $f(x) = x^2$ at the point (3, 9).

Solution: Observe that the graph of a function $y = f(x)$ can be parametrized by $x = t$ and $y = f(t)$ and hence $\mathbf{r}(t) = \langle t, f(t) \rangle$. In this case the formula for curvature reduces to

In[1201]:= **Clear[r, t, f]**
r[t_] = {t, f[t]}

Out[1202]= {t, f[t]}

In[1203]:= $\mathbf{T[t\_]} = \dfrac{\mathbf{r'[t]}}{\mathbf{Sqrt[r'[t].r'[t]]}}$

$\mathbf{\kappa = Sqrt[Simplify[T'[t].T'[t]]\,/\,Simplify[r'[t].r'[t]]]}$

Out[1203]= $\left\{ \dfrac{1}{\sqrt{1 + f'[t]^2}} \,,\, \dfrac{f'[t]}{\sqrt{1 + f'[t]^2}} \right\}$

Out[1204]= $\sqrt{\dfrac{f''[t]^2}{\left(1 + f'[t]^2\right)^3}}$

which is the same as $\kappa = \dfrac{|f''(x)|}{(1+(f'(x))^2)^{3/2}}$. With $f(x) = x^2$, we get

In[1205]:= $\mathbf{f[t\_] = t^2}$

$\mathbf{\kappa}$

Out[1205]= t^2

Out[1206]= $2 \sqrt{\dfrac{1}{\left(1 + 4\,t^2\right)^3}}$

At $x = t = 3$, the curvature becomes

In[1207]:= $\mathbf{\kappa\,/.\,t \to 3}$

Out[1207]= $\dfrac{2}{37\,\sqrt{37}}$

Here is a plot of the curvature along with the function.

In[1208]:= $\mathbf{Plot[\{f[t],\,\kappa\},\,\{t,\,0,\,3\}]}$

Out[1208]=

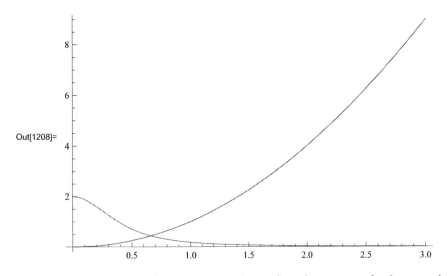

Example 13.10. Compute the curvature κ and the radius of curvature ρ for the curve defined by

$$r(t) = \left\langle 1 - t, \, t^2 + 1, \, \frac{2}{3} t^3 + 1 \right\rangle \text{ at } t = 1/2.$$

Solution: Again we begin by computing the unit tangent vector **T**:

In[1209]:= **Clear[r, T, t, κ]**

In[1210]:= **r[t_] = {1 - t, t^2 + 1, (2 / 3) t^3 + 1}**
r'[t]
T[t_] = r'[t] / Sqrt[Simplify[r'[t].r'[t]]]

Out[1210]= $\left\{ 1 - t, \, 1 + t^2, \, 1 + \dfrac{2\,t^3}{3} \right\}$

Out[1211]= $\left\{ -1, \, 2\,t, \, 2\,t^2 \right\}$

Out[1212]= $\left\{ -\dfrac{1}{\sqrt{\left(1 + 2\,t^2\right)^2}}, \, \dfrac{2\,t}{\sqrt{\left(1 + 2\,t^2\right)^2}}, \, \dfrac{2\,t^2}{\sqrt{\left(1 + 2\,t^2\right)^2}} \right\}$

We then compute the curvature using the same formula as in the previous example and evaluate it at $t = 1/2$:

In[1213]:= **κ = Sqrt[Simplify[T'[t].T'[t]] / Simplify[r'[t].r'[t]]]**
κ /. t → 1 / 2

Out[1213]= $2 \sqrt{\dfrac{1}{\left(1 + 2\,t^2\right)^4}}$

Out[1214]= $\dfrac{8}{9}$

Hence, the curvature $\kappa = 8/9$ at $t = 1/2$ and the corresponding radius of curvature is $\rho = 1/\kappa = 9/8$.

Curvature Formula (Cross Product)

There is an alternative formula for calculating the curvature of space curves that involves the cross product and eliminates the need to compute the unit tangent vector function:

$$\kappa = \frac{\| \mathbf{r}''(t) \times \mathbf{r}'(t) \|}{\| \mathbf{r}'(t) \|^3} = \frac{\| \mathbf{a}(t) \times \mathbf{v}(t) \|}{\| \mathbf{v}(t) \|^3}$$

Example 13.11. Compute the curvature $\kappa(t)$ and the radius of curvature for the helix defined by $\mathbf{r}(t) = \langle \cos t, \sin t, t \rangle$ for any real number t.

Solution: We first find the derivative of the unit tangent vector with respect to t.

In[1215]:= **Clear[r, T, t, κ]**
r[t_] = {Cos[t], Sin[t], t}
r'[t]
r''[t]

Out[1216]= {Cos[t], Sin[t], t}

Out[1217]= {-Sin[t], Cos[t], 1}

Out[1218]= {-Cos[t], -Sin[t], 0}

In[1219]:= **κ[t_] = Sqrt[Simplify[Cross[r''[t], r'[t]].Cross[r''[t], r'[t]]]] /**
      Sqrt[Simplify[r'[t].r'[t]]]³

Out[1219]= $\dfrac{1}{2}$

It follows that $\kappa = \frac{1}{2}$ and $\rho = 2$ for all values of t. Hence, our helix is a curve of constant curvature.

■ Exercises

In Exercises 1 and 2, find $\mathbf{r}'(t)$ and $\mathbf{T}(t)$ and evaluate $\mathbf{T}(2)$.

1. $\mathbf{r}(t) = (3 + 2t)\,\mathbf{i} + (2 - 5t)\,\mathbf{j} + 9t\,\mathbf{k}$ 2. $\mathbf{v}(t) = \langle \sin t, \cos t, 1 \rangle$

3. Use *Mathematica* to find the curvature function $k(x)$ for $y = \cos x$. Also plot $\kappa(x)$ for $0 \le x \le 1$. Where does the curvature assume its maximum value?

4. Determine the unit normal vectors to $r(t) = [t\,\mathbf{i} + \sin t\,\mathbf{j}]$ at $t = \frac{\pi}{4}$ and $t = \frac{3\pi}{4}$.

5. Determine the curvature of the vector-valued function $\mathbf{r}(t) = (3 + 2t)\,\mathbf{i} + 6t\,\mathbf{j} + (5 - t)\,\mathbf{k}$.

6. Find a formula for the curvature of the general helix $\mathbf{r}(t) = a\cos t\,\mathbf{i} + a\sin t\,\mathbf{j} + ct\,\mathbf{k}$.

■ 13.5. Motion in Three Space

Students should read Section 13.5 of Rogawski's *Calculus* [1] for a detailed discussion of the material presented in this section.

Recall that the velocity vector is the rate of the change of the position vector with respect to time while the acceleration vector represents the rate of change of the velocity vector with respect to time. Moreover, speed is defined to be the absolute value of the velocity vector. In short, we have the following:

$$\mathbf{v}(t) = \mathbf{r}'(t), \ s(t) = \|\mathbf{v}(t)\| \ \text{and} \ \mathbf{a}(t) = \mathbf{v}'(t) = \mathbf{r}''(t)$$

One can secure the velocity vector and the position function if the acceleration vector is known via integration. More specifically:

$\mathbf{v}(t) = \int_0^t \mathbf{a}(u)\,du + v_0$ where v_0 represents the initial velocity vector and $\mathbf{r}(t) = \int_0^t \mathbf{v}(u)\,du + v_0\,t + r_0$ where r_0 is the initial position.

Example 13.12. Find the velocity vector, the speed, and the acceleration vector for the vector-valued function $\mathbf{r}(t) = t^3\,\mathbf{i} + (1 - t)\,\mathbf{j} + 4t^2\,\mathbf{k}$ at time $t = 1$.

Solution:

In[1220]:= `Clear[r, v, s, a]`
`r[t_] = {t^3, 1 - t, 4 t^2}`
`v[t_] = r'[t]`
`s[t_] = Sqrt[v[t].v[t]]`
`a[t_] = r''[t]`
`v[1]`
`s[1]`
`a[1]`

Out[1221]= $\left\{t^3, 1 - t, 4 t^2\right\}$

Out[1222]= $\left\{3 t^2, -1, 8 t\right\}$

Out[1223]= $\sqrt{1 + 64 t^2 + 9 t^4}$

Out[1224]= $\{6 t, 0, 8\}$

Out[1225]= $\{3, -1, 8\}$

Out[1226]= $\sqrt{74}$

Out[1227]= $\{6, 0, 8\}$

Thus, $\mathbf{v}(1) = \mathbf{r}'(1) = 3\,\mathbf{i} - \mathbf{j} + 8\,\mathbf{k}$, $s(1) = \sqrt{74}$, and $\mathbf{a}(1) = 6\,\mathbf{i} + 8\,\mathbf{k}$.

Example 13.13. Find $\mathbf{r}(t)$ and $\mathbf{v}(t)$ if $\mathbf{a}(t) = t\,\mathbf{i} + 4\,\mathbf{j}$ subject to the initial conditions $\mathbf{v}(0) = 3\,\mathbf{i} - 2\,\mathbf{j}$ and $\mathbf{r}(0) = \mathbf{0}$.

Solution: We first solve for $\mathbf{v}(t)$ by integrating $\mathbf{a}(t)$:

In[1228]:= `Clear[r, v, a]`
`a[t_] = {t, 4}`
`v[t_] = Integrate[a[u], {u, 0, t}] + {v01, v02}`

Out[1229]= $\{t, 4\}$

Out[1230]= $\left\{\dfrac{t^2}{2} + v01,\ 4\,t + v02\right\}$

Here, the constant vector of integration $\mathbf{v}_0 = \langle v_{01}, v_{02}\rangle = \langle 3, -2\rangle$ equals the initial velocity:

In[1231]:= `Solve[v[0] == {3, -2}, {v01, v02}]`

Out[1231]= $\{\{v01 \to 3,\ v02 \to -2\}\}$

Thus, $\mathbf{v}(t) = \dfrac{t^2}{2}\,\mathbf{i} + 4\,t\,\mathbf{j} + (3\,\mathbf{i} - 2\,\mathbf{j})$.

In[1232]:= `v[t_] = v[t] /. {v01 → 3, v02 → -2}`

Out[1232]= $\left\{3 + \dfrac{t^2}{2},\ -2 + 4\,t\right\}$

Next, we solve for $\mathbf{r}(t)$ by integrating $\mathbf{v}(t)$:

In[1233]:= **r[t_] = Integrate[v[u], {u, 0, t}] + {r01, r02}**

Out[1233]= $\left\{ r01 + 3\,t + \dfrac{t^3}{6},\ r02 - 2\,t + 2\,t^2 \right\}$

Again, the constant vector of integration $\mathbf{r}_0 = \langle r_{01}, r_{02} \rangle = \langle 0, 0 \rangle$ equals the initial position:

In[1234]:= **Solve[r[0] == {0, 0}, {r01, r02}]**

Out[1234]= $\{\{ r01 \to 0,\ r02 \to 0 \}\}$

Hence, $\mathbf{r}(t) = \left(\dfrac{t^3}{6} + 3\,t \right) \mathbf{i} + \left(2\,t^2 - 2\,t \right) \mathbf{j}$.

Components of Acceleration

There are two components of acceleration: *tangential* and *normal*. More precisely, the acceleration vector **a** can be decomposed as $\mathbf{a} = a_T\,\mathbf{T} + a_N\,\mathbf{N}$, where $a_T = \dfrac{d^2 s}{dt^2} = \dfrac{\mathbf{a} \cdot \mathbf{v}}{\|\mathbf{v}\|}$ is the tangential component and $a_N = \kappa \left(\dfrac{ds}{dt} \right)^2 = \dfrac{\|\mathbf{a} \times \mathbf{v}\|}{\|\mathbf{v}\|}$ is the normal component. Moreover, one has $a_T^2 + a_N^2 = \|\mathbf{a}\|^2$ so that $a_N = \sqrt{\|\mathbf{a}\|^2 - a_T^2}$ and $a_T = \sqrt{\|\mathbf{a}\|^2 - a_N^2}$.

Example 13.14. Determine the tangential and normal components of acceleration for the vector function $\mathbf{r}(t) = \langle t^3, t^2, t \rangle$.

Solution:

In[1235]:= **Clear[r, v, s]**
      r[t_] = {t^3, t^2, t}
      r'[t]
      r''[t]

Out[1236]= $\left\{ t^3,\ t^2,\ t \right\}$

Out[1237]= $\left\{ 3\,t^2,\ 2\,t,\ 1 \right\}$

Out[1238]= $\{ 6\,t,\ 2,\ 0 \}$

In[1239]:= **speed = Simplify[Sqrt[r'[t].r'[t]]]**

Out[1239]= $\sqrt{1 + 4\,t^2 + 9\,t^4}$

The result in the last output represents the speed at time *t*. In order to secure the tangential component of the acceleration, we differentiate the previous output:

In[1240]:= **at = D[speed, t]**

Out[1240]= $\dfrac{8\,t + 36\,t^3}{2\,\sqrt{1 + 4\,t^2 + 9\,t^4}}$

The normal component of the acceleration is

In[1241]:= **an = $\sqrt{\texttt{r''[t].r''[t] - at^2}}$**

Out[1241]= $\sqrt{4 + 36\ t^2 - \dfrac{\left(8\ t + 36\ t^3\right)^2}{4\ \left(1 + 4\ t^2 + 9\ t^4\right)}}$

In[1242]:= **Simplify[an]**

Out[1242]= $2\ \sqrt{\dfrac{1 + 9\ t^2 + 9\ t^4}{1 + 4\ t^2 + 9\ t^4}}$

NOTE: The components of acceleration can also be found through the formulas $a_T = \frac{\mathbf{a} \cdot \mathbf{v}}{\|\mathbf{v}\|}$ and $a_N = \frac{\|\mathbf{a} \times \mathbf{v}\|}{\|\mathbf{v}\|}$, confirmed using *Mathematica* as follows:

In[1243]:= **at = r''[t].r'[t] / Sqrt[r'[t].r'[t]]**
    an = Sqrt[Cross[r''[t], r'[t]].Cross[r''[t], r'[t]]] / Sqrt[r'[t].r'[t]]

Out[1243]= $\dfrac{4\ t + 18\ t^3}{\sqrt{1 + 4\ t^2 + 9\ t^4}}$

Out[1244]= $\dfrac{\sqrt{4 + 36\ t^2 + 36\ t^4}}{\sqrt{1 + 4\ t^2 + 9\ t^4}}$

■ Exercises

In Exercises 1 and 2, calculate the velocity and acceleration vectors and the speed at the time indicated:

1. $\mathbf{r}(t) = t^2\,\mathbf{i} + (1 - t)\,\mathbf{j} + \left(5\,t^2\right)\mathbf{k}$, $t = 2$.   2. $\mathbf{r}(t) = \cos t\,\mathbf{i} + \sin t\,\mathbf{j} + \tan(2\,t)\,\mathbf{k}$, $t = \frac{\pi}{6}$.

3. Sketch the path $\mathbf{r}(t) = \left(1 - t^2\right)\mathbf{i} + (1 - t)\,\mathbf{j}$ for $-3 \le t \le 3$ and compute the velocity and acceleration vectors at $t = 0$, $t = 1$, and $t = 2$.

4. Find $\mathbf{v}(t)$ given $\mathbf{a}(t)$ and the initial velocity $\mathbf{v}_0$.

a. $\mathbf{a}(t) = t\,\mathbf{i} + 3\,\mathbf{j}$, $\mathbf{v}(0) = \frac{1}{2}\,\mathbf{i} + 2\,\mathbf{j}$ b. $\mathbf{a}(t) = e^{2\,t}\,\mathbf{i} + 0\,\mathbf{j} + (t + 2)\,\mathbf{k}$, $\mathbf{v}(0) = \mathbf{i} - 3\,\mathbf{j} + 2\,\mathbf{k}$

5. Find $\mathbf{r}(t)$ and $\mathbf{v}(t)$ given $\mathbf{a}(t)$ together with the initial velocity and position at rest:

a. $\mathbf{a}(t) = e^{3\,t}\,\mathbf{i} + 4\,t\,\mathbf{j} + (t - 2)\,\mathbf{k}$, $\mathbf{v}(0) = 0\,\mathbf{i} + 0\,\mathbf{j} + \mathbf{k}$, $\mathbf{r}(0) = 0\,\mathbf{i} + 3\,\mathbf{j} + 4\,\mathbf{k}$
b. $\mathbf{a}(t) = 0\,\mathbf{i} + 0\,\mathbf{j} + \sin t\,\mathbf{k}$, $\mathbf{v}(0) = \mathbf{i} + \mathbf{j}$, $\mathbf{r}(0) = \mathbf{i}$.

6. Find the decomposition of $\mathbf{a}(t)$ into its tangential and normal components at the indicated point:

a. $\mathbf{r}(t) = (3 - 4\,t)\,\mathbf{i} + (t + 1)\,\mathbf{j} + t^2\,\mathbf{k}$ at $t = 1$
b. $\mathbf{r}(t) = t\,\mathbf{i} + e^{-t}\,\mathbf{j} + t\,e^{-t}\,\mathbf{k}$ at $t = 0$

7. Show that the tangential and normal components of acceleration of the helix given by $\mathbf{r}(t) = (\cos t)\,\mathbf{i} + (\sin t)\,\mathbf{j} + t\,\mathbf{k}$ are equal to 0 and 1, respectively.

Chapter 14   Differentiation in Several Variables

Useful Tip: If you are reading the electronic version of this publication formatted as a *Mathematica* Notebook, then it is possible to view 3-D plots generated by *Mathematica* from different perspectives. First, place your screen cursor over the plot. Then drag the mouse while pressing down on the left mouse button to rotate the plot.

■ 14.1 Functions of Two or More Variables

Students should read Section 14.1 of Rogawski's *Calculus* [1] for a detailed discussion of the material presented in this section.

■ 14.1.1 Plotting Level Curves using ContourPlot

We begin with plotting level curves $f(x, y) = c$ of a function of two variables. The command to plot level curves is **Contour-Plot[f,{x,a,b},{y,c,d}]**.

Most of the options for **ContourPlot** are the same as those for **Plot**. In the following example, we consider the option **Image-Size**.

Example 14.1. Plot the level curves of $f(x, y) = x^2 + x y - y^2$.

Solution: Let us first plot the level curves using the default settings of *Mathematica*.

In[1245]:= **Clear[x, y, f]**
f[x_, y_] := x^2 + x y - y^2

In[1247]:= **ContourPlot[f[x, y], {x, -5, 5}, {y, -5, 5}, ImageSize → {250}]**

Out[1247]=

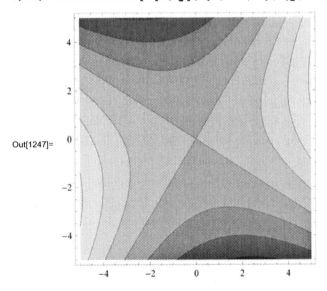

To get the level curves on the *xy*-plane without the shading, the colors, and the frame, but with the coordinate axes, we use the following options of **ContourPlot**.

In[1248]:= `ContourPlot[f[x, y], {x, -5, 5}, {y, -5, 5}, Frame → False,`
`    Axes → True, ContourShading → False, ImageSize → {250}]`

Out[1248]=

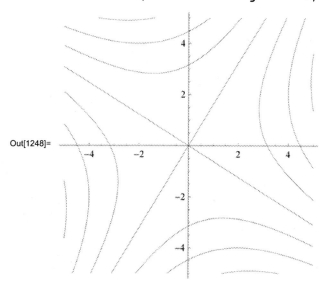

Contours is an option of **ContourPlot** that can be used in two different ways: **Contour→n** displays **n** equally spaced contour curves while **Contour→list** plots level curves $f(x, y) = c$ where c is an element of the list **list**.

To plot 15 level curves, we evaluate

In[1249]:= `ContourPlot[f[x, y], {x, -1, 1}, {y, -1, 1}, Contours → 15, ImageSize → {250} ]`

Out[1249]=

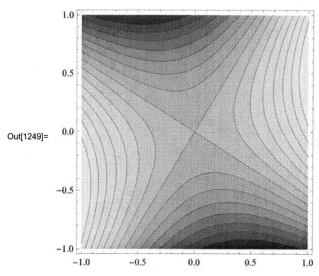

Here is an example when **list** = {−10, −5, −2, −1, 0, 1, 2, 5, 10}.

In[1250]:= `ContourPlot[f[x, y], {x, -5, 5}, {y, -5, 5},`
     `Contours → {-10, -5, -2, -1, 0, 1, 2, 5, 10}, ImageSize → {250}]`

Out[1250]=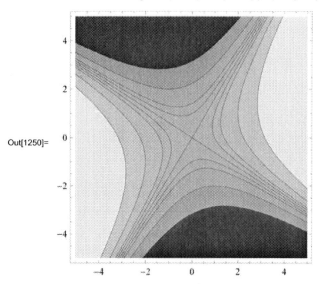

■ 14.1.2 Plotting Surfaces using Plot3D

Plot3D is the three-dimensional analog of the **Plot** command. Given an expression in two variables and the domain for the variables, **Plot3D** produces a surface plot.

The basic syntax to plot the graph of a function of two variables is **Plot3D[f,{x, a, b},{y, c, d}]**, where **f** is a function of x and y with $a \le x \le b$ and $c \le y \le d$.

The command to plot the graphs of two or more functions on the same coordinate axes is **Plot3D[{f, g, h, ... }, {x, a, b}, {y, c, d}]**, where **f, g, h, ...** are the functions to be plotted.

We will begin with the default settings of plotting a graph of a function of two variables.

Example 14.2. Plot $f(x, y) = \sin(x - \cos y)$.

Solution:

In[1251]:= `Plot3D[Sin[x - Cos[y]], {x, -3, 3}, {y, -3, 3}]`

Out[1251]=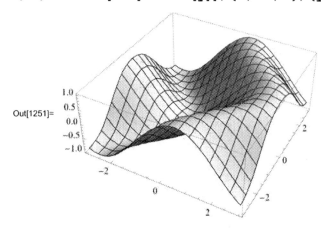

Example 14.3. Plot the graphs of $f(x, y) = 3x + 4y - 3$ and $g(x, y) = 10 \sin(xy)$ on the same axes.

Solution: We will use red color for the graph of *f* and blue for that of *g*. This is given using the option **PlotStyle**.

In[1252]:= `Plot3D[{3 x + 4 y - 3, 10 Sin[x y]}, {x, -5, 5},`
`{y, -5, 5}, PlotStyle → {Green, Blue}, ImageSize → {250}]`

Out[1252]=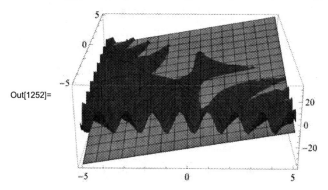

NOTE: One of the most significant improvements of *Mathematica 7.0* over the previous editions is its graphics capability. **Plot3D** has many options. Evaluate the command **Options[Plot3D]** to see the many options you have to plot a nice graph.

We will discuss some of these options below.

ViewPoint

In *Mathematica 7.0*, we can rotate the graph of a function of two variables by simply clicking on the graph and dragging the mouse around to see the graph from any point of view.

The option **ViewPoint** specifies the point in space from which the observer looks at a graphics object. The syntax for choosing a view point of a surface is **Plot3D[f[x, y], {x, a, b}, {y, c, d}, ViewPoint→{A, B, C}]**. The default value for **{A, B, C}** is {1.3,-2.4,2.0}. This may be changed by entering values directly.

To view a graph from directly in front {0, −2, 0}; in front and up {0, −2, 2}; in front and down {0, −2, −2}; left hand corner { −2, −2, 0}; directly above {0, 0, 2}.

Plot3D[f[x, y], {x, a, b}, {y, c, d}, ViewPoint → view] produces a plot viewed from **view**. The possible values of **view** are **Above** (along positive *z*-axis), **Below** (along negative *z*-axis), **Front** (along negative *y*-axis), **Back** (along positive *y*-axis), **Left** (along the negative *x*-axis), and **Right** (along the positive *x*-axis).

Example 14.4. Plot $f(x, y) = \cos x \sin y$ using **ViewPoint** option to view the graph from various view points.

Solution: We leave it to the reader to navigate all of the above choices. We will consider a few of them.

In[1253]:= `Clear[f]`
`f[x_, y_] = Cos[x] Sin[y]`

Out[1254]= `Cos[x] Sin[y]`

Here is a plot of the graph using the default setting for **ViewPoint**:

In[1255]:= **Plot3D[f[x, y] , {x, -2 Pi, 2 Pi}, {y, -2 Pi, 2 Pi} , PlotRange → All,
ImageSize → {250}]**

Out[1255]=

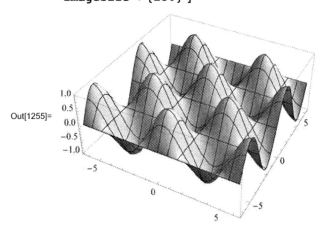

View from directly in front:

In[1256]:= **Plot3D[f[x, y] , {x, -2 Pi, 2 Pi}, {y, -2 Pi, 2 Pi}, ViewPoint → Front ,
PlotRange → All , ImageSize → {250}]**

Out[1256]=

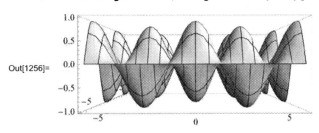

View from in front and up:

In[1257]:= **Plot3D[f[x, y] , {x, -2 Pi, 2 Pi}, {y, -2 Pi, 2 Pi}, ViewPoint → {0, -2, 2},
PlotRange → All, ImageSize → {250}]**

Out[1257]=

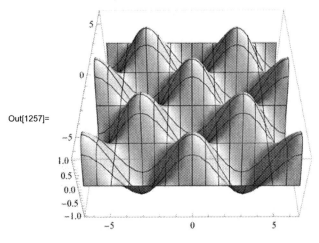

View from in front and down:

In[1258]:= `Plot3D[ f[x, y], {x, -2 Pi, 2 Pi}, {y, -2 Pi, 2 Pi}, ViewPoint → {0, -2, -2},`
`    PlotRange → All, ImageSize → {250}]`

Out[1258]=

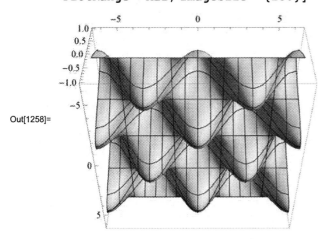

View from directly above:

In[1259]:= `Plot3D[ f[x, y], {x, -2 Pi, 2 Pi}, {y, -2 Pi, 2 Pi}, ViewPoint → Above,`
`    PlotRange → All, Ticks → {Automatic, Automatic, {-1, 0, 1}},`
`    ImageSize → {250}]`

Out[1259]=

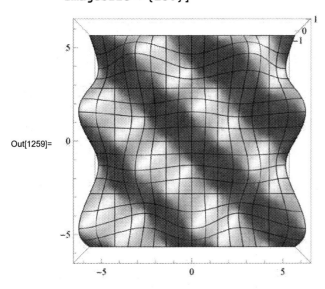

View from the right:

In[1260]:= `Plot3D[ f[x, y], {x, -2 Pi, 2 Pi}, {y, -2 Pi, 2 Pi}, ViewPoint → Right,`
`    PlotRange → All, ImageSize → {250}]`

Out[1260]=

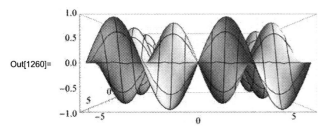

NOTE: As we pointed out earlier, we can also select different viewpoints by clicking on the graph and dragging the mouse around until we get the desired viewpoint.

Mesh, **MeshStyle**, **MeshShading**

The option **Mesh** specifies the type of mesh that should be drawn.

The option **MeshStyle** specifies the style in which a mesh should be drawn.

The option **MeshShading** is an option for specifying a list of colors to be used between mesh divisions.

We illustrate some uses of these options in the example below.

Example 14.5. Plot $f(x, y) = \cos x \sin y$ using various options involving **Mesh**.

Solution:

In[1261]:= **Clear[f]**
f[x_, y_] = Cos[x] Sin[y]

Out[1262]= $\cos[x] \sin[y]$

To plot a graph without a mesh we use the setting **Mesh→None**.

In[1263]:= **Plot3D[f[x, y], {x, -2 Pi, 2 Pi}, {y, -2 Pi, 2 Pi} , Mesh → None,**
ImageSize → {250}]

Out[1263]=

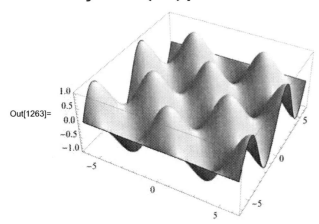

Mesh→n plots a surface with only $n \times n$ meshes.

In[1264]:= `Plot3D[ f[x, y], {x, -2 Pi, 2 Pi}, {y, -2 Pi, 2 Pi} , Mesh → 8 ,`
`ImageSize → {250}]`

Out[1264]=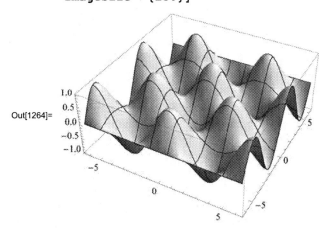

We can choose the color of the mesh using **MeshStyle**.

In[1265]:= `Plot3D[ f[x, y], {x, -2 Pi, 2 Pi}, {y, -2 Pi, 2 Pi} , MeshStyle →`
`{Red, Black}, ImageSize → {250} ]`

Out[1265]=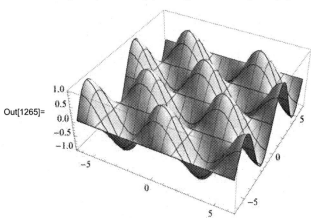

Here is another use of **MeshStyle**:

In[1266]:= `Plot3D[ f[x, y], {x, -2 Pi, 2 Pi}, {y, -2 Pi, 2 Pi} , MeshStyle →`
`{Dashing[0.01], None}, ImageSize → {250} ]`

Out[1266]=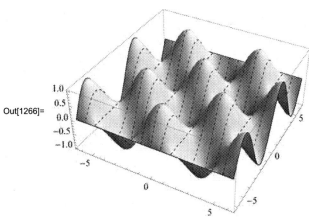

To display a plot with selected colors between meshes we use **MeshShading**:

In[1267]:= `Plot3D[f[x, y], {x, -2 Pi, 2 Pi}, {y, -2 Pi, 2 Pi},`
`   MeshShading → {{Blue, Red, White}, {Purple, Green, Black}}, ImageSize → {250} ]`

Out[1267]=

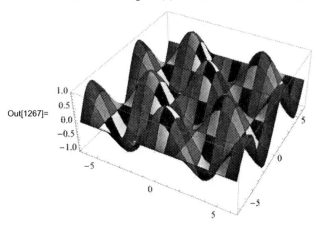

Here is a neat example in *Mathematica 7.0*:

In[1268]:= `Plot3D[ (x^2 - y^2) / (x^2 + y^2)^2, {x, -1.5, 1.5}, {y, -1.5, 1.5},`
`   BoxRatios → Automatic, PlotPoints → 25, MeshFunctions → {#3 &},`
`   MeshStyle → Purple, MeshShading → {None, Green, None, Yellow}, ImageSize → {250}]`

Out[1268]=

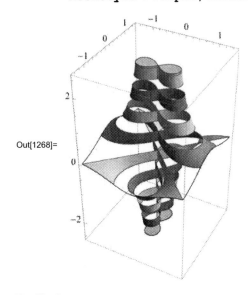

BoxRatios

The option **BoxRatios** specifies the ratio of the lengths of the sides of the box. This is analogous to specifying the **AspectRatio** of a two-dimensional plot. For **Plot3D**, the default setting is **BoxRatios→Automatic.**

Example 14.6. Plot $f(x, y) = e^{1-x^2-y^2}$ using the **BoxRatio** option.

Solution:

In[1269]:= **Clear[f]**

f[x_, y_] = E$^{1-x^2-y^2}$

Out[1270]= $e^{1-x^2-y^2}$

In[1271]:= **Plot3D[f[x, y], {x, -2, 2}, {y, -2, 2}, ImageSize → {250}]**

Out[1271]=

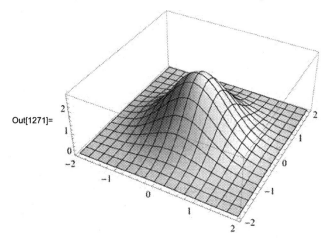

In[1272]:= **Plot3D[f[x, y], {x, -2, 2}, {y, -2, 2}, BoxRatios → {1, 1, 0.62`},**
ImageSize → {250}]

Out[1272]=

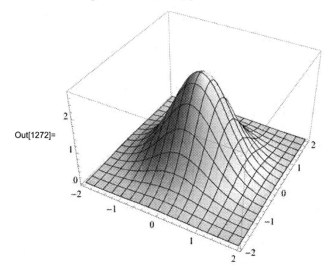

AxesLabel

The option **AxesLabel** is a command used to label the axes in plotting.

Example 14.7. Plot $f(x, y) = \sqrt{9 - x^2 - y^2}$ using the **AxesLabel** option.

Solution:

In[1273]:= **Clear[f]**

f[x_, y_] = $\sqrt{9 - x^2 - y^2}$

Out[1274]= $\sqrt{9 - x^2 - y^2}$

In[1275]:= `Plot3D[f[x, y], {x, -3, 3}, {y, -3, 3}, AxesLabel → {"x ", "y ", "z "},`
`ImageSize → {250}, ImagePadding → {{15, 15}, {15, 15}}]`

Out[1275]=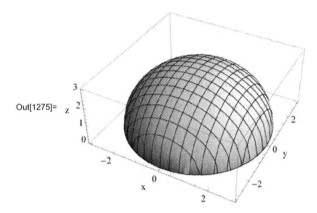

NOTE: To label a graph, use the **PlotLabel** option as shown following:

In[1276]:= `Plot3D[f[x, y], {x, -3, 3}, {y, -3, 3}, AxesLabel → {"x ", "y ", "z "},`
`PlotLabel → "Upper hemisphere", BoxRatios → Automatic, ImageSize → {250},`
`ImagePadding → {{15, 15}, {15, 25}}]`

Out[1276]=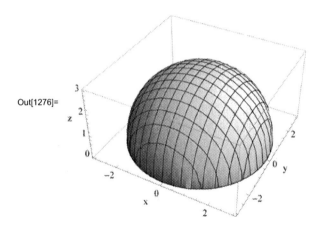

ColorFunction

The option **ColorFunction** specifies a function to apply to the values of the function being plotted to determine the color to use for a particular region on the *xy*-plane. It is an option for **Plot3D**, **ListPlot3D**, **DensityPlot**, and **ContourPlot**. The default setting for **ColorFunction** is **ColorFunction→Automatic**. **ColorFunction→Hue** yields a range of colors.

Example 14.8. Plot $f(x, y) = \sin(x^2 + y^2) + e^{1 - x^2 - y^2}$ in various colors using the **ColorFunction** option.

Solution:

In[1277]:= **Clear[f, x, y]**

f[x_, y_] = Sin[x² + y²] + E^{1-x²-y²}

Out[1278]= $e^{1-x^2-y^2} + \text{Sin}\left[x^2 + y^2\right]$

In[1279]:= **Plot3D[f[x, y], {x, -Pi, Pi}, {y, -Pi, Pi}, ColorFunction → Hue,**
ImageSize → {250}]

Out[1279]=

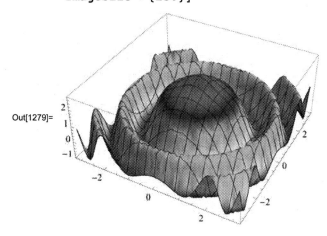

Here are other ways to use **ColorFunction**.

In[1280]:= **Plot3D[f[x, y], {x, -Pi, Pi}, {y, -Pi, Pi}, ColorFunction → "Rainbow",**
ImageSize → {250}]

Out[1280]=

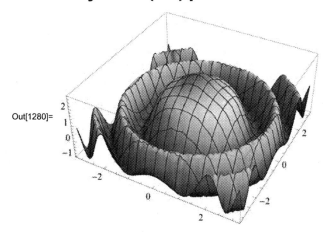

In[1281]:= `Plot3D[f[x, y], {x, -Pi, Pi}, {y, -Pi, Pi}, ColorFunction →`
`    "BlueGreenYellow", ImageSize → {250}]`

Out[1281]=

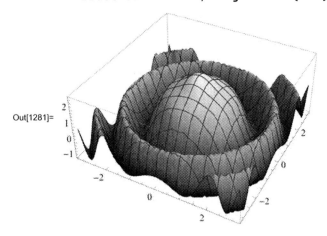

NOTE: We can use **PlotStyle** option to select color for graphs. The plot below uses this option.

In[1282]:= `Plot3D[f[x, y], {x, -Pi, Pi}, {y, -Pi, Pi}, PlotStyle → Yellow,`
`    ImageSize → {250} ]`

Out[1282]=

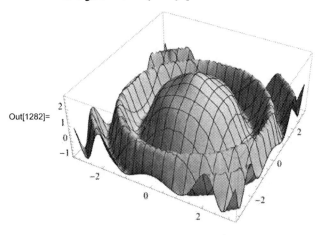

RegionFunction

The option **RegionFunction** specifies the region to include in the plot drawn.

Example 14.9. Plot $f(x, y) = \begin{cases} 10 \sin(3x - y), & \text{if } x^2 + y^2 < 4; \\ x^2 + y^2 - 5, & \text{otherwise} \end{cases}$.

Solution: We will use the command **RegionFunction** to specify the domain $x^2 + y^2 < 4$ as follows. Note that we have used **Show** to display the graphs.

```
In[1283]:= Clear[plot1, plot2]
         plot1 = Plot3D[10 Sin[3 x - y], {x, -4, 4}, {y, -4, 4}, PlotStyle → Blue,
             RegionFunction → Function[{x, y, z}, x^2 + y^2 < 4]];
         plot2 = Plot3D[ x² + y² - 5, {x, -4, 4}, {y, -4, 4}, PlotStyle → Red,
             RegionFunction → Function[{x, y, z}, x^2 + y^2 ≥ 4]];
         Show[plot1, plot2, ImageSize → {250}]
```

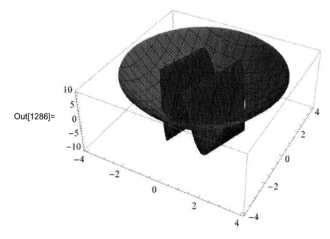

Out[1286]=

If we want to focus on a particular part of a surface defined by a function, we can use the option **RegionFunction**. The following example shows this point.

Example 14.10. Plot the graph of $f(x, y) = x^2 - 3xy - 2y^2$ and show the portion of the surface direclty above the unit circle centered at the origin.

Solution: We will use the option **ViewPoint**.

```
In[1287]:= Clear[plot1, plot2, f, x, y]
         f[x_, y_] = x² - 3 x y - 2 y²
         plot1 = Plot3D[f[x, y], {x, -4, 4}, {y, -4, 4}, PlotStyle → Blue,
             RegionFunction → Function[{x, y, z}, x^2 + y^2 < 1]];
         plot2 = Plot3D[f[x, y] , {x, -4, 4}, {y, -4, 4}, PlotStyle → Red,
             RegionFunction → Function[{x, y, z}, x^2 + y^2 > 1 ]];
         Show[plot1, plot2 , ViewPoint → Front, ImageSize → {250} ]
```

Out[1288]= $x^2 - 3 x y - 2 y^2$

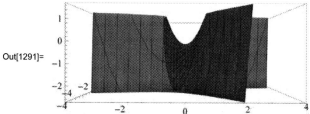

Out[1291]=

■ 14.1.3 Plotting Parametric Surfaces using ParametricPlot3D

ParametricPlot3D is a direct analog of **ParametricPlot**. Depending on the input, **ParametricPlot3D** produces a space curve or a surface. **ParametricPlot3D[{f, g, h}, {t, a, b }]** produces a three-dimensional space curve parametrized by the variable **t**, which runs from **a** to **b**. **ParametricPlot3D[{f, g, h}, {t, a, b },{u, c, d}]** produces a two-dimensional surface parametrized by **t**

and **u**. Options are given to **ParametricPlot3D** the same way as for **Plot3D**. Most of the options are the same.

Example 14.11. Plot the curve that is parametrized by $x = \sin t$, $y = \cos t$ and $z = t/3$ with $0 \le t \le 2\pi$.

Solution:

In[1292]:= `ParametricPlot3D[{Sin[t], Cos[t],` $\frac{t}{3}$ `}, {t, 0, 2 π}, ImageSize → {250},`

`ImagePadding → {{15, 15}, {15, 15}}]`

Out[1292]=

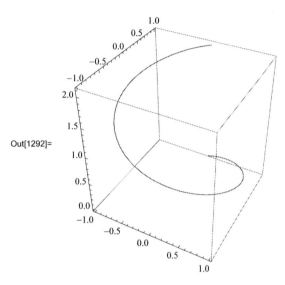

Example 14.12. Plot the surface that is parametrized by $x = u \cos u \, (4 + \cos (u + v))$, $y = u \sin u \, (4 + \cos (u + v))$, and $z = u \sin (u + v)$.

Solution:

In[1293]:= `ParametricPlot3D[{u Cos[u] (4 + Cos[u + v]), u Sin[u] (4 + Cos[u + v]), u Sin[u + v]},`
`{u, 0, 4 π}, {v, 0, 2 π}, ImageSize → {250}]`

Out[1293]=

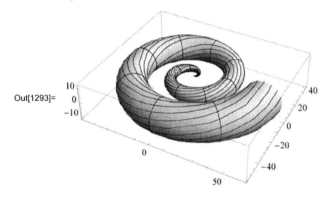

▪ 14.1.4 Plotting Level Surfaces using ContourPlot3D

ContourPlot3D is the command used to plot level surfaces of functions of three variables. Its syntax is **Contour-Plot3D[f,{x,a,b}, {y,c,d},{z,e,f}]**. Most of the Options for **ContourPlot3D** are the same as those of **Plot3D**. Below we will consider the option **Contours** of **ContourPlot3D**.

Example 14.13. Plot level surfaces of $f(x, y, z) = x^2 + y^2 + z^2$.

In[1294]:= `Clear[x, y, z, f]`
`f[x_, y_, z_] = x^2 + y^2 + z^2`
`ContourPlot3D[f[x, y, z], {x, -3, 3}, {y, -3, 3}, {z, -3, 3}, ImageSize → {250}]`

Out[1295]= $x^2 + y^2 + z^2$

Out[1296]=

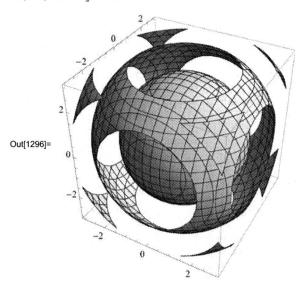

The following displays five (5) equally spaced contour surfaces of f.

In[1297]:= `ContourPlot3D[f[x, y, z], {x, -3, 3}, {y, -3, 3}, {z, -3, 3},`
`Contours → 5, ImageSize → {250}]`

Out[1297]=

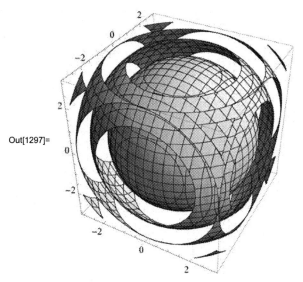

The following displays three level surfaces $f(x, y, z) = c$, where $c = 1, 4, 9$.

In[1298]:= `ContourPlot3D[f[x, y, z], {x, -3, 3}, {y, -3, 3}, {z, -3, 3},`
`Contours → {1, 4, 9}, ImageSize → {250}]`

Out[1298]=

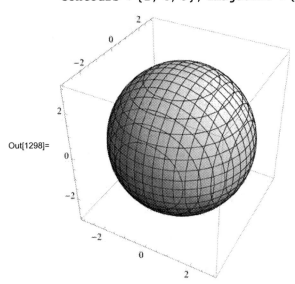

Notice that we only see one sphere. The other two are enclosed in the sphere of radius 3 corresponding to $c = 9$. One way to remedy this is to plot the level surfaces one by one. For this we use the **GraphicsArray** command. First, let us define the level surfaces as function of c:

In[1299]:= `Clear[c, plot]`
`plot[c_] := ContourPlot3D[f[x, y, z], {x, -3, 3}, {y, -3, 3}, {z, -3, 3},`
`Contours → {c}]`

Here are the three level surfaces corresponding to $c = 1, \ 4, \ 9$.

In[1301]:= `Show[GraphicsArray[{plot[1], plot[4], plot[9]}]]`

GraphicsArray::obs : GraphicsArray is obsolete. Switching to GraphicsGrid. ≫

Out[1301]=

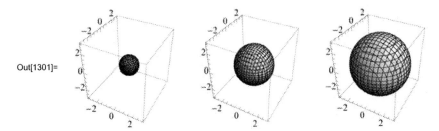

◼ Exercises

In Exercises 1 through 4, plot the level curves and the graphs of the given functions.

1. $f(x, y) = x y^5 - x^5 y$ for $-10 \le x \le 10, -10 \le y \le 10$

2. $f(x, y) = \frac{x^2 + 2 y}{1 + x^2 + y^2}$ for $-10 \le x \le 10, -10 \le y \le 10$

3. $f(x, y) = (\sin y) \, e^{\cos x}$ for $-2 \pi \le x \le 2 \pi, -2 \pi \le y \le 2 \pi$

4. $f(x, y) = \sin(x + \sin(y))$ for $-4 \pi \le x \le 4 \pi, -4 \pi \le y \le 4 \pi$

In Exercises 5 through 7, use at least two nondefault options to plot the given functions.

5. $f(x, y) = \sin(x - 2 y) \, e^{1/(y-x)}$ for $-2 \pi \le x \le 2 \pi, -2 \pi \le y \le 2 \pi$

6. $f(x, y) = 4 - 3 |x| - 2 |y|$ for $-10 \le x \le 10$, $-10 \le y \le 10$

7. $f(x, y) = \tanh^{-1}(x/y)$ for $-5 \le x \le 5$, $-5 \le y \le 5$

8. Plot $f(x, y) = \begin{cases} x^2 + y^2 - 4 & \text{if } x^2 + y^2 < 4 \\ 4 - x^2 + 3 y^2 & \text{otherwise} \end{cases}$

9. Plot the portion of the *helicoid (spiral ramp)* that is defined by:
$x = u \cos v$, $y = u \sin v$, $z = v$ for $0 \le u \le 3$ and $-2\pi \le v \le 2\pi$

10. Use **ContourPlot3D** to plot the level surfaces of the function $f(x, y, z) = 9 - x^2 - y^2 - z^2$.

▪ 14.2 Limits and Continuity

Students should read Section 14.2 of Rogawski's *Calculus* [1] for a detailed discussion of the material presented in this section.

▪ 14.2.1 Limits

If $f(x, y)$ is a function of x and y, and if the domain of f contains a circle around the point (a, b), we say that the limit of f at (a, b) is L if and only if $f(x, y)$ can be arbitrarily close to L for all (x, y) arbitrarily close (a, b).

More precisely, for a given $\epsilon > 0$, there exists a $\delta > 0$ such that for every (x, y) is in the domain of f,

$$0 < \sqrt{(x - a)^2 + (y - b)^2} < \delta \implies |f(x, y) - L| < \epsilon$$

If this is the case, we write

$$\lim_{(x,y) \to (a,b)} f(x, y) = L$$

The **Limit** command of *Mathematica* is restricted to functions of one variable. However, we can use it twice to find the limit of function of two variables provided the limit exists.

Example 14.14. Find $\lim_{(x,y) \to (3,4)} (x^2 + y^2)$.

Solution: We can easliy determine that the limit exists. We can find the limit by evaluating

In[1302]:= **Limit$\left[$Limit$\left[$x^2 + y^2, x $\to$ 3$\right]$, y $\to$ 4$\right]$**

Out[1302]= 25

The plot following confirms this.

In[1303]:= **Clear[plot1, plot2]**
plot1 = Plot3D$\left[x^2 + y^2, \{x, 1, 4\}, \{y, 3, 5\}\right]$;
plot2 = Graphics3D[{Red, PointSize[.025], Point[{3, 4, 25}]}];
Show[plot1, plot2, ImageSize → {250}, ImagePadding → {{15, 15}, {15, 15}}]

Out[1306]=

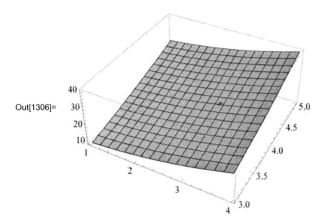

Example 14.15. Find $\lim_{(x,y)\to(4,1)} \frac{3x+y^2}{x-4y}$.

Solution: We will evaluate the limit in two different orders. The limit in which we use limit with x first and then with y is

In[1307]:= **Clear[f, x, y]**

$$f[x\_, y\_] = \frac{3 x + y^2}{x - 4 y}$$

Out[1308]= $\dfrac{3 x + y^2}{x - 4 y}$

The limit in which we use limit with x first and then with y is

In[1309]:= **Limit[Limit[f[x, y], x → 4], y → 1]**

Out[1309]= $-\infty$

The limit in which we use limit with y first and then with x is

In[1310]:= **Limit[Limit[f[x, y], y → 1], x → 4]**

Out[1310]= ∞

Here is the plot of the graph near the point (4, 1). Observe that the graph of the function is in green and the point (4, 1, 0) is in red. For a better comaprison, we have colored the xy-plane light blue. You may need to rotate the graph to see the point (4, 1, 0) on the xy-plane and see how the graph behaves when (x, y) is close to (4, 1).

In[1311]:= `Clear[plot1, plot2]`
`plot1 = Plot3D[{f[x, y], 0}, {x, 3, 5},`
`{y, 0, 2}, PlotStyle → {Green, LightBlue}, PlotPoints → 100];`
`plot2 = Graphics3D[{Red, PointSize[.025], Point[{4, 1, 0}]}];`
`Show[plot1, plot2, ImageSize → {250},`
`ImagePadding → {{15, 15}, {15, 15}}]`

Out[1314]=

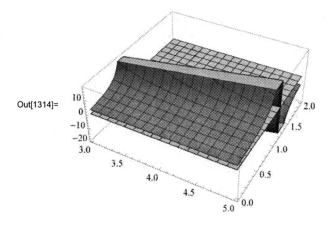

Here is the animation with *x* as the animation parameter.

Important Note: If you are reading the printed version of this publication, then you will not be able to view any of the animations generated from the **Animate** command in this chapter. If you are reading the electronic version of this publication formatted as a *Mathematica* Notebook, then evaluate each **Animate** command to view the corresponding animation. Just click on the arrow button to start the animation. To control the animation just click at various points on the sliding bar or else manually drag the bar.

In[1315]:= `Animate[Plot[f[x, y], {y, 0, 3}, PlotRange → {-20, 20}], {x, 3, 5}]`

Out[1315]=

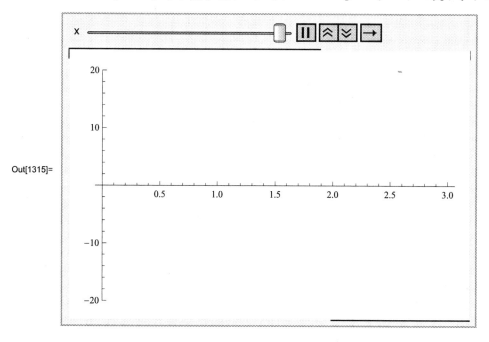

Example 14.16. Find $\lim_{(x,y)\to(0,0)} \frac{\sin x \sin y}{x\,y}$.

Solution: We will evaluate the limit in two different orders.

In[1316]:= `Clear[f, x, y]`

$$f[x\_, y\_] = \frac{Sin[x\,y]}{x\,y}$$

Out[1317]= $\dfrac{Sin[x\,y]}{x\,y}$

In[1318]:= `Limit[Limit[f[x, y], x → 0], y → 0]`

Out[1318]= 1

In[1319]:= `Limit[Limit[f[x, y], y → 0], x → 0]`

Out[1319]= 1

Here is the plot of the graph and the point (0, 0, 1).

In[1320]:= `Clear[plot1, plot2]`
`plot1 = Plot3D[f[x, y], {x, -1, 1}, {y, -1, 1}, PlotStyle → Green];`
`plot2 = Graphics3D[{Red, PointSize[.02], Point[{0, 0, 1}]}];`
`Show[plot1, plot2, ImageSize → {250}]`

Out[1323]=

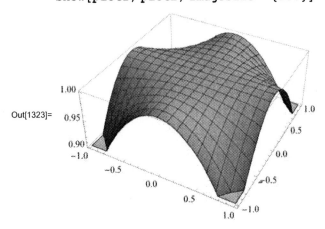

If we rotate this graph to a suitable position, we notice that the limit exists. Here are animations with x and y as animation parameters, respectively.

In[1324]:= **Animate[Plot[f[x, y], {x, -2, 2}, PlotRange → {0, 1}], {y, -2, 2}]**

Out[1324]=

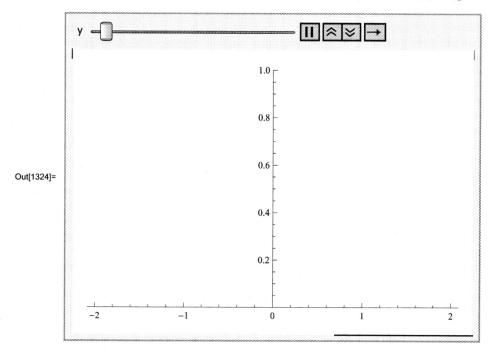

In[1325]:= **Animate[Plot[f[x, y], {y, -2, 2}, PlotRange → {0, 1}], {x, -2, 2}]**

Out[1325]=

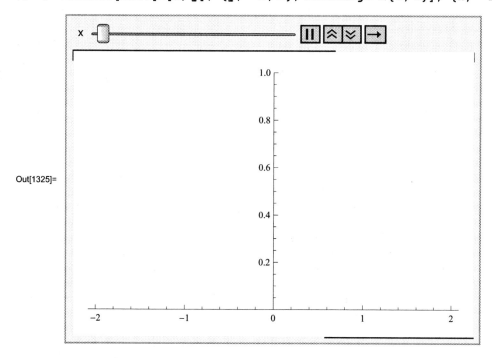

Example 14.17. Find $\lim_{(x,y)\to(0,0)} x \ln y$.

Solution:

In[1326]:= **Clear[f, x, y]**
f[x_, y_] = x Log[y]

Out[1327]= $x \, \text{Log}[y]$

In[1328]:= **Limit[Limit[f[x, y], x → 0], y → 0]**

Out[1328]= 0

In[1329]:= **Limit[Limit[f[x, y], y → 0], x → 0]**

Out[1329]= Indeterminate

In[1330]:= **Clear[plot1, plot2]**
plot1 =
  Plot3D[{f[x, y], 0}, {x, -1, 1}, {y, -1, 1}, PlotStyle → {Green, LightBlue}];
plot2 = Graphics3D[{Red, PointSize[.025], Point[{0, 0, 0}]}];
Show[plot1, plot2, ImageSize → {250},
  ImagePadding → {{15, 15}, {15, 15}}]

Out[1333]=

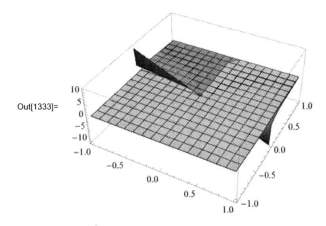

Here is the animation with *x* as the animation parameter.

In[1334]:= **Animate[Plot[f[x, y], {y, -2, 2}, PlotRange → {-10, 10}], {x, -2, 2}]**

Out[1334]=

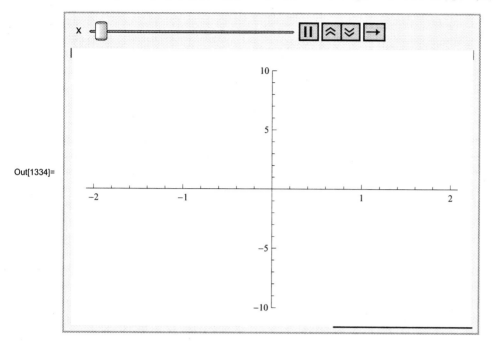

Example 14.18. Consider the function $f(x, y) = \frac{x y^2}{x^2 + y^4}$. Show that $\lim_{(x,y) \to (0,0)} f(x, y)$ does not exist.

Solution:

In[1335]:= **Clear[f, x, y]**

$$f[x\_, y\_] = \frac{x \, y^2}{x^2 + y^4}$$

Out[1336]= $\dfrac{x \, y^2}{x^2 + y^4}$

In[1337]:= **Limit[Limit[f[x, y], x → 0], y → 0]**

Out[1337]= 0

In[1338]:= **Limit[Limit[f[x, y], y → 0], x → 0]**

Out[1338]= 0

In[1339]:= **Limit[Limit[f[x, y], y → m x], x → 0]**

Out[1339]= 0

However, note that the limit along the curve $y = \sqrt{x}$ is

In[1340]:= **Limit[Limit[f[x, y], y → $\sqrt{x}$], x → 0]**

Out[1340]= $\dfrac{1}{2}$

Hence, the limit does not exist. Here is the plot of the function:

In[1341]:= **Plot3D[f[x, y], {x, -1, 1}, {y, -1, 1}, ImageSize → {250}]**

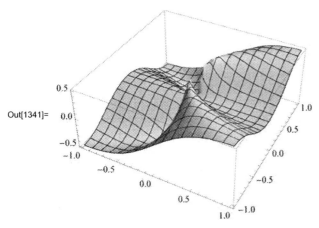

Out[1341]=

■ 14.2.2 Continiuty

Recall that a function f of two variables x and y is continuous at the point (a, b) if and only if $\lim_{(x,y)\to(a,b)} f(x, y) = f(a, b)$.

Example 14.19. Let $f(x, y) = \begin{cases} 1 - x^2 - y^2, & \text{if } x^2 + y^2 < 1 \\ 0, & \text{if } x^2 + y^2 \geq 1 \end{cases}$. Is f continuous?

Solution: Clearly, f is continuous at all points inside and outside the circle of radius 1. To check continuity on the unit circle, we let $x = r \cos t$ and $y = r \sin t$. We then let $r \to 1$.

In[1342]:= **Clear[x, y, r, s, t, f]**

f[x_, y_] = 1 - $\sqrt{x^2 + y^2}$

Out[1343]= $1 - \sqrt{x^2 + y^2}$

In[1344]:= **x = r Cos[t]**

y = r Sin[t]

Out[1344]= r Cos[t]

Out[1345]= r Sin[t]

In[1346]:= **Simplify[f[x, y]]**

Out[1346]= $1 - \sqrt{r^2}$

In[1347]:= **Limit[f[x, y], r → 1]**

Out[1347]= 0

The command below evaluates f on the circle.

In[1348]:= **Simplify[f[x, y] /. r → 1]**

Out[1348]= 0

Thus, the limit and the value of f are equal at all points on the unit circle. Hence, f is continuous everywhere. Here is the graph.

```
In[1349]:= Clear[plot1, plot2]
    plot1 = Plot3D[f[x, y], {x, -5, 5}, {y, -5, 5}, PlotStyle → Red,
        RegionFunction → Function[{x, y, z}, x^2 + y^2 < 1], Mesh → None];
    plot2 = Plot3D[ 0, {x, -5, 5}, {y, -5, 5}, PlotStyle → LightBlue,
        RegionFunction → Function[{x, y, z}, x^2 + y^2 ≥ 1], Mesh → None];
    Show[plot1, plot2, ImageSize → {250}]
```

Out[1352]=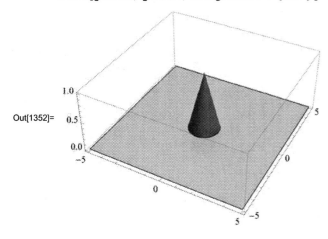

■ Exercises

In Exercises 1 through 4, find the limit, if it exists.

1. $\lim_{(x,y)\to(1,-1)}\left(2x^2y + xy^2\right)$ 2. $\lim_{(x,y)\to(1,1)}\frac{3x^2+y^2}{x^2-y}$

3. $\lim_{(x,y)\to(0,0)}\frac{\tan x \sin y}{xy}$ 4. $\lim_{(x,y)\to(0,0)} \sin x \ln y$

5. Consider the function $f(x, y) = \frac{x^2+y^2}{x^2+y^4}$. Show that $\lim_{(x,y)\to(0,0)} f(x, y)$ does not exist.

6. Let $f(x, y) = \begin{cases} x^2 - y^2, & \text{if } x + y < 0 \\ 2x + y, & \text{if } x + y \ge 0 \end{cases}$.

Is f continuous?

7. Let $f(x, y) = \frac{xy}{x^2+y^2}$. The domain of f is the whole plane without the origin. Is it possible to define $f(0, 0)$ so that f is continuous everywhere? Plot the graph of f to support your conclusions.

8. The domain of $f(x, y) = \frac{xy}{x+y}$ is the whole plane without the line $y = -x$. Is it possible to define $f(0, 0)$ so that f is continuous everywhere? Plot the graph of f to support your conclusions.

■ 14.3 Partial Derivatives

Students should read Section 14.3 of Rogawski's *Calculus* [1] for a detailed discussion of the material presented in this section.

Recall that the *Mathematica* command for the partial derivative of a function **f** with respect to **x** is **D[f, x]**, and **D[f,{x,n}]** gives the **n**th partial derivative of **f** with respect to **x**. The multiple (mixed) partial derivative of **f** with respect to x_1, x_2, x_3, ... is obtained by **D[f, x_1, x_2, x_3, ...]**. We can access this command from **BasicMathInput**. The symbols are $\partial_\square \square$ and $\partial_{\square,\square} \square$.

Example 14.20. Find the first partial derivatives of $x^3 + y^2$ with respect to x and y.

Solution: We give two methods of input.

Method 1: We can type all the inputs and the command as follows:

In[1353]:= `Clear[x, y]`
`D[x^3 + y^2, x]`

Out[1354]= $3 x^2$

In[1355]:= `D[x^3 + y^2, y]`

Out[1355]= $2 y$

Method 2: We can use the **BasicInput** palette to enter the inputs.

In[1356]:= $\partial_x \left(x^3 + y^2\right)$

Out[1356]= $3 x^2$

In[1357]:= $\partial_y \left(x^3 + y^2\right)$

Out[1357]= $2 y$

Example 14.21. Find the four second partial derivatives of $x^3 \sin(y) + e^{xy}$.

Solution: Let $z = x^3 \sin y + e^{xy}$. We again demonstrate two methods of input.

Method 1:

We can find z_{xx} by

In[1358]:= `Clear[x, y]`
`D[x^3 * Sin[y] + E^(x * y), {x, 2}]`

Out[1359]= $e^{xy} y^2 + 6 x \operatorname{Sin}[y]$

We can find z_{yy} by

In[1360]:= `D[x^3 * Sin[y] + E^(x * y), {y, 2}]`

Out[1360]= $e^{xy} x^2 - x^3 \operatorname{Sin}[y]$

We can find z_{xy} by

In[1361]:= `D[x^3 * Sin[y] + E^(x * y), x, y]`

Out[1361]= $e^{xy} + e^{xy} x y + 3 x^2 \operatorname{Cos}[y]$

z_{yx} is given by

In[1362]:= `D[x^3 * Sin[y] + E^(x * y), y, x]`

Out[1362]= $e^{xy} + e^{xy} x y + 3 x^2 \operatorname{Cos}[y]$

NOTE: Clairaut's Theorem states that if the mixed partial derivatives f_{xy} and f_{yx} are continuous at a point (x, y), then they are equal: $f_{xy} = f_{yx}$. The last two outputs confirm Clairaut's Theorem for this particular example.

Method 2: Here is the input using the palette symbol $\partial_{\square,\square}\square$:

In[1363]:= **Clear[x, y]**
$$\partial_{x,x}\left(x^3 * Sin[y] + e^{x*y}\right)$$
$$\partial_{y,y}\left(x^3 * Sin[y] + e^{x*y}\right)$$
$$\partial_{x,y}\left(x^3 * Sin[y] + e^{x*y}\right)$$
$$\partial_{y,x}\left(x^3 * Sin[y] + e^{x*y}\right)$$

Out[1364]= $e^{x\,y}\,y^2 + 6\,x\,Sin[y]$

Out[1365]= $e^{x\,y}\,x^2 - x^3\,Sin[y]$

Out[1366]= $e^{x\,y} + e^{x\,y}\,x\,y + 3\,x^2\,Cos[y]$

Out[1367]= $e^{x\,y} + e^{x\,y}\,x\,y + 3\,x^2\,Cos[y]$

Example 14.22. Evaluate the first partial derivatives of $x\,y + y\,z^2 + x\,z$ at $(-1, 2, 3)$.

Solution: Recall that **Expr** /. $\{x_1 \rightarrow a_1, x_2 \rightarrow a_2, x_3 \rightarrow a_3, ... \}$ is the command for substituting x_1 by a_1, x_2 by a_2, x_3 by a_3, ... , in **Expr**.

In[1368]:= **Clear[x,y,z]**
D[x*y + y*z^2 + x*z,x]/.{x-> -1, y->2, z->3}

Out[1369]= 5

In[1370]:= **D[x * y + y * z^2 + x * z, y] /. {x -> -1, y -> 2, z -> 3}**

Out[1370]= 8

In[1371]:= **D[x * y + y * z^2 + x * z, z] /. {x -> -1, y -> 2, z -> 3}**

Out[1371]= 11

Example 14.23. Let $f(x, y, z) = y\,e^x + x\,e^{-y}\ln z$. Find $f_{xxx}, f_{xyz}, f_{xzz}, f_{zxz}$, and f_{zzx}.

Solution: First, we define $f(x, y, z)$ in *Mathematica*. We can use the $\partial_{\square,\square}\square$ notation. Since the palette gives only two boxes for the variables, we need to add one more box. This can be done by using **CTRL +, (comma)**, that is, hold the CONTROL key and press the COMMA button. Note also that the command **D[f[x,y,z],x,y,z]** gives f_{xyz}. We demonstrate both methods.

In[1372]:= **Clear[x, y, z, f]**
$$f[x\_, y\_, z\_] := y * e^x + x * Log[z] * e^{-y}$$

In[1374]:= $\partial_{x,x,x}$ **f[x, y, z]**

Out[1374]= $e^x\,y$

In[1375]:= $\partial_{x,y,z}$ **f[x, y, z]**

Out[1375]= $-\dfrac{e^{-y}}{z}$

In[1376]:= $\partial_{x,z,z}$ **f[x, y, z]**

Out[1376]= $-\dfrac{e^{-y}}{z^2}$

In[1377]:= **D[f[x, y, z], z, x, z]**

Out[1377]= $-\dfrac{e^{-y}}{z^2}$

In[1378]:= **D[f[x, y, z], z, z, x]**

Out[1378]= $-\dfrac{e^{-y}}{z^2}$

Example 14.24. Let $f(x, y) = x y \frac{x^2-y^2}{x^2+y^2}$ if $(x, y) \neq (0, 0)$ and $f(0, 0) = 0$.

a) Find $f_x(x, y)$ and $f_y(x, y)$ for $(x, y) \neq (0, 0)$.

b) Use the limit definition to find $f_x(0, 0)$ and $f_y(0, 0)$.

c) Find $f_{x y}(x, y)$ and $f_{y x}(x, y)$ for $(x, y) \neq (0, 0)$.

d) Use the limit definition to find $f_{x y}(0, 0)$ and $f_{y x}(0, 0)$.

Solution: We will first define f using the **If** command.

In[1379]:= **Clear[x, y, f, fx, fy, fxy, fyx]**

$$f[x\_, y\_] = If\left[\{x, y\} \neq \{0, 0\}, \; x\,y\,\frac{x^2 - y^2}{x^2 + y^2}, \; 0\right]$$

Out[1380]= $If\left[\{x, y\} \neq \{0, 0\}, \; \dfrac{x\,y\,(x^2 - y^2)}{x^2 + y^2}, \; 0\right]$

a) Let **fx** and **fy** denote the partial derivatives with respect to x and y, respectively. Then

In[1381]:= **fx[x_, y_] = D[f[x, y], x]**
fy[x_, y_] = D[f[x, y], y]

Out[1381]= $If\left[\{x, y\} \neq \{0, 0\}, \; \left(-\dfrac{2\,x\,(x^2 - y^2)}{(x^2 + y^2)^2} + \dfrac{2\,x}{x^2 + y^2}\right)(x\,y) + \dfrac{y\,(x^2 - y^2)}{x^2 + y^2}, \; 0\right]$

Out[1382]= $If\left[\{x, y\} \neq \{0, 0\}, \; \left(-\dfrac{2\,y\,(x^2 - y^2)}{(x^2 + y^2)^2} - \dfrac{2\,y}{x^2 + y^2}\right)(x\,y) + \dfrac{x\,(x^2 - y^2)}{x^2 + y^2}, \; 0\right]$

If we use the **FullSimplify** command to simplify the preceding output, we get

In[1383]:= **FullSimplify[fx[x, y]]**
FullSimplify[fy[x, y]]

Out[1383]= $\begin{cases} \dfrac{y\,(x^4 + 4\,x^2\,y^2 - y^4)}{(x^2 + y^2)^2} & x \neq 0 \;||\; y \neq 0 \\ 0 & \text{True} \end{cases}$

Out[1384]= $\begin{cases} \dfrac{x\,(x^4 - 4\,x^2\,y^2 - y^4)}{(x^2 + y^2)^2} & x \neq 0 \;||\; y \neq 0 \\ 0 & \text{True} \end{cases}$

Thus, $f_x(x, y) = \dfrac{y(x^4 + 4\,x^3\,y^2 - y^4)}{(x^2+y^2)^2}$ and $f_y(x, y) = \dfrac{x(x^4 - 4\,x^2\,y^2 - y^4)}{(x^2+y^2)^2}$ if $(x, y) \neq (0, 0)$.

b) We use the limit definition $f_x(0, 0) = \lim_{h \to 0} \frac{f(0+h,0)-f(0,0)}{h}$ and $f_y(0, 0) = \lim_{k \to 0} \frac{f(0,0+k)-f(0,0)}{k}$ to find the partial derivatives at $(0, 0)$.

In[1385]:= **Clear[h, k]**

$$\text{\textbf{Limit}\left[\frac{\textbf{f[0+h, 0] - f[0, 0]}}{\textbf{h}}, \textbf{h} \rightarrow \textbf{0}\right]}$$

Out[1386]= 0

In[1387]:= **$\text{Limit}\left[\frac{\textbf{f[0, 0+k] - f[0, 0]}}{\textbf{k}}, \textbf{k} \rightarrow \textbf{0}\right]$**

Out[1387]= 0

Hence, $f_x(0, 0) = 0$ and $f_y(0, 0) = 0$.

c) To find the mixed second partial derivatives, we use **fx** and **fy** from the outputs in part a). Note that the **FullSimplify** command is used to to get a simplified form of the mixed partial derivatives.

In[1388]:= **fxy[x_, y_] = FullSimplify[D[fx[x, y], y]]**
fyx[x_, y_] = FullSimplify[D[fy[x, y], x]]

Out[1388]= $\begin{cases} \frac{(x-y)\ (x+y)\ (x^4+10\ x^2\ y^2+y^4)}{(x^2+y^2)^3} & x \neq 0\ ||\ y \neq 0 \\ 0 & \text{True} \end{cases}$

Out[1389]= $\begin{cases} \frac{(x-y)\ (x+y)\ (x^4+10\ x^2\ y^2+y^4)}{(x^2+y^2)^3} & x \neq 0\ ||\ y \neq 0 \\ 0 & \text{True} \end{cases}$

Thus, $f_{xy} = \frac{(x-y)(x+y)\left(x^4+10\,x^2\,y^2+y^4\right)}{\left(x^2+y^2\right)^3}$ and $f_{yx} = \frac{(x-y)(x+y)\left(x^4+10\,x^2\,y^2+y^4\right)}{\left(x^2+y^2\right)^3}$ for $(x, y) \neq (0, 0)$. Note that these two functions are equal for $(x, y) \neq (0, 0)$ in conformity with Clairaut's Theorem, since both are continuous when $(x, y) \neq (0, 0)$.

d) We use the limit definition of a partial derivative to compute $f_{xy}(0, 0)$ and $f_{yx}(0, 0)$. Recall that we have defined f_x as **fx[x,y]** and f_y as **fy[x,y]**.

Then $f_{xy}(0, 0)$ is given by

In[1390]:= **$\text{Limit}\left[\frac{\textbf{fx[0, 0+k] - fx[0, 0]}}{\textbf{k}}, \textbf{k} \rightarrow \textbf{0}\right]$**

Out[1390]= -1

and $f_{yx}(0, 0)$ is given by

In[1391]:= **$\text{Limit}\left[\frac{\textbf{fy[0+h, 0] - fy[0, 0]}}{\textbf{h}}, \textbf{h} \rightarrow \textbf{0}\right]$**

Out[1391]= 1

Thus, $f_{xy}(0, 0) = -1$ and $f_{yx}(0, 0) = 1$. Note that this implies that the mixed partial derivatives are not continuous at $(x, y) = (0, 0)$. To see this graphically, first consider the following graph of f, which confirms that f has partial derivatives everywhere.

In[1392]:= `Plot3D[f[x, y], {x, -3, 3}, {y, -3, 3}, ImageSize → {250}]`

Out[1392]=

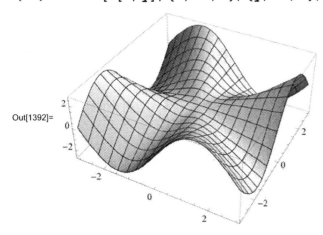

Here are the graphs of f_x and f_y, which now show why the second mixed partials at the origin are not equal.

In[1393]:= `Clear[plot1, plot2]`

`plot1 = Plot3D[fx[x, y], {x, -3, 3}, {y, -3, 3},`
`    PlotStyle → Red, AxesLabel → {"Graph of z=fx", None, None}] ;`

`plot2 = Plot3D[fy[x, y], {x, -3, 3}, {y, -3, 3}, PlotStyle → Blue,`
`    AxesLabel → {"Graph of z=fy", None, None}] ;`

`Show[GraphicsArray[{plot1, plot2}], ImageSize → {420}]`

GraphicsArray::obs : GraphicsArray is obsolete. Switching to GraphicsGrid. ≫

Out[1396]=

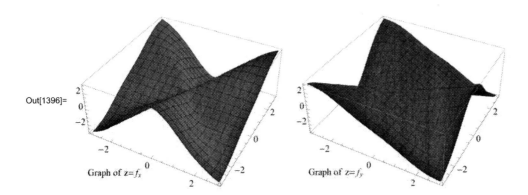

In addition, the graphs of f_{xy} and f_{yx} show the mixed partials are not continuous at the origin. This is the main reason why the inequalities of the mixed partials at the origin does not contradict Clairaut's Theorem.

```
In[1397]:= Clear[plot1, plot2]
        plot1 = Plot3D[fxy[x, y], {x, -3, 3}, {y, -3, 3},
            PlotStyle → Red, AxesLabel → {"Graph of z=fxy", None, None}];
        plot2 = Plot3D[fyx[x, y], {x, -3, 3}, {y, -3, 3}, PlotStyle → Blue,
            AxesLabel → {"Graph of z=fyx", None, None}];
        Show[GraphicsArray[{plot1, plot2}], ImageSize → {420}]
```

GraphicsArray::obs : GraphicsArray is obsolete. Switching to GraphicsGrid. ≫

Out[1400]=

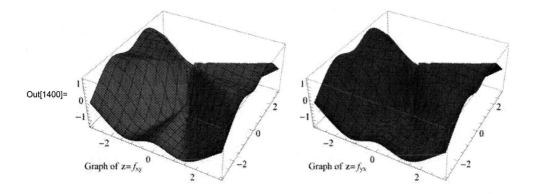

■ Exercises

1. Let $f(x, y) = \frac{(x-y)^2}{x^2+y^2}$. Find:

a. $f_x(1,0)$ b. $f_y(1, 0)$ c. f_{xy} d. f_{yx} e. f_{xxy}

2. Find the first partial derivatives of $z = x^3 y^2$ with respect to x and y.

3. Find the four second partial derivatives of $x^2 \cos(y) + \tan(x e^y)$.

4. Evaluate the first partial derivatives of $f(x, y, z) = e^{-z} xy + yz^2 + xz$ at $(-1, 2, 3)$.

5. Let $f(x, y, z) = \frac{x^4 y^3}{z^2+\sin x}$. Find $f_{xxx}, f_{xyz}, f_{xzz}, f_{zxz}$, and f_{zzx}.

6. Let $f(x, y) = \frac{x y^2}{x^2+y^4}$ if $(x, y) \neq (0, 0)$ and $f(0, 0) = 0$.

a. Find $f_x(x, y)$ and $f_y(x, y)$ for $(x, y) \neq (0, 0)$.

b. Use the limit definition to find $f_x(0, 0)$ and $f_y(0, 0)$.

c. Find $f_{xy}(x, y)$ and $f_{yx}(x, y)$ for $(x, y) \neq (0, 0)$.

d. Use the limit definition to find $f_{xy}(0, 0)$ and $f_{yx}(0, 0)$.

■ 14.4 Tangent Planes

Students should read Section 14.4 of Rogawski's *Calculus* [1] for a detailed discussion of the material presented in this section.

Let $z = f(x, y)$ be a function of two variables. The equation of the *tangent plane* at the point $(a, b, f(a, b))$ is given by

$$z = f_x(a, b) (x - a) + f_y(a, b) (y - b) + f(a, b)$$

Example 14.25. Let $f(x, y) = x^2 + y^2$.

a) Find the equation of the tangent plane to the graph of f at the point $(2, 1, 3)$.

b) Plot the graph of f and its tangent plane at $(2, 1, 3)$.

Solution: Here, $a = 2, b = 1$.

a)

In[1401]:= **Clear[f, x, y, z]**
  f[x_, y_] = x^2 + y^2

Out[1402]= $x^2 + y^2$

Thus, the equation the of the tangent plane is

In[1403]:= **A = ∂_x f[x, y] /. {x → 2, y → 1};**
  B = ∂_y f[x, y] /. {x → 2, y → 1};
  z = A (x - 2) + B (y - 1) + f[2, 1];
  Simplify[z]

Out[1406]= $-5 + 4 x + 2 y$

b) Here is a plot of the graph of f:

In[1407]:= **plot1 = Plot3D[{f[x, y], z}, {x, -10, 10}, {y, -10, 10}, PlotStyle → {Blue, Green}];**
  plot2 = ListPointPlot3D[{ {2, 1, 3}}, PlotStyle → {Red, PointSize[Large]}];
  Show[plot1, plot2, ImageSize → {250}, ImagePadding → {{15, 15}, {15, 15}}]

Out[1409]=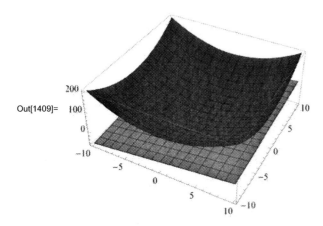

Example 14.26. Let $f(x, y) = x^2 y - 6 x y^2 + 3 y$. Find the points where the tangent plane to the graph of f is parallel to the xy-plane.

Solution: For the tangent plane to be parallel to the xy-plane, we must have $f_x = 0$ and $f_y = 0$.

In[1410]:= **Clear[f, x, y]**
  f[x_, y_] = x^2 y - 6 x y^2 + 3 y

Out[1411]= $3 y + x^2 y - 6 x y^2$

A tangent plane is parallel to the *xy*-plane at

In[1412]:= **Solve[{ D[f[x, y], x] == 0, D[f[x, y], y] == 0}]**

Out[1412]= $\left\{\left\{y \to -\frac{1}{3},\ x \to -1\right\},\ \left\{y \to 0,\ x \to -i\ \sqrt{3}\right\},\ \left\{y \to 0,\ x \to i\ \sqrt{3}\right\},\ \left\{y \to \frac{1}{3},\ x \to 1\right\}\right\}$

Rotate the following graph to see the points of tangencies.

In[1413]:= **Plot3D[{f[x, y], f[-1, -1 / 3], f[1, 1 / 3]}, {x, -1, 1},**
    {y, -1, 1}, PlotStyle → {LightBlue, Green, Red}, PlotRange → All,
    ImageSize → {250}, ImagePadding → {{15, 15}, {15, 15}}]

Out[1413]=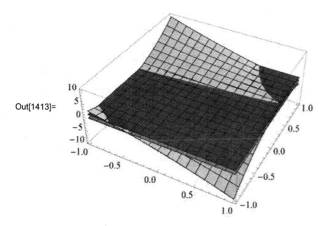

■ Exercises

1. Let $f(x, y) = x^3\, y + x\, y^2 - 3\, x + 4$.
a) Find a set of parametric equations of the normal line and an equation of the tangent plane to the surface at the point (1, 2).
b) Graph the surface, the normal line, and the tangent plane found in a).

2. Let $f(x,\ y) = x^2 + y^2$.
a. Find the equation of the tangent plane to the graph of f at the point (2, 1, 5).
b. Plot the graph of f and its tangent plane at (2, 1, 5).

3. Let $f(x,\ y) = e^{-y/x}$.
a. Find the equation of the tangent plane to the graph of f at the point (1, 0, 1).
b. Plot the graph of f and its tangent plane at (1, 0, 1).

4. Let $f(x,\ y) = \cos(x\,y)$. Find the points where the tangent plane to the graph of f is parallel to the *xy*-plane.

■ 14.5 Gradient and Directional Derivatives

Students should read Section 14.5 of Rogawski's *Calculus* [1] for a detailed discussion of the material presented in this section.

Recall that the notation for a vector such as $\mathbf{u} = 2\,\mathbf{i} + 5\,\mathbf{j} - 6\,\mathbf{k}$ in *Mathematica* is {2,5,-6}. The command for the *dot product* of two vectors $\mathbf{u}$ and $\mathbf{v}$ is obtained by typing **u.v**.

The *gradient* of f, denoted by ∇f, at (a, b) can be obtained by evaluating $\nabla f(a, b) = \langle \partial_x f(a, b),\ \partial_y f(a, b) \rangle$.

The *directional derivative* of f at (a, b) *in the direction of a unit vector* **u** is given by $D_{\mathbf{u}} f = \nabla f(a, b) \cdot \mathbf{u}$.

Example 14.27. Find the gradient and directional derivative of $f(x, y) = x^2 \sin 2 y$ at the point $\left(1, \frac{\pi}{2}, 0\right)$ in the direction of $\mathbf{v} = \left\langle \frac{3}{5}, -\frac{4}{5} \right\rangle$.

Solution:

In[1414]:= `Clear[f, v]`
`f[x_, y_] := x`^{2}` * Sin[2 y]`
$$v = \left\{ \frac{3}{5}, \frac{-4}{5} \right\}$$

Out[1416]= $\left\{ \frac{3}{5}, -\frac{4}{5} \right\}$

The gradient of f at $\left(1, \frac{\pi}{2}\right)$ is

In[1417]:= $\nabla f = \left\{ \partial_x f[x, y], \partial_y f[x, y] \right\} /. \left\{ x \to 1, y \to \frac{\pi}{2} \right\}$

Out[1417]= $\{0, -2\}$

Since **v** is a unit vector, the directional derivative is given by

In[1418]:= `direcderiv = v.`∇`f`

Out[1418]= $\frac{8}{5}$

Example 14.28. Find the gradient and directional derivative of $f(x, y, z) = x y + y z + x z$ at the point $(1, 1, 1)$ in the direction of $\mathbf{v} = 2\,\mathbf{i} + \mathbf{j} - \mathbf{k}$.

Solution:

In[1419]:= `Clear[x, y, z]`
`w = x * y + y * z + x * z`
`v = {2, 1, -1}`

Out[1420]= $x\,y + x\,z + y\,z$

Out[1421]= $\{2, 1, -1\}$

We normalize **v**:

In[1422]:= `unitvector = v / Norm[v]`

Out[1422]= $\left\{ \sqrt{\frac{2}{3}}, \frac{1}{\sqrt{6}}, -\frac{1}{\sqrt{6}} \right\}$

The gradient of $w = f(x, y, z)$ at $(1, 1, 1)$ is

In[1423]:= ∇w `= {D[w, x], D[w, y], D[w, z]} /. {x -> 1, y -> 1, z -> 1}`

Out[1423]= $\{2, 2, 2\}$

Hence, the directional derivative is given by

In[1424]:= **direcderiv = unitvector.∇w**

Out[1424]= $2\sqrt{\dfrac{2}{3}}$

Example 14.29. Plot the gradient vector field and the level curves of the function $f(x, y) = x^2 \sin 2\, y$.

Solution:

In[1425]:= **Clear[f, fx, fy, x, y]**
f[x_, y_] = x² - 3 x y + y - y²
fx = D[f[x, y], x]
fy = D[f[x, y], y]

Out[1426]= $x^2 + y - 3\,x\,y - y^2$

Out[1427]= $2\,x - 3\,y$

Out[1428]= $1 - 3\,x - 2\,y$

Thus, the gradient vector field is $\nabla f(x, y) = \langle\, 2\,x - 3\,y,\ 1 - 3\,x - 2\,y\,\rangle$. To plot this vector field, we need to download the package **VectorFieldPlots**, which is done by evaluating

In[1429]:= **Needs["VectorFieldPlots`"]**

General::obspkg :

VectorFieldPlots` is now obsolete. The legacy version being loaded may conflict with current Mathematica functionality. See the Compatibility Guide for updating information. ≫

Here is a plot of some level curves and the gradient field.

In[1430]:= **Clear[plot1, plot2]**
plot1 = ContourPlot[f[x, y], {x, -5, 5}, {y, -4, 4},
**   Axes → True, Frame → False, Contours → 15, ColorFunction → Hue] ;**
plot2 = VectorFieldPlot[{fx, fy}, {x, -5, 5}, {y, -4, 4},
**   Axes → True, Frame → False] ;**
Show[plot1, plot2, ImageSize → {250}]

Out[1433]=

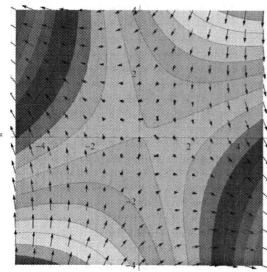

Example 14.30. Let the temperature T at a point (x, y) on a metal plate be given by $T(x, y) = \frac{x}{x^2+y^2}$.

a) Plot the graph of the temperature.
b) Find the rate of change of temperature at (3, 4), in the direction of $\mathbf{v} = \mathbf{i} - 2\,\mathbf{j}$.
c) Find the unit vector in the direction of which the temperature increases most rapidly at (3, 4).
d) Find the maximum rate of increase in the temperature at (3, 4).

Solution:

a) Here is the graph of T.

In[1434]:= **T[x_, y_] = $\dfrac{\mathbf{x}}{\mathbf{x}^2 + \mathbf{y}^2}$**

Out[1434]= $\dfrac{x}{x^2 + y^2}$

In[1435]:= **graphofT =**
  Plot3D[T[x, y], {x, -5, 5}, {y, -5, 5}, BoxRatios → {1, 1, 1}, ImageSize → Small]

Out[1435]=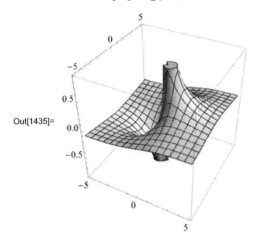

b) Let $\mathbf{u} = \frac{\mathbf{v}}{\|\mathbf{v}\|}$. Then $\mathbf{u}$ is a unit vector and the rate of change in temperature at (3, 4) in the direction of $\mathbf{v}$ is given by $D_{\mathbf{u}}\,T(3, 4) = \nabla f(3, 4) \cdot \mathbf{u}$.

In[1436]:= **∇T = {D[T[x, y], x], D[T[x, y], y]}**
  v = {1, -2}
  u = $\dfrac{\mathbf{v}}{\sqrt{\mathbf{v}.\mathbf{v}}}$
  u.∇T /. {x -> 3, y -> 4} // N

Out[1436]= $\left\{-\dfrac{2\,x^2}{\left(x^2 + y^2\right)^2} + \dfrac{1}{x^2 + y^2},\ -\dfrac{2\,x\,y}{\left(x^2 + y^2\right)^2}\right\}$

Out[1437]= $\{1, -2\}$

Out[1438]= $\left\{\dfrac{1}{\sqrt{5}},\ -\dfrac{2}{\sqrt{5}}\right\}$

Out[1439]= 0.0393548

Thus, the rate of change at (3, 4) in the direction $\mathbf{v}$ is 0.0393548. NOTE: The command //N in the last line of the previous input converts the output to decimal form.

c) The unit vector in the direction of which the temperature increases most rapidly at (3, 4) is given by

In[1440]:= $\dfrac{\nabla T}{Norm[\nabla T]}$ /. {x -> 3, y -> 4}

Out[1440]= $\left\{\dfrac{7}{25}, -\dfrac{24}{25}\right\}$

d) The maximum rate of increase in the temperature at (3,4) is the norm of the gradient at this point. This can be obtained by:

In[1441]:= **Norm[∇ T] /. {x -> 3, y -> 4}**

Out[1441]= $\dfrac{1}{25}$

■ **Exercises**

1. Find the gradient and directional derivative of $f(x, y) = \sin^{-1}(x\,y)$ at the point $\left(1, 1, \frac{\pi}{2}\right)$ in the direction of $\mathbf{v} = \langle 1, -1\rangle$.

2. Let $T(x, y) = e^{xy - y^2}$.
a. Find $\nabla T(x, y)$.
b. Find the directional derivative of $T(x, y)$ at the point (3, 5) in the dierection of $\mathbf{u} = 1/2\,\mathbf{i} + \sqrt{3}/2\,\mathbf{j}$.
c. Find the direction of greatest increase in T from the point (3, 5).

3. Plot the gradient vector field and the level curves of the function a $f(x, y) = \cos x \sin^2 y$.

4. Find the gradient and directional derivative of $f(x, y, z) = x\,y\,e^{yz} + \sin(xz)$ at the point (1, 1, 0) in the direction of $\mathbf{v} = \mathbf{i} - \mathbf{j} - \mathbf{k}$.

■ 14.6 The Chain Rule

Students should read Section 14.6 of Rogawski's *Calculus* [1] for a detailed discussion of the material presented in this section.

Example 14.31. Let $x = t^2 + s$, $y = t + s^2$ and $z = x \sin y$. Find the first partial derivatives of z with respect to s and t.

Solution:

In[1442]:= **Clear[x, y, z, s, t]**
x = t^2 + s
y = t + s^2
z = x Sin[y]

Out[1443]= $s + t^2$

Out[1444]= $s^2 + t$

Out[1445]= $\left(s + t^2\right) Sin\left[s^2 + t\right]$

In[1446]:= **D[z, s]**

Out[1446]= $2 s \left(s + t^2\right) Cos\left[s^2 + t\right] + Sin\left[s^2 + t\right]$

In[1447]:= **D[z, t]**

Out[1447]= $\left(s + t^2\right) \text{Cos}\left[s^2 + t\right] + 2 \text{ t Sin}\left[s^2 + t\right]$

Example 14.32. Find the partial derivatives of z with respect to x and y assuming that the equation $x^2 z - y z^2 = x y$ defines z as a function of x and y.

Solution:

In[1448]:= **Clear[x, y, z, r, t, s]**
eq = x² z[x, y] - y z[x, y]² == x y

Solve[D[eq, x], D[z[x, y], x]]
Solve[D[eq, y], D[z[x, y], y]]

Out[1449]= $x^2 z[x, y] - y z[x, y]^2 == x y$

Out[1450]= $\left\{\left\{z^{(1,0)}[x, y] \to \dfrac{-y + 2 x z[x, y]}{-x^2 + 2 y z[x, y]}\right\}\right\}$

Out[1451]= $\left\{\left\{z^{(0,1)}[x, y] \to \dfrac{x + z[x, y]^2}{x^2 - 2 y z[x, y]}\right\}\right\}$

Example 14.33. Let $f(x, y, z) = F(r)$, where $r = \sqrt{x^2 + y^2 + z^2}$ and F is a twice differentiable function of one variable.
a) Show that $\nabla f = F'(r) \frac{1}{r} (x \mathbf{i} + y \mathbf{j} + z \mathbf{k})$.
b) Find the Laplacian of f.

Solution:
a)

In[1452]:= **Clear[x, y, z, r, f, F]**
f[x_, y_, z_] = F[r]

r = $\sqrt{x^2 + y^2 + z^2}$

Out[1453]= $F[r]$

Out[1454]= $\sqrt{x^2 + y^2 + z^2}$

Here is the gradient of f:

In[1455]:= **gradf = {D[f[x, y, z], x], D[f[x, y, z], y], D[f[x, y, z], z]}**

Out[1455]= $\left\{\dfrac{x F'\left[\sqrt{x^2 + y^2 + z^2}\right]}{\sqrt{x^2 + y^2 + z^2}}, \dfrac{y F'\left[\sqrt{x^2 + y^2 + z^2}\right]}{\sqrt{x^2 + y^2 + z^2}}, \dfrac{z F'\left[\sqrt{x^2 + y^2 + z^2}\right]}{\sqrt{x^2 + y^2 + z^2}}\right\}$

With $r = \sqrt{x^2 + y^2 + z^2}$, the preceding output becomes

$$\nabla f(x, y, z) = \left\langle \tfrac{x F'(r)}{r}, \tfrac{y F'(r)}{r}, \tfrac{z F'(r)}{r} \right\rangle = F'(r) \tfrac{1}{r} \langle x, y, z \rangle$$

which proves part a).

b) Recall that the Laplacian of f, denoted by Δf, is defined by $\Delta f = f_{xx} + f_{yy} + f_{zz}$.

In[1456]:= **D[f[x, y, z], {x, 2}] + D[f[x, y, z], {y, 2}] + D[f[x, y, z], {z, 2}]**

Out[1456]= $-\dfrac{x^2\,F'\left[\sqrt{x^2+y^2+z^2}\,\right]}{\left(x^2+y^2+z^2\right)^{3/2}} - \dfrac{y^2\,F'\left[\sqrt{x^2+y^2+z^2}\,\right]}{\left(x^2+y^2+z^2\right)^{3/2}} - \dfrac{z^2\,F'\left[\sqrt{x^2+y^2+z^2}\,\right]}{\left(x^2+y^2+z^2\right)^{3/2}} +$

$\dfrac{3\,F'\left[\sqrt{x^2+y^2+z^2}\,\right]}{\sqrt{x^2+y^2+z^2}} + \dfrac{x^2\,F''\left[\sqrt{x^2+y^2+z^2}\,\right]}{x^2+y^2+z^2} + \dfrac{y^2\,F''\left[\sqrt{x^2+y^2+z^2}\,\right]}{x^2+y^2+z^2} + \dfrac{z^2\,F''\left[\sqrt{x^2+y^2+z^2}\,\right]}{x^2+y^2+z^2}$

We simplify this to get

In[1457]:= **Simplify[%]**

Out[1457]= $\dfrac{2\,F'\left[\sqrt{x^2+y^2+z^2}\,\right]}{\sqrt{x^2+y^2+z^2}} + F''\left[\sqrt{x^2+y^2+z^2}\,\right]$

which is the same as $\frac{2}{r}\,F'[r] + F''[r]$.

■ **Exercises**

1. Let $x = u^2 + \sin v$, $y = u\,e^{v/u}$, and $z = y^3 \ln x$. Find the first partial derivatives of z with respect to u and v.

2. Find the partial derivatives of z with respect to x and y assuming that the equation $x^2 z - y z^2 = x y$ defines z as a function of x and y.

3. Find an equation of the tangent plane to the surface $x z + 2 x^2 y + y^2 z^3 = 11$ at $(2, 1, 1)$.

■ **14.7 Optimization**

Students should read Section 14.7 of Rogawski's *Calculus* [1] for a detailed discussion of the material presented in this section.

Second Derivative Test: Suppose $f_x(a, b) = 0$ and $f_y(a, b) = 0$. Define

$$D(x, y) = f_{xx}\,f_{yy} - \left(f_{xy}\right)^2$$

The function D is called the *discriminant function.*

i) If $D(a, \,, b) > 0$ and $f_{xx}(a, b) > 0$, then $f(a, b)$ is a local minimum value.
ii) If $D(a, \,, b) > 0$ and $f_{xx}(a, b) < 0$, then $f(a, b)$ is a local maximum value.
iii) If $D(a, \,, b) < 0$, then $(a, b, f(a, b))$ is a saddle point on the graph of f.
iv) If $D(a, b) = 0$, then no conclusion can be drawn about the the point (a, b).

Example 14.34. Let $f(x, y) = x^4 - 4 x y + 2 y^2$.
a) Find all critical points of f.
b) Use the second derivative test to classify the critical points as local minimum, local maximum, saddle point, or neither.

Solution: Since **D** is used in *Mathematica* as the command for derivative, we will use **disc** for the discriminant function D.

In[1458]:= **Clear[f, x, y]**

f[x_, y_] = x^4 - 4 x y + 2 y^2

Out[1459]= $x^4 - 4 x y + 2 y^2$

a) The critical points are given by

In[1460]:= **cp = Solve[{D[f[x, y], x] == 0, D[f[x, y], y] == 0}]**

Out[1460]= $\{\{y \to -1, x \to -1\}, \{y \to 0, x \to 0\}, \{y \to 1, x \to 1\}\}$

b)

In[1461]:= **Clear[fxx, disc]**

fxx[x_, y_] = D[f[x, y], {x, 2}]

disc[x_, y_] = D[f[x, y], {x, 2}] * D[f[x, y], {y, 2}] - (D[D[f[x, y], x], y])^2

Out[1462]= $12 x^2$

Out[1463]= $-16 + 48 x^2$

In[1464]:= **TableForm[Table[{ cp[[k, 2, 2]], cp[[k, 1, 2]],**
disc[cp[[k, 2, 2]], cp[[k, 1, 2]]], fxx[cp[[k, 2, 2]], cp[[k, 1, 2]]],
f[cp[[k, 2, 2]], cp[[k, 1, 2]]]}, {k, 1, Length[cp]}],
TableHeadings → {{}, {"x ", "y ", " D(x,y) ", " f$_{xx}$ ", "f(x,y)"}}]

Out[1464]//TableForm=

x	y	D(x,y)	f$_{xx}$	f(x,y)
-1	-1	32	12	-1
0	0	-16	0	0
1	1	32	12	-1

By the second derivative test, we conclude that f has a local minimum value of -1 at $(-1, -1)$ and $(1, 1)$, and a saddle point at $(0, 0)$.

Here is the graph of f and the relevant points.

In[1465]:= **Clear[plot1, plot2]**
plot1 =
Plot3D[f[x, y], {x, -2, 2}, {y, -2, 2}, PlotStyle → LightBlue, PlotRange → 10];
plot2 = Graphics3D[{PointSize[Large], Red,
Point[Table[{ cp[[k, 2, 2]], cp[[k, 1, 2]], f[cp[[k, 2, 2]], cp[[k, 1, 2]]]},
{k, 1, Length[cp]}]]}, PlotRange → 10];
Show[plot1, plot2, ImageSize → {250}]

Out[1468]=

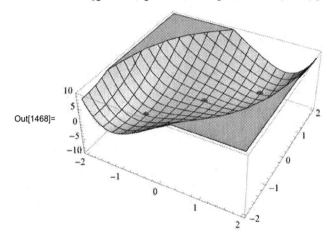

Example 14.35. Let $f(x, y) = x^3 + y^4 - 6x - 2y^2$.
a) Find all critical points of f.
b) Use the second derivative test to classify the critical points as local minimum, local maximum, saddle point, or neither.

Solution: Again, we will use **disc** to denote the discriminant function D since the letter **D** is used in *Mathematica* for the derivative command.

In[1469]:= **Clear[f, x, y]**
f[x_, y_] = x³ + y⁴ - 6 x - 2 y²

Out[1470]= $-6x + x^3 - 2y^2 + y^4$

a) The critical points are given by

In[1471]:= **cp = Solve[{D[f[x, y], x] == 0, D[f[x, y], y] == 0}]**

Out[1471]= $\left\{ \left\{ y \to -1, x \to -\sqrt{2} \right\}, \left\{ y \to -1, x \to \sqrt{2} \right\}, \left\{ y \to 0, x \to -\sqrt{2} \right\}, \right.$
$\left. \left\{ y \to 0, x \to \sqrt{2} \right\}, \left\{ y \to 1, x \to -\sqrt{2} \right\}, \left\{ y \to 1, x \to \sqrt{2} \right\} \right\}$

b)

In[1472]:= **Clear[fxx, disc]**
fxx[x_, y_] = D[f[x, y], {x, 2}]
disc[x_, y_] = D[f[x, y], {x, 2}] * D[f[x, y], {y, 2}] - (D[D[f[x, y], x], y])²

Out[1473]= $6x$

Out[1474]= $6x \left(-4 + 12 y^2\right)$

In[1475]:= `TableForm[Table[{ cp[[k, 2, 2]], cp[[k, 1, 2]],`
`disc[cp[[k, 2, 2]], cp[[k, 1, 2]]], fxx[cp[[k, 2, 2]], cp[[k, 1, 2]]],`
`f[cp[[k, 2, 2]], cp[[k, 1, 2]]]}, {k, 1, Length[cp]}],`
`TableHeadings → {{}, {"x ", "y ", " D(x,y) ", " fxx ", "f(x,y)"}}]`

Out[1475]//TableForm=

x	y	D(x, y)	f_{xx}	f(x, y)
$-\sqrt{2}$	-1	$-48\sqrt{2}$	$-6\sqrt{2}$	$-1 + 4\sqrt{2}$
$\sqrt{2}$	-1	$48\sqrt{2}$	$6\sqrt{2}$	$-1 - 4\sqrt{2}$
$-\sqrt{2}$	0	$24\sqrt{2}$	$-6\sqrt{2}$	$4\sqrt{2}$
$\sqrt{2}$	0	$-24\sqrt{2}$	$6\sqrt{2}$	$-4\sqrt{2}$
$-\sqrt{2}$	1	$-48\sqrt{2}$	$-6\sqrt{2}$	$-1 + 4\sqrt{2}$
$\sqrt{2}$	1	$48\sqrt{2}$	$6\sqrt{2}$	$-1 - 4\sqrt{2}$

By the second derivative test we conclude that f has local maximum value of $4\sqrt{2}$ at $\left(-\sqrt{2}, 0\right)$, local minimum value of $-1 - 4\sqrt{2}$ at $\left(\sqrt{2}, -1\right)$ and $\left(\sqrt{2}, 1\right)$, and saddle points at $\left(-\sqrt{2}, -1\right)$, $\left(\sqrt{2}, 0\right)$, and $\left(-\sqrt{2}, 1\right)$.

Here is the graph of f and the relevant points.

In[1476]:= `Clear[plot1, plot2]`
`plot1 = Plot3D[f[x, y], {x, -2.5, 2.5},`
`{y, -2.5, 2.5}, PlotStyle → LightBlue, PlotRange → 10];`
`plot2 = Graphics3D[{PointSize[Large], Red,`
`Point[Table[{ cp[[k, 2, 2]], cp[[k, 1, 2]], f[cp[[k, 2, 2]], cp[[k, 1, 2]]]},`
`{k, 1, Length[cp]}]]}, PlotRange → 10];`
`Show[plot1, plot2, ImageSize → {250}]`

Out[1479]=

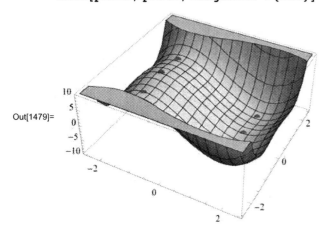

Example 14.36. Let $f(x, y) = 2x^2 - 3xy - x + y + y^2$ and let R be the rectangle in the xy-plane whose vertices are at $(0,0)$, $(2,0)$, $(2,2)$, and $(0,2)$.

a) Find all relative extreme values of f inside R.

b) Find the maximum and minimum values of f on R.

Solution:

In[1480]:= **Clear[f, x, y, disc]**
f[x_, y_] = 2 x² - 3 x * y - x + y + y² + 5

Out[1481]= $5 - x + 2 x^2 + y - 3 x y + y^2$

In[1482]:= **Solve$\left[\left\{\partial_x f[x, y] == 0, \partial_y f[x, y] == 0\right\}, \{x, y\}\right]$**

Out[1482]= $\{\{x \to 1, y \to 1\}\}$

In[1483]:= **disc[x_, y_] = $\partial_{x,x} f[x, y] * \partial_{y,y} f[x, y] - \left(\partial_{x,y} f[x, y]\right)^2$**

Out[1483]= -1

In[1484]:= **$\partial_{x,x} f[x, y]$ /. {x -> 1, y -> 1}**
disc[x, y] /. {x -> 1, y -> 1}

Out[1484]= 4

Out[1485]= -1

Thus, $(1, 1)$ is the local minimum point of f inside R and its local minimum value is $f(1, 1) = 5$. Next, we find the extreme values of f on the boundary of the rectangle. This is done by considering f as a function of one variable corresponding to each side of R. Let $f_1 = f(x, 0)$, $f_2 = f(x, 2)$, for x between 0 and 2, and $f_3 = f(0, y)$ and $f_4 = f(2, y)$, for y between 0 and 2. We now proceed as follows:

In[1486]:= **Clear[f1, f2, f3, f4]**
f1 = f[x, 0]
f2 = f[x, 2]
f3 = f[0, y]
f4 = f[2, y]

Out[1487]= $5 - x + 2 x^2$

Out[1488]= $11 - 7 x + 2 x^2$

Out[1489]= $5 + y + y^2$

Out[1490]= $11 - 5 y + y^2$

In[1491]:= **Solve[D[f1, x] == 0]**

Out[1491]= $\left\{\left\{x \to \frac{1}{4}\right\}\right\}$

In[1492]:= **Solve[D[f2, x] == 0]**

Out[1492]= $\left\{\left\{x \to \frac{7}{4}\right\}\right\}$

In[1493]:= **Solve[D[f3, y] == 0]**

Out[1493]= $\left\{\left\{y \to -\frac{1}{2}\right\}\right\}$

In[1494]:= **Solve[D[f4, y] == 0]**

Out[1494]= $\left\{\left\{y \to \frac{5}{2}\right\}\right\}$

Thus, points on the boundary of R that are critical points of f are $\left(\frac{1}{4},\ 0\right)$ and $\left(\frac{7}{4},\ 2\right)$. Observe that the points $(0,\ -1/2)$ and $\left(2,\ \frac{5}{2}\right)$ are outside the rectangle R. The four vertices of R at $(0,0)$, $(2,0)$, $(0,2)$ and $(2,2)$ are also critical points. Can you explain why? We now evaluate f at each of these points and at $(1,\ 1)$ (the relative minimum point found earlier) using the substitution command and compare the results.

In[1495]:= $\mathbf{f[x, y]}\ /.\ \left\{\left\{x \to \dfrac{1}{4},\ y \to 0\right\},\ \left\{x \to \dfrac{7}{4},\ y \to 2\right\},\right.$
$\{x \to 0,\ y \to 0\},\ \{x \to 2,\ y \to 0\},$
$\left.\{x \to 0,\ y \to 2\},\ \{x \to 2,\ y \to 2\},\ \{x \to 1,\ y \to 1\}\right\}$

Out[1495]= $\left\{\dfrac{39}{8},\ \dfrac{39}{8},\ 5,\ 11,\ 11,\ 5,\ 5\right\}$

Thus, the minimum value of f is $39/8$, which occurs at $(1/4, 0)$ and also at $(7/4, 2)$. The maximum value of f is 6, which is attained at $(2, 0)$ and also at $(0, 2)$. Here is the graph of f over the rectangle R.

In[1496]:= `Clear[plot1, plot2, plot3]`
`plot1 = Plot3D[{f[x, y], 0}, {x, 0, 2},`
`    {y, 0, 2}, PlotStyle → {Green, Blue}, PlotRange → All];`
`plot2 = Graphics3D[{PointSize[Large], Red ,`
`    Point[{ {1 / 4, 0, f[1 / 4, 0]}, {7 / 4, 2, f[7 / 4, 2]} }]}, PlotRange → All ];`
`plot3 = Graphics3D[{PointSize[Large], Black ,`
`    Point[{ {2, 0, f[2, 0]}, {0, 2, f[2, 0]}}]}, PlotRange → All ];`
`Show[plot1, plot2 , plot3, ImageSize → {250}, ImagePadding → {{15, 15}, {15, 15}}]`

Out[1500]=

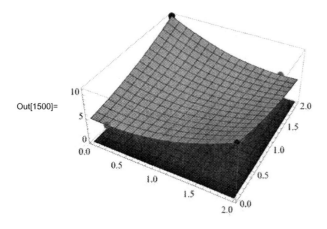

■ Exercises

1. Let $f(x,\ y) = x^4 - 4\,x\,y + 2\,y^2$.
a. Find all critical points of f.
b. Use the second derivative test to classify the critical points as local minimum, local maximum, saddle point, or neither.
c. Plot the graph of f and the local extreme points and saddle points, if any.

2. Let $f(x,\ y) = (x + y)\ln\!\left(x^2 + y^2\right)$, for $(x,\ y) \ne (0,\ 0)$.
a. Find all critical points of f.
b. Use the second derivative test to classify the critical points as local minimum, local maximum, saddle point, or neither.
c. Plot the graph of f and the local extreme points and saddle points, if any.

3. Let $f(x, y) = 2 x^2 - 3 x y - x + y + y^2$ and let R be the rectangle in the xy-plane whose vertices are at $(0, 0)$, $(2, 0)$, $(2, 2)$, and $(0, 2)$.

a. Find all relative extreme values of f inside R.

b. Find the maximum and minimum values of f on R.

c. Plot the graph of f and the local extreme points and saddle points, if any.

■ 14.8 Lagrange Multipliers

Students should read Section 14.8 of Rogawski's *Calculus* [1] for a detailed discussion of the material presented in this section.

Example 14.37. Let $f(x, y) = x y$ and $g(x, y) = x^2 + y^2 - 4$.

a) Plot the level curves of f and g as well as their gradient vectors.

b) Find the maximum and minimum values of f subject to the constraint $g(x, y) = 0$.

Solution:

a) We will define f and g and compute their gradients. Recall that we need to evaluate the command **Needs["`VectorFieldPlots`"]** before we plot the gradient fields.

```
In[1501]:= Clear[f, g, fx, fy, gx, gy, x, y]
        f[x_, y_] = 2 x + 3 y
        g[x_, y_] = x² + y² - 4
        fx = D[f[x, y], x]
        fy = D[f[x, y], y]
        gx = D[g[x, y], x]
        gy = D[g[x, y], y]
```

Out[1502]= $2 x + 3 y$

Out[1503]= $-4 + x^2 + y^2$

Out[1504]= 2

Out[1505]= 3

Out[1506]= $2 x$

Out[1507]= $2 y$

```
In[1508]:= Needs["VectorFieldPlots`"]
```

In[1509]:= `Clear[plot1, plot2, plot3, plot4]`
`plot1 = ContourPlot[x² + y² - 4, {x, -2, 2}, {y, -2, 2},`
`    Frame → False, Axes → True, ContourShading → False, PlotRange → All];`
`plot2 = ContourPlot[2 x + 3 y, {x, -2, 2}, {y, -2, 2}, Frame → False,`
`    Axes → True, ContourShading → False, PlotRange → All];`
`plot3 = VectorFieldPlot[{fx, fy}, {x, -2, 2}, {y, -2, 2},`
`    Axes → True, Frame → False, ColorFunction → Hue];`
`plot4 = VectorFieldPlot[{gx, gy}, {x, -2, 2}, {y, -2, 2},`
`    Axes → True, Frame → False, ColorFunction → Hue];`
`Show[plot1, plot2, plot3, plot4, ImageSize → {250}]`

Out[1514]=

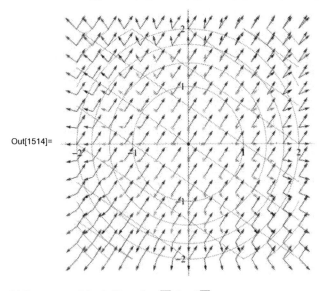

b) Let us use l for λ. To solve $\nabla f = l \nabla g$ we compute

In[1515]:= `Solve[{fx == l gx, fy == l gy, g[x, y] == 0}]`

Out[1515]= $\left\{\left\{l \to -\frac{\sqrt{13}}{4}, x \to -\frac{4}{\sqrt{13}}, y \to -\frac{6}{\sqrt{13}}\right\}, \left\{l \to \frac{\sqrt{13}}{4}, x \to \frac{4}{\sqrt{13}}, y \to \frac{6}{\sqrt{13}}\right\}\right\}$

Thus, $\left(-\frac{4}{\sqrt{13}}, -\frac{6}{\sqrt{13}}\right)$ and $\left(\frac{4}{\sqrt{13}}, \frac{6}{\sqrt{13}}\right)$ are the critical points. We evaluate f at these points to determine the absolute maximum and the absolute minimum of f on the graph of $g(x, y) = 0$.

In[1516]:= $f\left[-\frac{4}{\sqrt{13}}, -\frac{6}{\sqrt{13}}\right]$

$f\left[\frac{4}{\sqrt{13}}, \frac{6}{\sqrt{13}}\right]$

Out[1516]= $-2\sqrt{13}$

Out[1517]= $2\sqrt{13}$

Hence, f attains its absolute minimum value of $-2\sqrt{13}$ at $\left(-\frac{4}{\sqrt{13}}, -\frac{6}{\sqrt{13}}\right)$ and absolute maximum value of $-2\sqrt{13}$ at $\left(\frac{4}{\sqrt{13}}, \frac{6}{\sqrt{13}}\right)$.

Here is a combined plot of the gradients of f (in black) and g (in red) at the critical points.

In[1518]:= **Clear[plot1, plot2, plot3, plot4, plot5, plot6]**
plot1 = ContourPlot[g[x, y], {x, -3, 3}, {y, -3, 3},
    Contours → {0}, Frame → False, Axes → True, ContourShading → False];

plot2 = ListPlot$\left[\left\{\left\{-\dfrac{4}{\sqrt{13}}, -\dfrac{6}{\sqrt{13}}\right\}, \left\{\dfrac{4}{\sqrt{13}}, \dfrac{6}{\sqrt{13}}\right\}\right\}\right]$;

In[1521]:= **plot3 = Graphics$\Big[$Arrow$\Big[$**

    $\left\{\left\{-\dfrac{4}{\sqrt{13}}, -\dfrac{6}{\sqrt{13}}\right\}, \left\{-\dfrac{4}{\sqrt{13}}, -\dfrac{6}{\sqrt{13}}\right\} + \{\text{fx, fy}\}\;/.\;\left\{x \to \dfrac{-4}{\sqrt{13}}, y \to \dfrac{-6}{\sqrt{13}}\right\}\right\}\Big]\Big]$;

In[1522]:= **plot4 = Graphics$\Big[$**

    Arrow$\left[\left\{\left\{\dfrac{4}{\sqrt{13}}, \dfrac{6}{\sqrt{13}}\right\}, \left\{\dfrac{4}{\sqrt{13}}, \dfrac{6}{\sqrt{13}}\right\} + \{\text{fx, fy}\}\;/.\;\left\{x \to \dfrac{4}{\sqrt{13}}, y \to \dfrac{6}{\sqrt{13}}\right\}\right\}\right]\Big]$;

In[1523]:= **plot5 = Graphics$\Big[\Big\{$Red, Arrow$\Big[\Big\{\left\{-\dfrac{4}{\sqrt{13}}, -\dfrac{6}{\sqrt{13}}\right\}$,**

    $\left\{-\dfrac{4}{\sqrt{13}}, -\dfrac{6}{\sqrt{13}}\right\} + \{\text{gx, gy}\}\;/.\;\left\{x \to \dfrac{-4}{\sqrt{13}}, y \to \dfrac{-6}{\sqrt{13}}\right\}\Big\}\Big]\Big\}\Big]$;

In[1524]:= **plot6 = Graphics$\Big[\Big\{$Red, Arrow$\Big[$**

    $\left\{\left\{\dfrac{4}{\sqrt{13}}, \dfrac{6}{\sqrt{13}}\right\}, \left\{\dfrac{4}{\sqrt{13}}, \dfrac{6}{\sqrt{13}}\right\} + \{\text{gx, gy}\}\;/.\;\left\{x \to \dfrac{4}{\sqrt{13}}, y \to \dfrac{6}{\sqrt{13}}\right\}\right\}\Big]\Big\}\Big]$;

In[1525]:= **Show[plot1, plot2, plot3, plot4, plot5, plot6,**
    PlotRange → All, AspectRatio → Automatic, ImageSize → {250}]

Out[1525]=

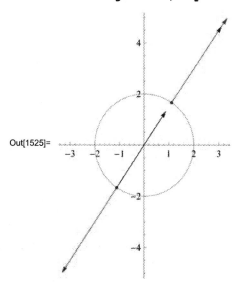

■ Exercises

1. Let $f(x, y) = 4 x^2 + 9 y^2$ and $g(x, y) = x y - 4$.

a. Plot the level curves of f and g as well as their gradient vectors.

b. Find the maximum and minimum values of f subject to $g(x, y) = 0$.

2. Find the maximum and minimum values of $f(x, y, z) = x^3 - 3 y^2 + 4 z$ subject to the constraint $g(x, y, z) = x + y z - 4 = 0$.

3. Find the maximum area of a rectangle that can be inscribed in the ellipse $\frac{x^2}{a^2} + \frac{y^2}{b^2} = 1$.

4. Find the maximum volume of a box that can be inscribed in the sphere $x^2 + y^2 + z^2 = 4$.

Chapter 15   Multiple Integration

Useful Tip: If you are reading the electronic version of this publication formatted as a *Mathematica* Notebook, then it is possible to view 3-D plots generated by *Mathematica* from different perspectives. First, place your screen cursor over the plot. Then drag the mouse while pressing down on the left mouse button to rotate the plot.

■ 15.1 Double Integral over a Rectangle

Students should read Section 15.1 of Rogawski's *Calculus* [1] for a detailed discussion of the material presented in this section.

Integration can be generalized to functions of two or more variables. As the integral of a single-variable function defines area of a plane region under the curve, it is natural to consider a double integral of a two-variable function that defines volume of a solid under a surface. This definition can be made precise in terms of double Riemann sums where rectangular columns (as opposed to rectangles) are used as building blocks to approximate volume (as opposed to area). The exact volume is then obtained as a limit where the number of columns increases without bound.

■ 15.1.1 Double Integrals and Riemann Sums

Let $f(x, y)$ be a function of two variables defined on a rectangular domain $R = [a, b] \times [c, d]$ in $\mathbb{R}^2$. Let $P = \{a = x_0 < x_1 < ... < x_m = b, c = y_0 < y_1 < ... < y_n = d\}$ be an arbitrary partition of R into a grid of $m \cdot n$ rectangles, where m and n are integers. For each sub-rectangle $R_{ij} = [x_{i-1}, x_i] \times [y_{j-1}, y_j]$ denote by ΔA_{ij} its area and choose an arbitrary base point $(x_{ij}, y_{ij}) \in R_{ij}$, where $x_{ij} \in [x_{i-1}, x_i]$ and $y_{ij} \in [y_{j-1}, y_j]$. The product $f(x_{ij}, y_{ij}) \Delta A_{ij}$ represents the volume of the ij-rectangular column situated between the surface and the xy-plane. We then define the *double Riemann sum* S_p of $f(x, y)$ on R with respect to P to be the total volume of all these columns:

$$S_P = \sum_{i=1}^{m} \sum_{j=1}^{n} f(x_{ij}, y_{ij}) \Delta A_{ij}$$

Define $\| P \|$ to be the maximum dimension of all the sub-rectangles. The *double integral* of $f(x, y)$ on the rectangle R is then defined as the limit of S_P as $\| P \| \to 0$:

$$\int \int_R f(x, y) \, dA = \lim_{\|P\| \to 0} \sum_{i=1}^{m} \sum_{j=1}^{n} f(x_{ij}, y_{ij}) \Delta A_{ij}$$

If the limit exists regardless of the choice of partition and base points, then the double integral is said to exist. Otherwise, the double integral does not exist.

MIDPOINT RULE (Uniform Partitions): Let us consider uniform partitions P, where the points $\{x_i\}$ and $\{y_j\}$ are evenly spaced, that is, $x_i = a + i \Delta x$, $y_j = b + j \Delta y$ for $i = 0, 1, ..., m$ and $j = 0, 1, ..., n$, and with $\Delta x = (b - a)/m$ and $\Delta y = (d - c)/n$. Then the corresponding double Riemann sum is

$$S_{m,n} = \sum_{i=1}^{m} \sum_{j=1}^{n} f(x_{ij}, y_{ij}) \Delta x \Delta y$$

Here is a subroutine called **MDOUBLERSUM** that calculates the double Riemann sum $S_{m,n}$ of $f(x, y)$ over a rectangle R for uniform partitions using the center midpoint of each sub-rectangle as base point, that is, $x_{ij} = (x_{i-1} + x_i)/2 = a + (i - 1/2) \Delta x$ and $y_{ij} = (y_{j-1} + y_j)/2 = c + (j - 1/2) \Delta y$.

In[1526]:= **Clear[f]**

MDOUBLERSUM[a_ , b_ , c_ , d_ , m_ , n_] :=
Sum[f[a + (i - 1 / 2) * (b - a) / m, c + (j - 1 / 2) * (d - c) / n] * (b - a) / m * (d - c) / n,
{i, 1, m}, {j, 1, n}]

Example 15.1. Approximate the volume of the solid bounded below the surface $f(x) = x^2 + y^2$ and above the rectangle $R = [-1, 1] \times [-1, 1]$ on the *xy*-plane using a uniform partition with $m = 10$ and $n = 10$ and center midpoints as base points. Then experiment with larger values of *m* and *n* and conjecture an answer for the exact volume.

Solution: We calculate the approximate volume for $m = 10$ and $n = 10$ using the subroutine MDOUBLERSUM:

In[1528]:= **f[x_ , y_] = x^2 + y^2;**

MDOUBLERSUM[-1, 1, -1, 1, 10, 10]

Out[1529]= $\dfrac{66}{25}$

In[1530]:= **N[%]**

Out[1530]= 2.64

In[1531]:= **Table[MDOUBLERSUM[-1, 1, -1, 1, 10 * k, 10 * k], {k, 1, 10}]**

Out[1531]= $\left\{ \dfrac{66}{25}, \dfrac{133}{50}, \dfrac{1798}{675}, \dfrac{533}{200}, \dfrac{1666}{625}, \dfrac{3599}{1350}, \dfrac{3266}{1225}, \dfrac{2133}{800}, \dfrac{16198}{6075}, \dfrac{3333}{1250} \right\}$

In[1532]:= **N[%]**

Out[1532]= {2.64, 2.66, 2.6637, 2.665, 2.6656, 2.66593, 2.66612, 2.66625, 2.66634, 2.6664}

It appears that the exact volume is 8/3. To prove this, we evaluate the double Riemann sum $S_{m,n}$ in the limit as $m, n \to \infty$:

In[1533]:= **Clear[S, m, n];**

S[m_ , n_] = Simplify[MDOUBLERSUM[-1, 1, -1, 1, m, n]]

Out[1534]= $\dfrac{4}{3} \left(2 - \dfrac{1}{m^2} - \dfrac{1}{n^2} \right)$

In[1535]:= **Limit[Limit[S[m, n], m → Infinity], n → Infinity]**

Out[1535]= $\dfrac{8}{3}$

To see this limiting process visually, evaluate the following subroutine, called **DOUBLEMIDPT**, which plots the surface of the function corresponding to the double integral along with the rectangular columns defined by the double Riemann sum considered in the previous subroutine **MDOUBLERSUM**.

```
In[1536]:= Clear[f];
        DOUBLEMIDPT[f_, {a_, b_, m_}, {c_, d_, n_}] := Module[
          {dx, dy, i, j, xstar, ystar, mrect, plot},
          dx = N[(b - a) / m];
          xstar = Table[a + i * dx, {i, 0, m}];
          dy = N[(d - c) / n];
          ystar = Table[c + j * dy, {j, 0, n}];
          mcolumn = Table[Cuboid[{xstar[[i]], ystar[[j]], 0},
              {xstar[[i + 1]], ystar[[j + 1]], f[(xstar[[i]] + xstar[[i + 1]]) / 2,
                (ystar[[j]] + ystar[[j + 1]]) / 2]}], {i, 1, m}, {j, 1, n}];
          plot = Plot3D[f[x, y], {x, a, b}, {y, c, d}, Filling → Bottom];
          Show[plot, Graphics3D[mcolumn], ImageSize → {300}]]
```

```
In[1538]:= f[x_, y_] := x^2 + y^2;
        DOUBLEMIDPT[f, {-1, 1, 10}, {-1, 1, 10}]
```

Out[1539]=

Here is an animation that demonstrates how the volume of the rectangular columns approach that of the solid in the limit as $m, n \to \infty$:

Important Note: If you are reading the printed version of this publication, then you will not be able to view any of the animations generated from the **Animate** command in this chapter. If you are reading the electronic version of this publication formatted as a *Mathematica* Notebook, then evaluate each **Animate** command to view the corresponding animation. Just click on the arrow button to start the animation. To control the animation just click at various points on the sliding bar or else manually drag the bar.

In[1540]:= `Animate[DOUBLEMIDPT[f, {-1, 1, a}, {-1, 1, a}] , {a, 5, 50, 5 }]`

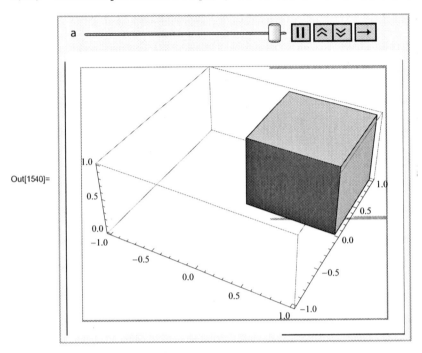

Out[1540]=

■ 15.1.2 Double Integrals and Iterated Integrals in *Mathematica*

The *Mathematica* command for evaluating double integrals is the same as that for evaluating integrals of a single-variable function, except that two limits of integration must be specified, one for each independent variable. Thus:

Integrate[f[x,y],{x,a,c},{y,c,d}] analytically evaluates the double integral $\int\int_R f(x, y)\, dA$ over the rectangle $R = [a, b] \times [c, d]$.

NIntegrate[f[x,y],{x,a,c},{y,c,d}] numerically evaluates the double integral $\int\int_R f(x, y)\, dA$ over the rectangle $R = [a, b] \times [c, d]$.

Iterated Integrals: In practice, one does not actually use the limit definition in terms of Riemann sums to evaluate double integrals, but instead apply **Fubini's Theorem** to easily compute them in terms of iterated integrals:

Fubini's Theorem: (Rectangular Domains) If $R = \{(x, y) : a \le x \le b, c \le y \le d\}$, then

$$\int\int_R f(x, y)\, dA = \int_a^b \int_c^d f(x, y)\, dy\, dx = \int_c^d \int_a^b f(x, y)\, dx\, dy$$

Thus, *Mathematica* will naturally apply Fubini's Theorem whenever possible to analytically determine the answer. Depending on the form of the double integral, *Mathematica* may resort to more sophisticated integration techniques, such as contour integration, which are beyond the scope of this text.

Example 15.2. Calculate the volume of the solid bounded below by the surface $f(x) = x^2 + y^2$ and above the rectangle $R = [-1, 1] \times [-1, 1]$.

Solution: The volume of the solid is given by the double integral $\int\int_R f(x, y)\, dA$. To evaluate it, we use the **Integrate** command:

In[1541]:= **f[x_, y_] := x^2 + y^2;**
Integrate[f[x, y], {x, -1, 1}, {y, -1, 1}]

Out[1542]= $\dfrac{8}{3}$

This confirms the conjecture that we made in the previous example for the exact volume.

NOTE: Observe that we obtain the same answer by explicitly computing this double integral as an integrated integral as follows. Moreover, for rectangular domains, the order of integration does not matter.

In[1543]:= **Integrate[Integrate[f[x, y], {x, -1, 1}], {y, -1, 1}]**
Integrate[Integrate[f[x, y], {y, -1, 1}], {x, -1, 1}]

Out[1543]= $\dfrac{8}{3}$

Out[1544]= $\dfrac{8}{3}$

Example 15.3. Compute the double integral $\iint_R x\, e^{-y^2}\, dA$ on the rectangle $R = [0, 1] \times [0, 1]$.

Solution: Observe that the **Integrate** command here gives us an answer in terms of the non-elementary error function **Erf**:

In[1545]:= **Integrate[x * E^(-y^2), {x, 0, 1}, {y, 0, 1}]**

Out[1545]= $\dfrac{1}{4} \sqrt{\pi}\ \text{Erf}[1]$

This is because the function $f(x, y) = x\, e^{-y^2}$ has no elementary anti-derivative with respect to y due to the Gaussian factor e^{-y^2} (bell curve). Thus, we instead use the **NIntegrate** Command to numerically approximate the double integral:

In[1546]:= **NIntegrate[x * E^(-y^2), {x, 0, 1}, {y, 0, 1}]**

Out[1546]= 0.373412

■ Exercises

1. Consider the function $f(x, y) = 16 - x^2 - y^2$ defined over the rectangle $R = [0, 2] \times [-1, 3]$.
a. Use the subroutine **MDOUBLERSUM** to compute the double Riemann sum $S_{m,n}$ of $f(x, y)$ over R for $m = 2$ and $n = 2$.
b. Repeat part a) by generating a table of double Riemann sums for $m = 10 k$ and $n = 10 k$ where $k = 1, 2, ..., 10$. Make a conjecture for the exact value of $\iint_R f(x, y)\, dA$.
c. Find a formula for $S_{m,n}$ in terms of m and n. Verify your conjecture in part b) by evaluating $\lim_{m,n \to \infty} S_{m,n}$.
d. Directly compute $\iint_R f(x, y)\, dA$ using the **Integrate** command.

2. Repeat Exercise 1 but with $f(x, y) = (1 + x)(1 + y)(1 + x\, y)$ defined over the rectangle $R = [0, 1] \times [0, 1]$.

3. Evaluate the double integral $\displaystyle\int\int \sqrt{x^4 + y^4}\ dA$ over the rectangle $R = [-2, 1] \times [-1, 2]$ using both the **Integrate** and **NIntegrate** commands. How do the two answers compare?

4. Calculate the volume of the solid lying under the surface $z = e^{-y}(x + y^2)$ and over the rectangle $R = [0, 2] \times [0, 3]$. Then make a plot of this solid.

5. Repeat Exercise 4 but with $z = \sin\left(x^2 + y^2\right)$ and rectangle $R = \left[-\sqrt{\pi}\,,\,\sqrt{\pi}\,\right] \times \left[-\sqrt{\pi}\,,\,\sqrt{\pi}\,\right]$.

6. Evaluate the double integral $\iint_R f(x,\ y)\,dA$ where $f(x,\ y) = x\,y\,\cos\left(x^2 + y^2\right)$ and $R = [-\pi,\ \pi] \times [-\pi,\ \pi]$. Does your answer make sense? Make a plot of the solid corresponding to this double integral to intuitively explain your answer. HINT: Consider symmetry.

7. Find the volume of solid bounded between the two hyperbolic paraboloids (saddles) $z = 1 + x^2 - y^2$ and $z = 3 - x^2 + y^2$ over the rectangle $R = [-1,\ 1] \times [-1,\ 1]$.

8. Find the volume of the solid bounded by the planes $z = 2\,x$, $z = -3\,x + 2$, $y = 0$, $y = 1$, and $z = 0$.

■ 15.2 Double Integral over More General Regions

Students should read Section 15.2 of Rogawski's *Calculus* [1] for a detailed discussion of the material presented in this section.

For domains of integration that are non-rectangular but still *simple*, that is, bounded between two curves, Fubini's Theorem continues to hold. There are two types to consider:

Fubini's Theorem: (Simple Domains)

Type I (Vertically Simple): If $D = \{(x,\ y) : a \le x \le b,\ \alpha(x) \le y \le \beta(x)\}$, then

$$\iint_D f(x,\ y)\,dA = \int_a^b \int_{\alpha(x)}^{\beta(x)} f(x,\ y)\,dy\,dx$$

The corresponding *Mathematica* command is **Integrate[f[x,y],{x,a,b},{y,α[x],β[x]}]**.

Type II (Horizontally Simple): If $D = \{(x,\ y) : c \le y \le d,\ \alpha(y) \le x \le \beta(y)\}$, then

$$\iint_D f(x,\ y)\,dA = \int_c^d \int_{\alpha(y)}^{\beta(y)} f(x,\ y)\,dx\,dy$$

The corresponding *Mathematica* command is **Integrate[f[x,y],{y,c,d},{x,α[y],β[y]}]**.

Warning: Be careful not to reverse the order of integration prescribed for either type. For example, evaluating the command **Integrate[f[x,y],{y,α[x],β[x]},{x,a,b}]** for Type I (x and y are reversed) will lead to incorrect results.

Example 15.4. Calculate the volume of the solid bounded below by the surface $f(x,\ y) = 1 - x^2 + y^2$ and above the domain D bounded by $x = 0$, $x = 1$, $y = x$, and $y = 1 + x^2$.

Solution: We observe that $x = 0$ and $x = 1$ represent the left and right boundaries, respectively, of D. Therefore, we plot the graphs of the other two equations along the x-interval $[0, 2]$ to visualize D (shaded in the following plot):

In[1547]:= **Clear[x, y]**
plot1 = Plot[{x, 1 + x^2}, {x, 0, 1}, Filling → {1 → {2}}, ImageSize → 250]

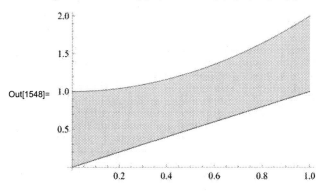

Out[1548]=

Here is a plot of the corresponding solid situated over *D*:

In[1549]:= **f[x_, y_] = 1 - x^2 + y^2;**
plot3 = Plot3D[f[x, y], {x, 0, 1}, {y, x, 1 + x^2}, Filling → Bottom,
ViewPoint → {1, 1, 1}, PlotRange → {0, 4}, ImageSize → {250}]

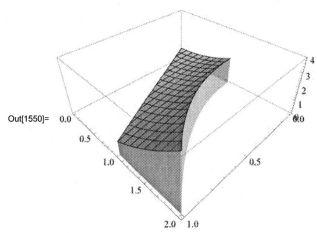

Out[1550]=

To compute the volume of this solid given by $\iint_D f(x, y)\, dA$, we describe *D* as a vertically simple domain where $0 \le x \le 1$ and $x \le y \le 1 + x^2$ and apply Fubini's Theorem to evaluate the corresponding iterated integral $\int_0^1 \int_x^{1+x^2} f(x, y)\, dy\, dx$ (remember to use the correct order of integration):

In[1551]:= **Integrate$\left[$f[x, y], {x, 0, 1}, $\left\{$y, x, 1 + x$^2\right\}\right]$**

Out[1551]= $\dfrac{29}{21}$

Example 15.5. Evaluate the double integral $\iint_D \sin\left(y^2\right) dA$, where *D* is the domain bounded by $x = 0$, $y = 2$, and $y = x$.

Solution: We first plot the graphs of $x = 0$, $y = 2$, and $y = x$ to visualize the domain *D*:

In[1552]:= `plot1 = ContourPlot[{x == 0, y == 2, y == x},`
`{x, -0.5, 2.5}, {y, -0.5, 2.5}, ImageSize → {250}]`

Out[1552]=

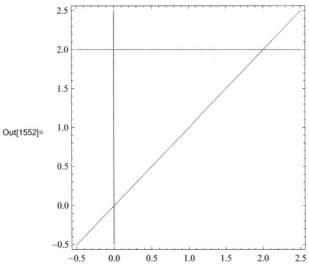

It follows that D is the triangular region bounded by these graphs, which we shade in the following plot to make clear:

In[1553]:= `plot2 = Plot[x, {x, 0, 2}, Filling → 2];`
`Show[plot1, plot2, ImageSize → {250}]`

Out[1554]=

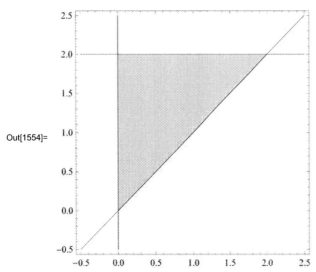

To compute the given double integral, we describe D as a horizontally simple domain, where $0 \le y \le 2$ and $0 \le x \le y$ and apply Fubini's Theorem to evaluate the corresponding iterated integral $\int_0^2 \int_0^y \sin(y^2) \, dx \, dy$ (again, remember to use the correct order of integration):

In[1555]:= `Integrate[Sin[y^2], {y, 0, 2}, {x, 0, y}]`

Out[1555]= $\text{Sin}[2]^2$

In[1556]:= `N[%]`

Out[1556]= 0.826822

NOTE: It is also possible to view D as a vertically simple domain, where $0 \le x \le 2$ and $x \le y \le 2$. The corresponding iterated integral $\int_0^2 \int_x^2 \sin(y^2) \, dy \, dx$ gives the same answer, as it should by Fubini's Theorem:

In[1557]:= **Integrate[Sin[y^2], {x, 0, 2}, {y, x, 2}]**

Out[1557]= $\text{Sin}[2]^2$

Observe that it is actually impossible to evaluate this iterated integral by hand since there is no elementary formula for the anti-derivative of $\sin(y^2)$ with respect to y. Thus, if necessary, *Mathematica* automatically switches the order of integration by converting from one type to the other.

■ Exercises

In Exercises 1 through 4, evaluate the given iterated integrals and plot the solid corresponding to each one.

1. $\int_0^1 \int_0^{x^2} (4 - x^2 + y^2) \, dy \, dx$ 2. $\int_0^4 \int_0^{\sqrt{2-y^2}} x^2 \, y \, dx \, dy$

3. $\int_0^\pi \int_0^{\sin\theta} r^2 \cos\theta \, dr \, d\theta$ 4. $\int_0^1 \int_0^x \frac{y}{1+xy} \, dy \, dx$

In Exercises 5 through 8, evaluate the given double integrals and plot the solid corresponding to each one.

5. $\iint_D (x + y) \, dA$, $D = \{(x, y) : 0 \le x \le 3, \, 0 \le y \le \sqrt{x}\}$

6. $\iint_D \sqrt{x + y} \, dA$, $D = \{(x, y) : 0 \le x \le 1 - y^2, \, 0 \le y \le 1\}$

7. $\iint_D e^{x+y} \, dA$, where $D = \{(x, y) : x^2 + y^2 \le 4\}$

8. $\iint_D \frac{y}{x+1} \, dA$, where D is the following shaded diamond region:

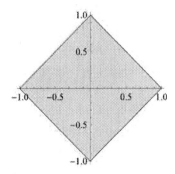

In Exercises 9 through 12, calculate the volume of the given solid S:

9. S is bounded under the paraboloid $z = 16 - x^2 - y^2$ and above the region bounded between the line $y = x$ and the parabola $y = 6 - x^2$.

10. S is bounded under the right circular cone $z = \sqrt{x^2 + y^2}$ and above the disk $x^2 + y^2 \le 1$.

11. S is bounbed between the plane $z = 5 + 2x + 2y$ and the paraboloid $z = 12 - x^2 - y^2$. HINT: Equate the two surfaces to obtain the equation of the domain.

12. S is bounded between the cylinders $x^2 + y^2 = 1$ and $y^2 + z^2 = 1$.

■ 15.3 Triple Integrals

Students should read Section 15.3 of Rogawski's *Calculus* [1] for a detailed discussion of the material presented in this section.

Once the notion of a double integral is well established, it is straightforward to generalize it to triple (and even higher-order) integrals for functions of three variables defined over a solid region in space. Here is the definition of a triple integral in terms of triple Riemann sums for a function $f(x, y, z)$ defined on a box region $B = \{(x, y, z) : a \le x \le b, c \le y \le d, p \le z \le q\}$ (refer to your calculus text for details):

$$\iiint_B f(x, y) \, dV = \lim_{\|P\| \to \infty} \sum_{i=1}^{m} \sum_{j=1}^{n} \sum_{k=1}^{p} f(x_{ijk}, y_{ijk}) \Delta V_{ijk}$$

where the notation is analogous to that used for double integrals in Section 15.1 of this text. Of course, Fubini's Theorem also generalizes to triple integrals:

Fubini's Theorem: (Box Domains) If $B = \{(x, y, z) : a \le x \le b, c \le y \le d, p \le z \le q\}$, then

$$\iiint_B f(x, y) \, dV = \int_a^b \int_c^d \int_p^q f(x, y) \, dz \, dy \, dx$$

The corresponding *Mathematica* commands are:

Integrate[f[x,y,z],{x,a,c},{y,c,d},{z,e,f}] analytically evaluates the triple integral $\iiint_B f(x, y) \, dV$ over the box $B = [a, b] \times [c, d] \times [e, f]$.

NIntegrate[f[x,y],{x,a,c},{y,c,d},{z,e,f}] numerically evaluates the triple integral $\iiint_B f(x, y) \, dV$ over the rectangle $B = [a, b] \times [c, d] \times [e, f]$.

NOTE: For box domains, the order of integration does not matter so that it is possible to write five other versions of triple iterated integrals besides the one given in Fubini's Theorem.

Example 15.6. Calculate the triple integral $\iiint_B x \, y \, z \, dV$ over the box $B = [0, 1] \times [2, 3] \times [4, 5]$.

Solution: We use the **Integrate** command to calculate the given triple integral.

In[1558]:= **Integrate[x y z, {x, 0, 1}, {y, 2, 3}, {z, 4, 5}]**

Out[1558]= $\dfrac{45}{8}$

Volume as Triple Integral: Recall that if a solid region W is bounded between two surfaces $\psi(x, y)$ and $\phi(x, y)$, where both are defined on the same domain D with $\psi(x, y) \le \phi(x, y)$, then its volume V can be expressed by the triple integral

$$V = \iiint_W 1 \, dV = \iint_D \int_{\psi(x,y)}^{\phi(x,y)} 1 \, dz \, dA$$

Example 15.7. Calculate the volume of the solid bounded between the surfaces $z = 4x^2 + 4y^2$ and $z = 16 - 4x^2 - 4y^2$ on the rectangular domain $[-1, 1] \times [-1, 1]$.

Solution: Here is a plot of the solid:

In[1559]:= `Plot3D[{4 x^2 + 4 y^2, 16 - 4 x^2 - 4 y^2}, {x, -1, 1}, {y, -1, 1},`
`    Filling → {1 → 8, 2 → 8}, ImageSize → {250}, ImagePadding → {{15, 15}, {15, 15}}]`

Out[1559]=

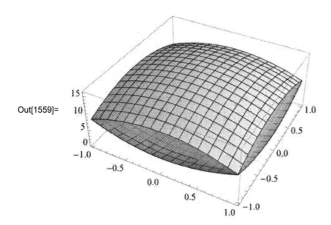

The volume of the solid is given by the triple iterated integral $\int_{-1}^{1}\int_{-1}^{1}\int_{4\,x^2+4\,y^2}^{16-4\,x^2-4\,y^2} 1\, dz\, dy\, dx$:

In[1560]:= `Integrate[1, {x, 0, 1}, {y, -1, 0}, {z, 4 x^2 + 4 y^2, 16 - 4 x^2 - y^2}]`

Out[1560]= $\dfrac{35}{3}$

■ Exercises

In Exercises 1 through 4, evaluate the given iterated integrals:

1. $\int_{0}^{1}\int_{0}^{x}\int_{0}^{y^2}(x+y+z)\,dz\,dy\,dx$

2. $\int_{0}^{3}\int_{0}^{\sin y}\int_{0}^{y+z}x\,y\,z\,dx\,dz\,dy$

3. $\int_{0}^{\pi}\int_{0}^{\theta}\int_{0}^{r\cos\theta}r\,z^2\,dz\,dr\,d\theta$

4. $\int_{0}^{1}\int_{\sqrt{x}}^{1}\int_{0}^{1-y}z\log(1+x\,y)\,dz\,dy\,dx$

In Exercises 5 through 8, evaluate the given triple integrals:

5. $\iiint_{W}(x+y\,z)\,dV$, where $W=\{(x,\,y,\,z):0\le x\le 1,\ 0\le y\le\sqrt{x}\ ,\ 0\le z\le y^2\}$.

6. $\iiint_{W}\sin y\,dV$, where W lies under the plane $z=1+x+y$ and above the triangular region bounded by $x=0$, $x=2$, and $y=3\,x$.

7. $\iiint_{W}z\,dV$, where W is bounded by the paraboloid $z=4-x^2-y^2$ and $z=0$.

8. $\iiint_{W}f(x,\,y,\,z)\,dV$, where $f(x,\,y,\,z)=z^2$ and W is bounded between the cone $z=\sqrt{x^2+y^2}$ and $z=9$.

9. The triple integral $\int_{0}^{1}\int_{x/2}^{1-x/2}\int_{0}^{2-x-2\,y}dz\,dy\,dx$ represents the volume of a solid S. Evaluate this integral. Then make a plot of S and describe it.

10. Midpoint Rule for Triple Integrals:

a. Develop a subroutine called **MTRIPLERSUM** to compute the triple Riemann sum of the triple integral $\iiint_{B}f(x,\,y,\,z)\,dV$ over the box domain $B=\{(x,\,y,\,z):a\le x\le b,\ c\le y\le d,\ p\le z\le q\}$ for uniform partitions and using the center midpoint of each sub-box as base point. HINT: Modify the subroutine **MDOUBLERSUM** in Section 15.1 of this text.

b. Use your subroutine **MTRIPLESUM** in part a) to compute the triple Riemann sum of $\iiint_{B}(x^2+y^2+z^2)^{3/2}\,dV$ over the box $B=\{(x,\,y,\,z):0\le x\le 1,\ 0\le y\le 2,\ 0\le z\le 3\}$ by dividing B into 48 equal sub-boxes, that is, cubes having side length of 1/2.

c. Repeat part b) by dividing B into cubes having side length of $1/4$ and more generally into cubes having side length of $1/2^n$ for n sufficiently large in order to obtain an approximation accurate to 2 decimal places.

d. Verify your answer in part c) using *Mathematica*'s **NIntegrate** command.

■ 15.4 Integration in Polar, Cylindrical, and Spherical Coordinates

Students should read Section 15.4 of Rogawski's *Calculus* [1] for a detailed discussion of the material presented in this section.

■ 15.4.1 Double Integrals in Polar Coordinates

The following Change of Variables Formula converts a double integral in rectangular coordinates to one in polar coordinates:

Change of Variables Formula (Polar Coordinates):

I. Polar Rectangles: If $R = \{(r, \theta) : \theta_1 \le \theta \le \theta_2, r_1 \le r \le r_2\}$, then

$$\iint_R f(x, y)\, dA = \int_{\theta_1}^{\theta_2} \int_{r_1}^{r_2} f(r\cos\theta, r\sin\theta)\, r\, dr\, d\theta$$

II. Polar Regions: If $D = \{(r, \theta) : \theta_1 \le \theta \le \theta_2, \alpha(\theta) \le r \le \beta(\theta)\}$, then

$$\iint_D f(x, y)\, dA = \int_{\theta_1}^{\theta_2} \int_{\alpha(\theta)}^{\beta(\theta)} f(r\cos\theta, r\sin\theta)\, r\, dr\, d\theta$$

Example 15.8. Calculate the volume of the solid region bounded by the paraboloid $f(x) = 4 - x^2 - y^2$ and the *xy*-plane using polar coordinates.

Solution: We first plot the paraboloid:

```
In[1561]:= f[x_, y_] = 4 - x^2 - y^2
          Plot3D[f[x, y], {x, -2, 2}, {y, -2, 2}, PlotRange → {0, 4}, ImageSize → {250}]
```

Out[1561]= $4 - x^2 - y^2$

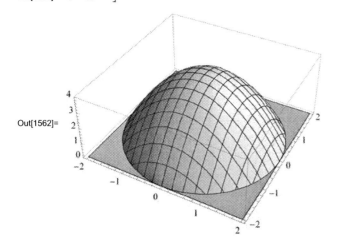

Out[1562]=

The circular domain D can be easily described in polar coordinates by the polar rectangle $R = \{(r, \theta) : 0 \le r \le 2, 0 \le \theta \le 2\pi\}$. Thus, the volume of the solid is given by the corresponding double integral $\int_0^{2\pi} \int_0^2 f(r\cos\theta, r\sin\theta)\, r\, dr\, d\theta$ in polar coordinates:

In[1563]:= **Clear[r, θ];**
Integrate[r * f[r * Cos[θ], r * Sin[θ]], {r, 0, 2}, {θ, 0, 2 Pi}]

Out[1564]= 8π

Observe that here $f(x, y)$ simplifies nicely in polar coordinates:

In[1565]:= **f[r * Cos[θ], r * Sin[θ]]**
Simplify[%]

Out[1565]= $4 - r^2 \text{Cos}[\theta]^2 - r^2 \text{Sin}[\theta]^2$

Out[1566]= $4 - r^2$

NOTE: Evaluating the same double integral in rectangular coordinates by hand would be quite tedious. This is not a problem with *Mathematica*, however:

In[1567]:= **Integrate[f[x, y], {x, -2, 2}, {y, -Sqrt[4 - x^2], Sqrt[4 - x^2]}]**

Out[1567]= 8π

■ 15.4.2 Triple Integrals in Cylindrical Coordinates

The following Change of Variables Formula converts a triple integral in rectangular coordinates to one in cylindrical coordinates:

Change of Variables Formula (Cylindrical Coordinates): If a solid region W is described by $\theta_1 \le \theta \le \theta_2$, $\alpha(\theta) \le r \le \beta(\theta)$, and $z_1(r, \theta) \le z \le z_2(r, \theta)$, then

$$\iiint_W f(x, y, z) \, dV = \int_{\theta_1}^{\theta_2} \int_{\alpha(\theta)}^{\beta(\theta)} \int_{z_1(r,\theta)}^{z_2(r,\theta)} f(r \cos \theta, r \sin \theta, z) \, r \, dz \, dr \, d\theta$$

Example 15.9. Use cylindrical coordinates to calculate the triple integral $\iiint_W z \, dV$, where W is the solid region bounded above by the plane $z = 8 - x - y$, below by the paraboloid $z = 4 - x^2 - y^2$, and inside the cylinder $x^2 + y^2 = 4$.

Solution: Since W lies inside the cylinder $x^2 + y^2 = 4$, this implies that it has a circular base on the *xy*-plane given by the same equation, which can be described in polar coordinates by $0 \le \theta \le 2\pi$ and $0 \le r \le 2$. Here is a plot of all three surfaces (plane, paraboloid, and cylinder):

```
In[1568]:= plotplane = Plot3D[8 - x - y, {x, -2, 2}, {y, -2, 2}];
        plotparaboloid = Plot3D[4 - x^2 - y^2, {x, -2, 2}, {y, -2, 2}];
        plotcylinder =
           ParametricPlot3D[{2 * Cos[θ], 2 * Sin[θ], z}, {θ, 0, 2 π}, {z, 0, 12}];
        Show[plotplane, plotparaboloid, plotcylinder, PlotRange → All, ImageSize → {250}]
```

Out[1571]=

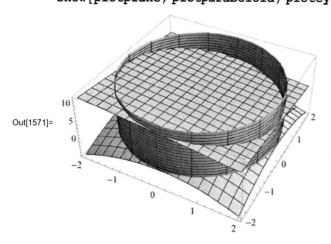

Since W is bounded in z by $4 - x^2 - y^2 \le z \le 8 - x - y$, or in cylindrical coordinates, $4 - r\cos\theta - r\sin\theta \le z \le 4 - r^2$, it follows that the given triple integral transforms to

$$\int_0^{2\pi} \int_0^2 \int_{4-r^2}^{4-r\cos\theta-r\sin\theta} z\, r\, dz\, dr\, d\theta$$

Evaluating this integral in *Mathematica* yields the answer

```
In[1572]:= Integrate[z * r, {θ, 0, 2 π}, {r, 0, 2},
           {z, 4 - r * Cos[θ] - r * Sin[θ], 8 + r * Cos[θ] + r * Sin[θ]}]
```

Out[1572]= $96\,\pi$

■ 15.4.3 Triple Integrals in Spherical Coordinates

The following Change of Variables Formula converts a triple integral in rectangular coordinates to one in spherical coordinates:

Change of Variables Formula (Spherical Coordinates): If a solid region W is described by $\theta_1 \le \theta \le \theta_2$, $\phi_1 \le \phi \le \phi_2$, and $\rho_1(\theta, \phi) \le \rho \le \rho_2(\theta, \phi)$, then

$$\iiint_W f(x, y, z)\, dV = \int_{\theta_1}^{\theta_2} \int_{\phi_1}^{\phi_2} \int_{\rho_1(\theta,\phi)}^{\rho_2(\theta,\phi)} f(\rho\cos\theta\sin\phi,\ \rho\sin\theta\sin\phi,\ \rho\cos\phi)\, \rho^2\, \sin\phi\, d\rho\, d\phi\, d\theta$$

Example 15.10. Use spherical coordinates to calculate the volume of the solid W lying inside the sphere $x^2 + y^2 + z^2 = z$ and above the cone $z = \sqrt{x^2 + y^2}$.

Solution: In spherical coordinates, the equation of the sphere is given by

$$\rho^2 = \rho\,\cos\phi$$

or equivalently, $\rho = \cos\phi$. Similarly, the equation of the cone transforms to

$$\rho\cos\phi = \sqrt{(\rho\cos\theta\sin\phi)^2 + (\rho\sin\theta\sin\phi)^2}\ = \rho\,\sin\phi$$

It follows that $\cos\phi = \sin\phi$, or $\phi = \pi/4$. Therefore, the cone makes an angle of 45 degrees with respect to the *z*-axis, as shown in the following plot along with the top half of the sphere:

In[1573]:= **Clear[ρ]**

plotcone = ParametricPlot3D[{ρ Cos[θ] Sin[Pi / 4], ρ Sin[θ] Sin[Pi / 4], ρ Cos[Pi / 4]},
{θ, 0, 2 Pi}, {ρ, 0, Sqrt[2] / 2}];

plotsphere = ParametricPlot3D[{Cos[ϕ] Cos[θ] Sin[ϕ],
Cos[ϕ] Sin[θ] Sin[ϕ], Cos[ϕ] Cos[ϕ]}, {θ, 0, 2 Pi}, {ϕ, 0, Pi / 4}];

Show[plotcone, plotsphere, PlotRange $\rightarrow$ All, ViewPoint $\rightarrow$ {1, 1, 1 / 4},
ImageSize $\rightarrow$ {250}]

Out[1576]=

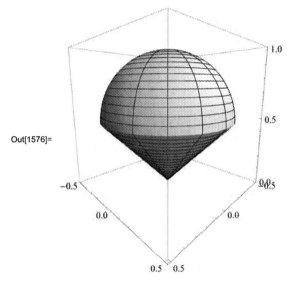

It is now clear that the solid *W* is described by $0 \le \theta \le 2\pi$, $0 \le \phi \le \pi/4$, and $0 \le \rho \le \cos\phi$. Thus, its volume is given by the triple integral

$$\int_0^{2\pi} \int_0^{\pi/4} \int_0^{\cos\phi} \rho^2 \sin\phi \, d\rho \, d\phi \, d\theta$$

which in *Mathematica* evaluates to

In[1577]:= **Integrate[ρ^2 * Sin[ϕ], {θ, 0, 2 Pi}, {ϕ, 0, Pi / 4}, {ρ, 0, Cos[ϕ]}]**

Out[1577]= $\dfrac{\pi}{8}$

■ Exercises

In Exercises 1 through 4, evaluate the given double integral by converting to polar coordinates:

1. $\int_{-1}^{1} \int_{-\sqrt{1-x^2}}^{\sqrt{1-x^2}} \left(1 - x^2 - y^2\right) dy \, dx$ 2. $\int_0^2 \int_0^{\sqrt{4-x^2}} e^{-(x^2+y^2)} \, dy \, dx$

3. $\iint_D x \log y \, dA$, where *D* is the annulus (donut-shaped region) with inner radius 1 and outer radius 3.

4. $\iint_D \arctan \frac{y}{x} \, dA$, where *D* is the region inside the cardioid $r = 1 + \cos t$.

5. Use polar coordinates to calculate the volume of the solid that lies below the paraboloid $z = x^2 + y^2$ and inside the cylinder $x^2 + y^2 = 2y$.

6. Evaluate the triple integral $\int_0^2 \int_0^{\sqrt{4-x^2}} \int_0^{\sqrt{4-x^2-y^2}} (x^2 + y^2) \, dz \, dy \, dx$ by converting to cylindrical coordinates.

7. Use cylindrical coordinates to calculate the triple integral $\int\int\int_W (x^2 + y^2) \, dV$, where W is the solid bounded between the two paraboloids $z = x^2 + y^2$ and $z = 8 - x^2 - y^2$.

8. Evaluate the triple integral $\int_{-2}^2 \int_{-\sqrt{4-x^2}}^{\sqrt{4-x^2}} \int_{\sqrt{x^2+y^2}}^{\sqrt{4-x^2-y^2}} (x^2 + y^2 + z^2) \, dz \, dy \, dx$ by converting to spherical coordinates.

9. The solid defined by the spherical equation $\rho = \sin \phi$ is called the *torus*.
a. Plot the torus.
b. Calculate the volume of the torus.

10. Ice-Cream Cone: A solid W in the shape of an ice-cream cone is bounded below by the cylinder $z = \sqrt{x^2 + y^2}$ and above by the sphere $x^2 + y^2 + z^2 = 8$. Plot W and determine its volume.

■ 15.5 Applications of Multiple Integrals

Students should read Section 15.5 of Rogawski's *Calculus* [1] for a detailed discussion of the material presented in this section.

Mass as Double Integral: Consider a lamina (thin plate) D in $\mathbb{R}^2$ with continous mass density $\rho(x, y)$. Then the mass of D is given by the double integral

$$M = \int\int_D \rho(x, y) \, dA$$

where the domain of integration is given by the region that describes the lamina D.

Example 15.11. Calculate the mass of the lamina D bounded between the parabola $y = x^2$ and $y = 4$ with density $\rho(x, y) = y$.

Solution: Here is a plot of the lamina D (shaded):

In[1578]:= **Plot[{x^2, 4}, {x, -2, 2}, ImageSize → {250}, Filling → {2 → {1}}]**

Out[1578]=

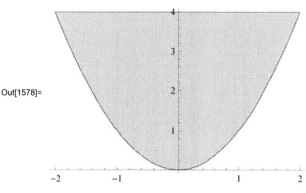

We can view D as a Type I region described by $-2 \le x \le 2$ and $x^2 \le y \le 4$. Thus. the mass of the lamina is given by the double integral:

In[1579]:= **Integrate[y, {x, -2, 2}, {y, x^2, 4}]**

Out[1579]= $\dfrac{128}{5}$

NOTE: Mass of a lamina can also be interpreted as the volune of the solid bounded by its density function over D as shown in the following plot:

In[1580]:= **Plot3D[y, {x, -2, 2}, {y, 0, 4}, RegionFunction -> (#1^2 < #2 < 4 &),**
   Filling → Bottom, Mesh → None, ImageSize → 250]

Out[1580]=

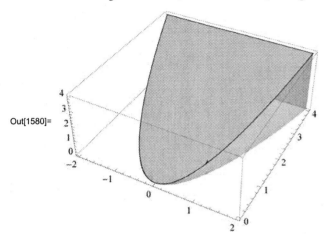

Example 15.12. Suppose a circular metal plate D, bounded by $x^2 + y^2 = 9$, has electrical charge density $\rho(x, y) = \sqrt{9 - x^2 - y^2}$. Calculate the total charge of the plate.

Solution: Here is a plot of the metal plate D (shaded):

In[1581]:= **Integrate[y, {x, -2, 2}, {y, x^2, 4}]**

Out[1581]= $\dfrac{128}{5}$

In[1582]:= **Plot[{Sqrt[9 - x^2], -Sqrt[9 - x^2]}, {x, -3, 3},**
   ImageSize → {250}, Filling → {2 → {1}}, AspectRatio → 1]

Out[1582]=

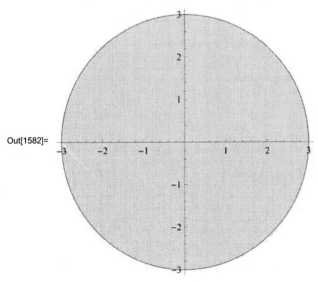

We shall calculate the total charge of the plate using polar coordinates, which will simplify the corresponding double integral. Since $\rho(r, \theta) = \sqrt{9 - r^2}$ and D is a simple polar region described by $r = 3$, the total charge is

In[1583]:= **Integrate[Sqrt[9 - r^2] * r, {r, 0, 3}, {theta, 0, 2 Pi}]**

Out[1583]= $18\,\pi$

Mass as Triple Integral: We can extend the notion of mass to a solid region W in $\mathbb{R}^3$. Suppose W is bounded between two surfaces $z = \psi(x, y)$ and $z = \phi(x, y)$, where both are defined on the same domain D with $\psi(x, y) \le \phi(x, y)$, and has density $\rho(x, y, z)$. Then the mass of W can be expressed by the triple integral

$$M = \int\int\int_W \rho(x, y, z)\,dV = \int\int_D\int_{\psi(x,y)}^{\phi(x,y)} \rho(x, y, z)\,dz\,dA$$

Example 15.13. Calculate the mass of the solid region W bounded between the planes $z = 1 - x - y$ and $z = 1 + x + y$ and situated over the triangular domain D bounded by $x = 0$, $y = 0$, and $y = 1 - x$. Assume the density of W is given by $\rho(x, y, z) = 1 + x^2 + y^2$.

Solution: Here is a plot of the solid region W:

In[1584]:= **Plot3D[{1 - x - y, 1 + x + y}, {x, 0, 1}, {y, 0, 1 - x}, ViewPoint → {1, 1, 1},**
      Filling → {1 → 1, 2 → 1}, Ticks → {Automatic, Automatic, {1, 2}},
      ImageSize → {250}, ImagePadding → {{15, 15}, {15, 15}}]

Out[1584]=

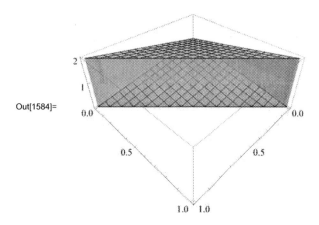

The mass of the solid is given by the triple iterated integral $\int_0^1 \int_0^{1-x} \int_{1-x-y}^{1+x+y} \left(1 + x^2 + y^2\right) dz\,dy\,dx$:

In[1585]:= **Integrate[1 + x^2 + y^2, {x, 0, 1}, {y, 0, 1 - x}, {z, 1 - x - y, 1 + x + y}]**

Out[1585]= $\dfrac{14}{15}$

Center of Mass: Given a lamina D in $\mathbb{R}^2$, its *center of mass* (x_{CM}, y_{CM}) (or balance point) is defined as the ratio of its moments (with respect to the coordinate axes) to its mass:

$$x_{CM} = \frac{M_y}{M}, \quad y_{CM} = \frac{M_x}{M}$$

where the moments M_y and M_x are defined by

$$M_y = \frac{1}{A}\int\int_D x\,\rho(x, y)\,dA, \quad M_x = \frac{1}{A}\int\int_D y\,\rho(x, y)\,dA$$

NOTE: In case the lamina has uniform density, that is, $\rho(x, y) = 1$, then the center of mass is the same as the *centroid* whose coordinates represent averages of the coordinates over the lamina.

Center of mass (and centroid) can be naturally extended to solid objects in $\mathbb{R}^3$. Refer to your textbook for further details.

Example 15.14. Calculate the mass of the solid region W bounded between the planes $z = 1 - x - y$ and $z = 1 + x + y$ and situated over the triangular domain D bounded by $x = 0$, $y = 0$, and $y = 1 - x$. Assume the density of W is given by $\rho(x, y, z) = 1 + x^2 + y^2$.

■ Exercises

In Exercises 1 and 2, find the mass of the given lamina D.
1. D is bounded between $y = \sin(\pi x)$ and $y = 0$ along the interval $[0, 1]$ and has density $\rho(x, y) = x(1 - x)$.
2. D is bounded by the lines $y = x + 1$, $y = -2x - 2$, and $x = 1$ and has density $\rho(x, y) = 1 + y^2$.

3. Find the center of mass of the lamina D in Exercises 1 and 2.

4. Find the centroid of the lamina in Exercises 1 and 2. Compare the centroid of each lamina with its center of mass.

In Exercises 5 and 6, find the mass of the given solidi object W.
5. W is the interior of the tetrahedron enclosed by the planes $x = 0$, $y = 0$, $z = 0$, and $z = 1 - x - y$ and has density $\rho(x, y, z) = 1 - z$.

6. W is the ice-cream cone bounded below by the cylinder $z = \sqrt{x^2 + y^2}$ and above by the sphere $x^2 + y^2 + z^2 = 8$ and has density $\rho(x, y, z) = z^2$.

7. Find the center of mass of the tetrahedron in Exercises 5 and 6. Refer to your textbook for appropriate formulas.

8. Find the centroid of the tetrahedron in Exercises 5 and 6. Compare this with its center of mass. Refer to your textbook for appropriate formulas.

■ 15.6 Change of Variables

Students should read Section 15.6 of Rogawski's *Calculus* [1] for a detailed discussion of the material presented in this section.

A change of variables is often useful for simplifying integrals of a single variable (commonly referred to as *u*-substitution):

$$\int_a^b f(x) \, dx = \int_c^d f(g(u)) \, g'(u) \, du$$

where $x = g(u)$, $a = g(c)$, and $b = g(d)$. This substitution formula allows one to transformation an integral in the variable x to one in a new variable u. Observe that the interval $[c, d]$ is mapped to interval $[a, b]$ under the function g.

This technique can be extended to double integrals of the form $\iint_D f(x, y) \, dx \, dy$, where a change of variables is described by a transformation $G(u, v) = (x, y)$, which maps a region D_0 in the uv-coordinate plane to the region D in the xy-coordinate plane.

The following Change of Variables Formula converts a double integral from the xy-coordinate system to a new coordinate system defined by u and v:

Change of Variables Formula (Coordinate Transformation): If $G(u, v) = (x(u, v), y(u, v))$ is a C^1-mapping from D_0 to D, then

$$\iint_D f(x, y) \, dx \, dy = \iint_{D_0} f(x(u, v), y(u, v)) \left| \frac{\partial(x, y)}{\partial(u, v)} \right| du \, dv$$

where $\left| \frac{\partial(x,y)}{\partial(u,v)} \right|$, referred to as the *Jacobian* of G and also denoted by $\mathrm{Jac}(G)$, is given by

$$\mathrm{Jac}(G) = \left| \frac{\partial(x,\,y)}{\partial(u,\,v)} \right| = \left| \begin{matrix} \frac{\partial x}{\partial u} & \frac{\partial x}{\partial v} \\ \frac{\partial y}{\partial u} & \frac{\partial y}{\partial v} \end{matrix} \right| = \frac{\partial x}{\partial u}\frac{\partial y}{\partial v} - \frac{\partial x}{\partial v}\frac{\partial y}{\partial u}$$

The Jacobian relates the area of any infinitesimal region inside D_0 with the corresponding region inside $D = G(D_0)$. In fact, if G is a linear map, then $\mathrm{Jac}(G)$ is constant and is equal in magnitude to the ratio of the areas of D to that of D_0:

Jacobian of a Linear Map: If $G(u,\,v) = (A\,u + C\,v,\, B\,u + D\,v)$ is a linear mapping from D_0 to D, then $\mathrm{Jac}(G)$ is constant with value

$$\mathrm{Jac}(G) = \left| \begin{matrix} A & C \\ B & D \end{matrix} \right| = A\,D - B\,C$$

Moreover,

$$\mathrm{Area}(D) = |\mathrm{Jac}(G)|\,\mathrm{Area}(D_0)$$

Refer to your textbook for a detailed discussion of transformations of plane regions.

Example 15.12. Make an appropriate changes of variables to calculate the double integral $\iint_D x\,y\,d\,A$, where D is the region bounded by the curves $x\,y = 1$, $x\,y = 2$, $x\,y^2 = 1$, and $x\,y^2 = 2$.

Solution: Here is a plot of the shaded region D bounded by the four given curves:

```
In[1586]:= plot1 = ContourPlot[{x * y == 1, x * y == 2, x * y^2 == 1, x * y^2 == 2},
        {x, 0, 5}, {y, 0, 5}, AspectRatio → Automatic, ImageSize → {250}];
    plot2 = ContourPlot[1, {x, 0, 5}, {y, 0, 5}, AspectRatio → Automatic,
        RegionFunction → Function[{x, y}, 1 < x y < 2 && 1 < x y^2 < 2],
        ImageSize → {250}, PlotPoints → 100];
    Show[
     plot1,
     plot2]
```

Out[1588]=

Observe that D is rather complicated. Since D can be described by the inequalities $1 < x\,y < 2$ and $1 < x\,y^2 < 2$, we make the natural change of variables $u = x\,y$ and $v = x\,y^2$, which transforms D to a simple square region D_0 in the *uv*-plane bounded by

$u = 1, u = 2, v = 1,$ and $v = 2$:

In[1589]:= `ContourPlot[1, {u, 0, 3}, {v, 0, 3}, ImageSize → {250},`
`    RegionFunction → Function[{u, v}, 1 < u < 2 && 1 < v < 2]]`

Out[1589]=

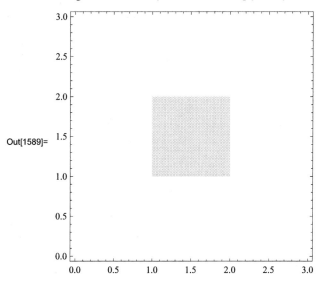

To find the formula for our transformation $G(u, v) = (x(u, v), y(u, v))$ that maps D_0 to D, we solve for x and y in terms of u and v:

In[1590]:= `Clear[sol, x, y, u, v]`
`    sol = Solve[{u == x * y, v == x * y^2}, {x, y}]`

Out[1591]= $\left\{\left\{x \to \dfrac{u^2}{v}, \ y \to \dfrac{v}{u}\right\}\right\}$

It follows that $G(u, v) = \left(u^2/v, \ v/u\right)$ and the corresponding Jacobian is

In[1592]:= `x = sol[[1, 1, 2]]`
`    y = sol[[1, 2, 2]]`
`    Jac = D[x, u] * D[y, v] - D[x, v] * D[y, u]`

Out[1592]= $\dfrac{u^2}{v}$

Out[1593]= $\dfrac{v}{u}$

Out[1594]= $\dfrac{1}{v}$

Thus, the given integral transforms to $\iint_D x\,y\,dA = \iint_{D_0} \dfrac{u}{v}\,dA = \int_1^2\int_1^2 \dfrac{u}{v}\,dv\,du$ with value

In[1595]:= `Integrate[u / v, {u, 1, 2}, {v, 1, 2}]`

Out[1595]= $\dfrac{3\,\mathrm{Log}[2]}{2}$

▪ Exercises

1. Consider the transformation $G(u, v) = (2\,u + v, u - 3\,v)$.

a. Set $D = G(D_0)$ where $D_0 = \{0 \le u \le 1, 0 \le v \le 2\}$. Make a plot of D and describe its shape.

b. Compute Jac(G).

c. Compare the area of D with that of D_0. How does this relate to Jac(G)?

2. Compute the area of the ellipse $\frac{x^2}{4} + \frac{y^2}{9} = 1$ by viewing it as a transformation of the unit circle $u^2 + v^2 = 1$ under a linear map $G(u, v) = (x(u, v), y(u, v))$ and using the area relationship described by Jac(G).

3. Evaluate the integral $\iint_D x\, y\, d A$, where D is the region in the first quadrant bounded by the equations $y = x$, $y = 4\,x$, $x\,y = 1$, and $x\,y = 4$. HINT: Consider the change of variables $u = x\,y$ and $v = y$.

4. Evaluate the integral $\iint_D (x + y)/(x - y)\, d A$, where D is the parallelogram bounded by the lines $x - y = 1$, $x - y = 3$, $2\,x + y = 0$, and $2\,x + y = 2$. HINT: Consider the change of variables $u = x - y$ and $v = 2\,x + y$.

5. Evaluate the integral $\iint_D \frac{y}{x}\, d A$, where D is the region bounded by the circles $x^2 + y^2 = 1$, $x^2 + y^2 = 4$ and lines $y = x$, $y = 3\,x$. HINT: Consider the change of variables $u = x^2 + y^2$ and $v = y/x$.

Chapter 16   Line and Surface Integrals

Useful Tip: If you are reading the electronic version of this publication formatted as a *Mathematica* Notebook, then it is possible to view 3-D plots generated by *Mathematica* from different perspectives. First, place your screen cursor over the plot. Then drag the mouse while pressing down on the left mouse button to rotate the plot.

■ 16.1 Vector Fields

Students should read Section 16.1 of Rogawski's *Calculus* [1] for a detailed discussion of the material presented in this section.

Let F_1, F_2, and F_3 be functions of x, y, and z. The vector-valued function

$$\mathbf{F}(x,\ y,\ z) = \langle F_1(x,\ y,\ z),\ F_2(x,\ y,\ z),\ F_3(x,\ y,\ z)\rangle$$

is called a *vector field*. We have already encountered a vector field in the form of the gradient of a function. Other useful examples of vector fields are the gravitational force, the velocity of fluid, magnetic fields, and electric fields.

We use the *Mathematica* commands **VectorFieldPlot** and **VectorFieldPlot3D** to plot the graphs of vector fields. However, before using these commands, it is advisable to load the **VectorFieldPlots** package. This is done by evaluating

In[1596]:= **Needs["VectorFieldPlots`"]**

Example 16.1. Draw the following vector fields.
a) $\mathbf{F}(x,\ y) = \langle \sin y,\ \cos x\rangle$ b) $\mathbf{F}(x,\ y,\ z) = \langle y,\ x+z,\ 2x-y\rangle$

Solution:
a)

In[1597]:= **Clear[F, x, y, z]**
        F[x_, y_] = {Sin[y], Cos[x]}

Out[1598]= {Sin[y], Cos[x]}

In[1599]:= **VectorFieldPlot[F[x, y], {x, -5, 5}, {y, -4, 4}, ImageSize → {250}]**

Out[1599]=

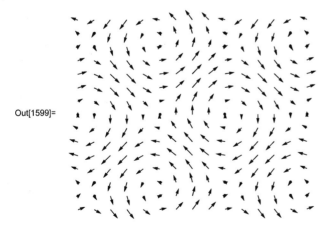

Here is another display of the preceding vector field with some options specified.

In[1600]:= `VectorFieldPlot[F[x, y], {x, -5, 5}, {y, -4, 4}, Axes → True,`
       `AxesOrigin → {0, 0}, Frame → False, ColorFunction → Hue, ImageSize → {250}]`

Out[1600]=

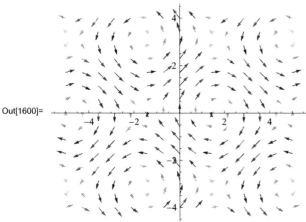

To see other available options of **VectorFieldPlot**, evaluate the command **Options[VectorFieldPlot]**.

b) We shall use two of the options of **VectorFieldPlot3D**, which does not have as many options as **VectorFieldPlot**. (Again, you can find these by evaluating **Options[VectorFieldPlot3D]**.)

In[1601]:= `Clear[F, x, y, z]`
       $F[x\_, y\_, z\_] = \{y z^2, x z^2, 2 x y z\}$
       `VectorFieldPlot3D[F[x, y, z], {x, -3, 3}, {y, -3, 3}, {z, -3, 3},`
        `ColorFunction → Hue, VectorHeads → True, ImageSize → {250}]`

Out[1602]= $\left\{y z^2, x z^2, 2 x y z\right\}$

Out[1603]=

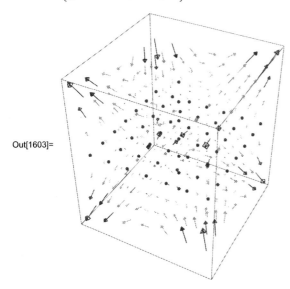

Example 16.2. Draw the unit radial vector fields:

a) $F(x, y) = \left\langle \dfrac{x}{\sqrt{x^2+y^2}}, \dfrac{y}{\sqrt{x^2+y^2}} \right\rangle$ b) $F(x, y, z) = \left\langle \dfrac{x}{\sqrt{x^2+y^2+z^2}}, \dfrac{y}{\sqrt{x^2+y^2+z^2}}, \dfrac{z}{\sqrt{x^2+y^2+z^2}} \right\rangle$

Solution: For convenience, we define both vector fields to be 0 at the origin. We shall use the **If** command to do so.

a)

In[1604]:= `Clear[F, x, y]`

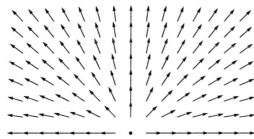

`VectorFieldPlot[F[x, y], {x, -3, 3}, {y, -3, 3}, ImageSize → {250}]`

Out[1605]= $\text{If}\left[x^2 + y^2 \neq 0, \dfrac{\{x, y\}}{\sqrt{x^2 + y^2}}, \{0, 0\}\right]$

Out[1606]=

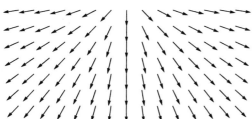

b)

In[1607]:= `Clear[F, x, y, z]`

$$F[x\_, y\_, z\_] = If\left[x^2 + y^2 + z^2 \neq 0, \frac{\{x, y, z\}}{\sqrt{x^2 + y^2 + z^2}}, \{0, 0, 0\}\right]$$

`VectorFieldPlot3D[F[x, y, z], {x, -3, 3}, {y, -3, 3}, {z, -3, 3},`
`  ColorFunction → Hue, VectorHeads → True, ImageSize → {250}]`

Out[1608]= $If\left[x^2 + y^2 + z^2 \neq 0, \frac{\{x, y, z\}}{\sqrt{x^2 + y^2 + z^2}}, \{0, 0, 0\}\right]$

Out[1609]=

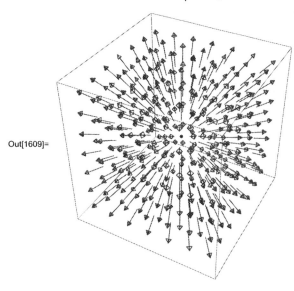

■ Exercises

In Exercise 1 through 4, draw the given vector fields.

1. $\mathbf{F}(x, y) = \langle y^2 - 2xy, \ xy + 6x^2 \rangle$

2. $\mathbf{F}(x, y, z) = \langle \sin x, \cos y, xz \rangle$

3. $\mathbf{F}(x, y) = \left\langle -\frac{y}{\sqrt{x^2+y^2}}, \frac{x}{\sqrt{x^2+y^2}} \right\rangle$

4. $\mathbf{F}(x, y, z) = \langle x + \cos(xz), y \sin(xy), xz \cos(yz) \rangle$

In Exerices 5 and 6, calculate and plot the gradient vector field for each of the following functions.

5. $f(x, y) = \ln(x + y^2)$

6. $f(x, y, z) = \sin x \ (\cos z / y)$

■ 16.2 Line Integrals

Students should read Section 16.2 of Rogawski's *Calculus* [1] for a detailed discussion of the material presented in this section.

Suppose C is a smooth curve in space whose parametric equations are given by

$$x = x(t), \ y = y(t), \ z = z(t)$$

where $a \leq t \leq b$. Let $C_1, \ C_2, \ C_3, \ ...., \ C_N$ be a partition of the curve C with arc length $\Delta s_1, \ \Delta s_2, \ \Delta s_3, \ ... , \ \Delta s_N$ and let $P_1, \ P_2, \ P_3, \ ... , \ P_N$ be points on the subarcs.

If $f(x, y, z)$ is a function that is continuous on the curve C, then the *line integral of f* is defined by

$$\int_C f(x, y, z) \, ds = \lim_{\Delta s_i \to 0} \sum_{i=1}^{N} f(P_i) \, \Delta s_i$$

NOTE: If $\mathbf{c}(t) = \langle x(t), \ y(t), \ z(t) \rangle$ is the vector equation of the curve C, then it can be shown (refer to your calculus textbook) that

$$\int_C f(x, y, z) \, ds = \int_a^b f(\mathbf{c}(t)) \, \|\mathbf{c}'(t)\| \, dt$$

In addition, if $\mathbf{F}(x, y, z) = \langle F_1, F_2, F_3 \rangle$ is a vector field that is continuous on C, then the *line integral* of $\mathbf{F}$ over C is given by

$$\int_C \mathbf{F}(x, y, z) \cdot d\mathbf{s} = \int_C (\mathbf{F} \cdot \mathbf{T}) \, ds = \int_a^b \mathbf{F}(\mathbf{c}(t)) \cdot \mathbf{c}'(t) \, dt$$

where $\mathbf{T}$ is the unit vector $\mathbf{T} = \frac{\mathbf{c}'(t)}{\|\mathbf{c}'(t)\|}$ and $\mathbf{F} \cdot \mathbf{T}$ is the dot product of $\mathbf{F}$ and $\mathbf{T}$.

Example 16.3. Find $\int_C f(x, y, z) \, ds$, where $f(x, y, z) = x\, y + z^2$ and C is given by $x = t$, $y = t^2$, and $z = t^3$, for $0 \le t \le 1$.

Solution:

```
In[1610]:= Clear[x, y, z, t, f, c]
        f[x_, y_, z_] = x^2 y + x z
        x[t_] = t
        y[t_] = t^2
        z[t_] = t^3
        c[t_] = {x[t], y[t], z[t]}
```

Out[1611]= $x^2\, y + x\, z$

Out[1612]= t

Out[1613]= t^2

Out[1614]= t^3

Out[1615]= $\left\{t, \ t^2, \ t^3\right\}$

In[1616]:= $\int_0^1 \mathbf{f[x[t], y[t], z[t]]\ Norm[c'[t]]\ dt}$

Out[1616]= $-\dfrac{1}{76545\sqrt{\dfrac{7}{2}\left(2\,i+\sqrt{5}\,\right)}}$

$\left(2\,(-1)^{1/4}\left(84\,987\,(-1)^{3/4}\sqrt{2\,i+\sqrt{5}}\,-532\,i\,\sqrt{14}\ \text{EllipticE}\left[\text{ArcSin}\left[\dfrac{3+3\,i}{\sqrt{2\left(-2\,i+\sqrt{5}\,\right)}}\right],\right.\right.\right.$

$\left.\dfrac{2\,i-\sqrt{5}}{2\,i+\sqrt{5}}\right]-266\,\sqrt{70}\ \text{EllipticE}\left[\text{ArcSin}\left[\dfrac{3+3\,i}{\sqrt{2\left(-2\,i+\sqrt{5}\,\right)}}\right],\dfrac{2\,i-\sqrt{5}}{2\,i+\sqrt{5}}\right]+$

$415\,i\,\sqrt{14}\ \text{EllipticF}\left[\text{ArcSin}\left[\dfrac{3+3\,i}{\sqrt{2\left(-2\,i+\sqrt{5}\,\right)}}\right],\dfrac{2\,i-\sqrt{5}}{2\,i+\sqrt{5}}\right]+$

$\left.\left.266\,\sqrt{70}\ \text{EllipticF}\left[\text{ArcSin}\left[\dfrac{3+3\,i}{\sqrt{2\left(-2\,i+\sqrt{5}\,\right)}}\right],\dfrac{2\,i-\sqrt{5}}{2\,i+\sqrt{5}}\right]\right)\right)$

Here is a numerical approximation of the preceding line integral.

In[1617]:= **NIntegrate[f[x[t], y[t], z[t]] Norm[c'[t]], {t, 0, 1}]**

Out[1617]= 1.16521

Example 16.4. Find $\int_C \mathbf{F}(x, y, z)\cdot d\mathbf{s}$, where $\mathbf{F}(x, y, z) = \langle x\,z,\ z\,y^2,\ y\,x^2\rangle$ and the curve C is given by $x = 2\,t$, $y = \sin t$, and $z = \cos t$, $0 \le t \le 2\,\pi$.

Solution:

In[1618]:= **Clear[x, y, z, t, f, c]**
F[x_, y_, z_] = {x z, z y², y x²}
x[t_] = 2 t
y[t_] = Sin[t]
z[t_] = Cos[t]
c[t_] = {x[t], y[t], z[t]}

Out[1619]= $\{x\, z,\ y^2\, z,\ x^2\, y\}$

Out[1620]= 2 t

Out[1621]= Sin[t]

Out[1622]= Cos[t]

Out[1623]= {2 t, Sin[t], Cos[t]}

In[1624]:= $\int_0^{2\,Pi}$ **F[x[t], y[t], z[t]].c'[t] ⅆt**

Out[1624]= $\dfrac{9\,\pi}{4} - \dfrac{16\,\pi^3}{3}$

In[1625]:= **N[%]**

Out[1625]= -158.298

■ Exercises

1. Find $\int_C f(x, y, z)\, ds$, where:

a. $f(x, y, z) = x\, y^2 - 4zy$ and C is given by $x = 2\, t$, $y = t^{2/3}$, and $z = 1 - 3\, t^2$, for $0 \le t \le 1$.

b. $f(x, y, z) = \frac{yz}{x}$ and C is given by $x = \ln t$, $y = t^2$, and $z = 3\, t$, for $3 \le t \le 5$.

2. Find $\int_C \mathbf{F}(x, y) \cdot d\mathbf{s}$, where:

a. $\mathbf{F}(x, y) = \left\langle e^{3\,x-2\,y},\ e^{2\,x+3\,y} \right\rangle$ and C is given by $x = 2\, t$, $y = \sin t$, $0 \le t \le \pi$

b. $\mathbf{F}(x, y) = \left\langle x^2,\ yx + y^2 \right\rangle$ and C is the unit circle center at the origin.

3. Find $\int_C \mathbf{F}(x, y, z) \cdot d\mathbf{s}$, where:

a. $\mathbf{F}(x, y, z) = \langle xyz,\ -xz,\ xy \rangle$ and C is given by $x = t$, $y = 2\, t^2$, $z = 3\, t$ $0 \le t \le 1$

b. $\mathbf{F}(x, y, z) = \left\langle xy^3,\ z + x^2,\ z^3 \right\rangle$ and C is the line segment joining $(-1,\ 2,\ -1)$ and $(1,\ 3,\ 4)$.

■ 16.3 Conservative Vector Fields

Students should read Section 16.3 of Rogawski's *Calculus* [1] for a detailed discussion of the material presented in this section.

Let $\mathbf{F}(x, y, z) = \langle F_1, F_2, F_3 \rangle$ be a vector field. Let C_1 and C_2 be any two different curves with the same initial point P and end point Q. We say that the vector field $\mathbf{F}$ is *path independent* if

$$\int_{C_1} \mathbf{F}(x, y, z) \cdot d\mathbf{s} = \int_{C_2} \mathbf{F}(x, y, z) \cdot d\mathbf{s}$$

A vector field that is path independent is called *conservative*.

NOTE 1: A vector field **F** is conservative if

$$\int_C \mathbf{F}(x, y, z) \cdot d\mathbf{s} = 0$$

for every closed curve C.

NOTE 2: If $\mathbf{F} = \nabla u$ is the gradient of a function $u = u(x, y, z)$, then we say that u is the *potential* of **F**. Moreover, if the end points of C are P and Q, we have

$$\int_C \mathbf{F}(x, y, z) \cdot d\mathbf{s} = u(P) - u(Q)$$

In particular, if the curve is closed, that is, if $P = Q$, then

$$\int_C \mathbf{F}(x, y, z) \cdot d\mathbf{s} = 0$$

Therefore, gradient is conservative. The converse of this statement is true if its domain is an open connected domain.

NOTE 3: Let $F = \langle F_1, F_2 \rangle$. If $\mathbf{F} = \nabla u = \left\langle \frac{\partial u}{\partial x}, \frac{\partial u}{\partial y} \right\rangle$, then $F_1 = \frac{\partial u}{\partial x}$ and $F_2 = \frac{\partial u}{\partial y}$. Taking the partial derivative of F_1 with respect to y and that of F_2 with respect to x and using the fact that $\frac{\partial^2 u}{\partial x \partial y} = \frac{\partial^2 u}{\partial y \partial x}$, we see that F_1 and F_2 must satisfy

$$\frac{\partial F_1}{\partial y} = \frac{\partial F_2}{\partial x}$$

This equation is used to check if a vector field is conservative. In that case, we solve $F_1 = \frac{\partial u}{\partial x}$ for u by integrating with respect to x and then use the equation $F_2 = \frac{\partial u}{\partial y}$ to find the constant of integration. Here is an example.

Example 16.5. Show that the vector function $\mathbf{F} = \langle 3 x^2 - 2 xy + 2, \ 6 y^2 - x^2 + 3 \rangle$ is conservative and find its potential.

Solution: Here, $F_1 = x y^2$ and $F_2 = x^2 y$. We now compare $\frac{\partial F_1}{\partial y}$ and $\frac{\partial F_2}{\partial x}$ to verify if **F** is conservative.

In[1626]:= `Clear[x, y, F1, F2]`
`F1[x_, y_] = 3 x^2 - 2 x y + 2`
`F2[x_, y_] = 6 y^2 - x^2 + 3`

Out[1627]= $2 + 3 x^2 - 2 x y$

Out[1628]= $3 - x^2 + 6 y^2$

In[1629]:= `D[F1[x, y], y]`
`D[F2[x, y], x]`

Out[1629]= $-2 x$

Out[1630]= $-2 x$

Thus, the vector field is conservative. To find its potential u, we integrate $F_1 = \frac{\partial u}{\partial x}$ with respect to x to get

In[1631]:= **Clear[h, u]**
   u = Integrate[F1[x, y], x] + h[y]

Out[1632]= $2 x + x^3 - x^2 y + h[y]$

Note that the addition of $h(y)$ is necessary because the constant of integration may depend on y. We now solve the equation $F_2 = \frac{\partial u}{\partial y}$ for $h'(y)$.

In[1633]:= **Clear[sol]**
   sol = Solve[D[u, y] == F2[x, y], h'[y]]

Out[1634]= $\left\{\left\{h'[y] \to 3\left(1 + 2 y^2\right)\right\}\right\}$

This means that $h'(y) = 3\left(1 + 2 y^2\right)$.

In[1635]:= **Integrate[sol[[1, 1, 2]], y]**

Out[1635]= $3 y + 2 y^3$

Hence, $h(y) = 3 y + 2 y^2$ and so $u(x, y) = 2 x + x^3 - x^2 y + 3 y + 2 y^3$ is the potential of **F**.

NOTE 4: Let $\mathbf{F} = \langle F_1, F_2, F_3 \rangle$. If $\mathbf{F} = \nabla u = \left(\frac{\partial u}{\partial x}, \frac{\partial u}{\partial y}, \frac{\partial u}{\partial z}\right)$, then $F_1 = \frac{\partial u}{\partial x}$, $F_2 = \frac{\partial u}{\partial y}$ and $F_3 = \frac{\partial u}{\partial z}$. Taking the partial derivative of F_1 with respect to y and that of F_2 with respect to x and using the fact that $\frac{\partial^2 u}{\partial x \partial y} = \frac{\partial^2 u}{\partial y \partial x}$, we see that F_1 and F_2 must satisfy

$$\frac{\partial F_1}{\partial y} = \frac{\partial F_2}{\partial x}$$

Taking the partial derivative of F_1 with respect to z and that of F_3 with respect to x and using the fact that $\frac{\partial^2 u}{\partial x \partial z} = \frac{\partial^2 u}{\partial z \partial x}$, we see that F_1 and F_3 must satisfy

$$\frac{\partial F_1}{\partial z} = \frac{\partial F_3}{\partial x}$$

The preceding two equations can be used to check if a vector field is conservative. If this the case, we solve $F_1 = \frac{\partial u}{\partial x}$ for u by integrating with respect to x and then use $F_2 = \frac{\partial u}{\partial y}$ to find the constant of integration. We show this by the following example.

Example 16.6. Show that the vector function $\mathbf{F} = \langle yz + yz \cos(xy), \ xz + xz \cos(xy), \ xy + \sin(xy)\rangle$ is conservative and find its potential.

Solution: Here, $F_1 = y z + y z \cos(x y)$, $F_2 = x z + x z \cos(x y)$, and $F_3 = x y + \sin(x y)$.

In[1636]:= **Clear[x, y, F1, F2, F3]**
   F1[x_, y_, z_] = y z + y z Cos[x y]
   F2[x_, y_, z_] = x z + x z Cos[x y]
   F3[x_, y_, z_] = x y + Sin[x y]

Out[1637]= $y z + y z \cos[x y]$

Out[1638]= $x z + x z \cos[x y]$

Out[1639]= $x y + \sin[x y]$

We now compare $\frac{\partial F_1}{\partial y}$ and $\frac{\partial F_2}{\partial x}$:

In[1640]:= `D[F1[x, y, z], y]`
`D[F2[x, y, z], x]`

Out[1640]= $z + z \, \text{Cos}[x \, y] - x \, y \, z \, \text{Sin}[x \, y]$

Out[1641]= $z + z \, \text{Cos}[x \, y] - x \, y \, z \, \text{Sin}[x \, y]$

Next, we compare $\frac{\partial F_1}{\partial z}$ and $\frac{\partial F_2}{\partial x}$:

In[1642]:= `D[F1[x, y, z], z]`
`D[F3[x, y, z], x]`

Out[1642]= $y + y \, \text{Cos}[x \, y]$

Out[1643]= $y + y \, \text{Cos}[x \, y]$

Thus, the vector field is conservative. To find its potential u, we integrate $F_1 = \frac{\partial u}{\partial x}$ with repsetct to x to get

In[1644]:= `Clear[u, h]`
`u = Integrate[F1[x, y, z], x] + h[y, z]`

Out[1645]= $x \, y \, z + h[y, z] + z \, \text{Sin}[x \, y]$

Note that the addition of $h(y, z)$ is necessary because the constant of intgeration can depend on y and z. We now solve the equation $F_2 = \frac{\partial u}{\partial y}$ for $\frac{\partial h}{\partial y}$.

In[1646]:= `Clear[sol]`
`sol = Solve[D[u, y] == F2[x, y, z], ∂_y h[y, z]]`

Out[1647]= $\left\{ \left\{ h^{(1,0)}[y, z] \to 0 \right\} \right\}$

This means that $\frac{\partial h}{\partial y} = 0$ and hence h is a function of z only. Next, we solve the equation $F_3 = \frac{\partial u}{\partial z}$ for $\frac{\partial h}{\partial z}$.

In[1648]:= `Clear[sol2]`
`sol2 = Solve[D[u, z] == F3[x, y, z], ∂_z h[y, z]]`

Out[1649]= $\left\{ \left\{ h^{(0,1)}[y, z] \to 0 \right\} \right\}$

Hence, $\frac{\partial h}{\partial z} = 0$ and we can take $h = 0$. Therefore, $u = x \, y \, z + z \sin(x \, y)$ is the potential for the vector field **F**.

■ **Exercises**

1. Show that the vector field $\mathbf{F} = \left\langle y^3 - 3 x^2 \, y, \; 3 \, xy^2 - x^3 \right\rangle$ is conservative and find its potential.

2. Show that the vector field $\mathbf{F} = \left\langle y \, z + \frac{2 \, xy}{z}, \; xz + \frac{x^2}{z}, \; xy - \frac{x^2 \, y}{z^2} \right\rangle$ is conservative and find its potential.

3. Determine whether the vector field $\mathbf{F} = \left\langle x^2, \; yx + e^z, \; y \, e^z \right\rangle$ is conservative. If it is, find its potential.

■ 16.4 Parametrized Surfaces and Surface Integrals

Students should read Section 16.4 of Rogawski's *Calculus* [1] for a detailed discussion of the material presented in this section.

A *parametrized surface* is a surface whose points are given in the form

$$G(u, v) = (x(u, v), \ y(u, v), \ z(u, v))$$

where u and v (called *parameters*) are independent variables used to describe a domain D (called the *parameter domain*).

The command for plotting parametrized surfaces is **ParametricPlot3D**. This command has been discussed in Section 14.1.2 of this text.

Example 16.7. Plot the parametrized surface defined by $G(u, v) = (\cos u \sin v,\ 4 \sin u \cos v,\ \cos v)$ over the domain $D = \{(u, v) \mid 0 \le u \le 2\pi,\ 0 \le v \le 2\pi\}$.

Solution:

In[1650]:= `ParametricPlot3D[{ Cos[u] Sin[v], 4 Sin[u] Cos[v], Cos[v]},`
`{u, 0, 2 Pi}, {v, 0, 2 Pi}, ImageSize → {250}]`

Out[1650]=

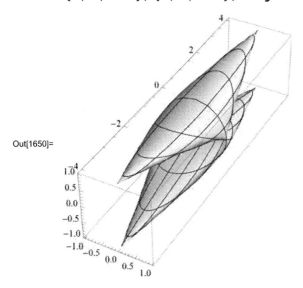

Example 16.8. Plot the parametrized surface defined by $G(u, v) = \left(u \cos v,\ u \sin v,\ 1 - u^2\right)$ over the domain $D = \{(u, v) \mid 0 \le u \le 1,\ 0 \le v \le 2\pi\}$.

Solution:

In[1651]:= `ParametricPlot3D[{u Cos[v] , u Sin[v] , 1 - u²}, {u, 0, 1},`
`{v, 0, 2 Pi}, ColorFunction → "BlueGreenYellow", ImageSize → {250},`
`ImagePadding → {{15, 15}, {15, 15}}]`

Out[1651]=

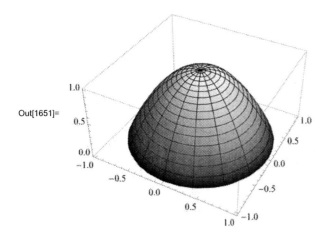

NOTE: On a parametrized surface $G(u, v) = (x(u, v),\ y(u, v),\ z(u, v))$, if we fix one of the variables, we get a curve on the surface. The plot following shows the curves corresponding to $u = 3/4$ (latitude) and $v = 5\pi/3$ (longitude).

```
In[1652]:= Clear[plot1, plot2, plot3]
        plot1 = ParametricPlot3D[{u Cos[v] , u Sin[v] , 1 - u²},
            {u, 0, 1}, {v, 0, 2 Pi}, ColorFunction → "BlueGreenYellow"];
        plot2 = ParametricPlot3D[{ 3 / 4 Cos[v] , 3 / 4 Sin[v] , 7 / 16},
            {v, 0, 2 Pi}, PlotStyle → {Thickness[0.01], Red}];
        plot3 = ParametricPlot3D[{ u Cos[5 Pi / 3] , u Sin[5 Pi / 3] , 1 - u²},
            {u, 0, 1}, PlotStyle → {Thickness[0.01], Blue}];
        Show[plot1, plot2, plot3, PlotRange → All, ImageSize → {250},
          ImagePadding → {{15, 15}, {15, 15}}]
```

Out[1656]=

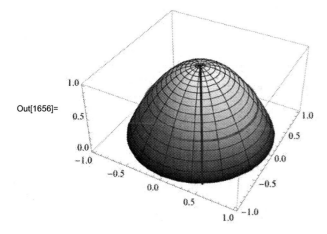

Let $P = G(u_0, v_0)$ be a point on the parametrized surface S. For fixed $v = v_0$, the tangent vector to the curve $G(u, v_0)$ at (u_0, v_0) is given by

$$\mathbf{T}_u = \frac{\partial G}{\partial u} (u_0, v_0)$$

while the tangent vector for $G(u_0, v)$ corresponding to a fixed $u = u_0$ is given by

$$\mathbf{T}_v = \frac{\partial G}{\partial v} (u_0, v_0)$$

These two vectors are tangent to the surface S. Thus, the normal vector $\mathbf{n}$ to the tangent plane at $G(u_0, v_0)$ is given by

$$\mathbf{n}(P) = \mathbf{n}(u_0, v_0) = \mathbf{T}_u \times \mathbf{T}_v$$

Example 16.9. Consider the parametrized surface $G(u, v) = \left(u \cos v, \ u \sin v, \ 1 - v^2 \right)$.

a) Find $\mathbf{T}_u$, $\mathbf{T}_v$, and $\mathbf{n}$.
b) Find the equation of the tangent plane at $(1/2, \ 5\pi/3)$.
c) Plot the tangent plane and surface.

Solution: Let us define G as a function of u and v in *Mathematica*.

```
In[1657]:= Clear[G, u, v]
        G[u_, v_] = {u Cos[v], u Sin[v], 1 - u²}
```

Out[1658]= $\left\{ u \cos[v], u \sin[v], 1 - u^2 \right\}$

a) We use **Tu** for $\mathbf{T}_u$ and **Tv** for $\mathbf{T}_v$. We evaluate these as functions of u and v.

In[1659]:= **Clear[Tu, Tv, n]**
Tu[u_, v_] = D[G[u, v], u]
Tv[u_, v_] = D[G[u, v], v]
n[u_, v_] = Cross[Tu[u, v], Tv[u, v]]

Out[1660]= $\{Cos[v], Sin[v], -2u\}$

Out[1661]= $\{-u Sin[v], u Cos[v], 0\}$

Out[1662]= $\{2 u^2 Cos[v], 2 u^2 Sin[v], u Cos[v]^2 + u Sin[v]^2\}$

b) The normal vector to the tangent plane at $(1/2, 5\pi/3)$ is

In[1663]:= **Clear[normal]**
normal = n[1 / 2, 5 Pi / 3]

Out[1664]= $\left\{\dfrac{1}{4}, -\dfrac{\sqrt{3}}{4}, \dfrac{1}{2}\right\}$

The tangent plane passes through the point

In[1665]:= **Clear[point]**
point = G[1 / 2, 5 Pi / 3]

Out[1666]= $\left\{\dfrac{1}{4}, -\dfrac{\sqrt{3}}{4}, \dfrac{3}{4}\right\}$

Thus, the equation of the tangent plane is given by

In[1667]:= **Clear[tplane]**
tplane = normal.({x, y, z} - point) == 0

Out[1668]= $\dfrac{1}{4}\left(-\dfrac{1}{4} + x\right) - \dfrac{1}{4}\sqrt{3}\left(\dfrac{\sqrt{3}}{4} + y\right) + \dfrac{1}{2}\left(-\dfrac{3}{4} + z\right) == 0$

which simplifies to

In[1669]:= **Simplify[tplane]**

Out[1669]= $2x + 4z == 5 + 2\sqrt{3}\ y$

c) Here is the plot of the surface and the tangent plane. Observe that we have used **ColorFunction** and **ColorFunctionScaling** options.

```
In[1670]:= Clear[plot1, plot2]
        plot1 = ParametricPlot3D[G[u, v],
            {u, 0, 1}, {v, 0, 2 Pi}, ColorFunction → "BlueGreenYellow"];
        plot2 = ContourPlot3D[2 x + 4 z == 5 + 2 √3 y, {x, -3, 3}, {y, -3, 3},
            {z, -4, 4}, ColorFunction → Function[{x, y, z}, Hue[Mod[z, 1]]],
            ColorFunctionScaling → False];
        Show[plot1, plot2, ImageSize → {250}, ImagePadding → {{15, 15}, {15, 15}}]
```

Out[1673]=

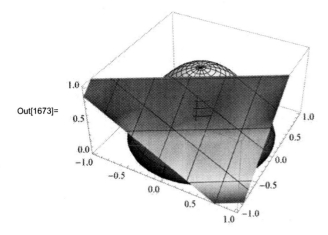

NOTE: The area $A(S)$ of a parametrized surface S: $G(u, v) = (x(u, v), y(u, v), z(u, v))$, where $(u, v) \in D$, is given by

$$A(S) = \iint_D \| \mathbf{n}(u, v) \| \, du \, dv$$

If $f(x, y, z)$ is continuous at all points of S, then the surface area of f over S is given by

$$\iint_S f(x, y, z) \, dS = \iint_D f(G(u, v)) \| \mathbf{n}(u, v) \| \, du \, dv$$

Example 16.10. Show the following:
a) The area of the cylinder of height h and radius r is $2 \pi r h$.
b) The area of the sphere of radius r is $4 \pi r^2$.

Solution:
a) A parametric equation of the cylinder of height h and radius r can be given by

$$x = r \cos v, \, y = r \sin v, \text{ and } z = u, \text{ where } 0 \le v \le 2 \pi, 0 \le u \le h$$

Thus, the cylinder is given by $G(u, v) = (r \cos u, \, r \sin u, \, v)$.

```
In[1674]:= Clear[ G, u, v, r]
        G[u_, v_] = {r Cos[v], r Sin[v], u}
Out[1675]= {r Cos[v], r Sin[v], u}
```

Here is a plot of the cylinder with $r = 3$ and $h = 5$:

In[1676]:= **r = 3; h = 5;**

ParametricPlot3D[G[u, v], {u, 0, h}, {v, 0, 2 Pi}]

Out[1677]=

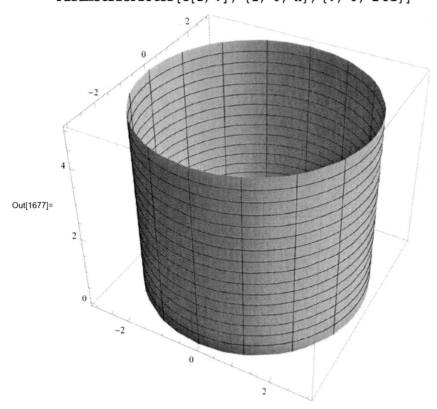

To compute the surface area of the cylinder, we need to compute its normal vector.

In[1678]:= **Clear[Tu, Tv, n, r, h]**

Tu[u_, v_] = D[G[u, v], u];

Tv[u_, v_] = D[G[u, v], v];

n[u_, v_] = Cross[Tu[u, v], Tv[u, v]]

Out[1681]= $\{-r \cos[v], -r \sin[v], 0\}$

Here is a plot of the cylinder with its normal vector for $r = 3$ and $h = 5$:

```
In[1682]:= r = 3; h = 5;
    Clear[plot1, plot2]
    plot1 = ParametricPlot3D[G[u, v], {u, 0, h}, {v, 0, 2 Pi}];
    plot2 = VectorFieldPlot3D[n[u, v], {u, 0, h},
        {v, -2 Pi, 2 Pi}, {z, -3, 3}, VectorHeads → True, PlotPoints → 15];
    Show[plot1, plot2, ImageSize → {250}]
    Clear[r, h]
```

Out[1686]=

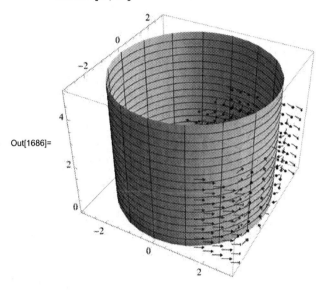

The surface area is

```
In[1688]:= SArea = ∫₀ʰ ∫₀²ᴾⁱ Norm[n[u, v]] dv du
```

Out[1688]= $2 \, h \, \pi \, \text{Abs}[r]$

Since $r > 0$, $|r| = r$ and hence the preceding output is $2 \pi r h$.

b) A parametric equation of the sphere of radius r is

$$x = r \cos u \sin v, \, y = r \sin u \sin v, \, z = r \cos v$$

where $0 \le u \le 2 \pi$ and $0 \le v \le \pi$. Thus, the sphere is given by $G(u, v) = (r \cos u \sin v, \, r \sin u \sin v, \, r \cos v)$.

```
In[1689]:= Clear[G, u, v, r]
    G[u_, v_] = {r Cos[u] Sin[v], r Sin[u] Sin[v], r Cos[v]}
```

Out[1690]= $\{r \, \text{Cos}[u] \, \text{Sin}[v], \, r \, \text{Sin}[u] \, \text{Sin}[v], \, r \, \text{Cos}[v]\}$

Here is a plot of the sphere with $r = 3$.

In[1691]:= **r = 3;**
ParametricPlot3D[G[u, v], {u, 0, 2 Pi}, {v, 0, Pi}, ImageSize → {250}]

Out[1692]=

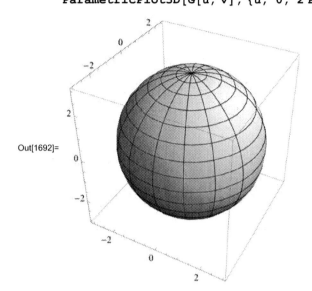

To compute the surface area of the sphere, we need to compute its normal vector.

In[1693]:= **Clear[Tu, Tv, n, r]**
Tu[u_, v_] = D[G[u, v], u];
Tv[u_, v_] = D[G[u, v], v];
n[u_, v_] = Cross[Tu[u, v], Tv[u, v]]

Out[1696]= $\{-r^2 \text{Cos}[u] \text{Sin}[v]^2, -r^2 \text{Sin}[u] \text{Sin}[v]^2,$
$-r^2 \text{Cos}[u]^2 \text{Cos}[v] \text{Sin}[v] - r^2 \text{Cos}[v] \text{Sin}[u]^2 \text{Sin}[v]\}$

Here is a plot of the sphere with its normal vector for $r = 3$.

In[1697]:= **r = 3; h = 5;**
Clear[plot1, plot2]
plot1 = ParametricPlot3D[G[u, v], {u, 0, 2 Pi}, {v, 0, h}];
plot2 = VectorFieldPlot3D[n[u, v], {u, -2 Pi, 2 Pi},
    {v, 0, h}, {z, -3, 3}, VectorHeads → True, PlotPoints → 10];
Show[plot1, plot2, ImageSize → {250}]
Clear[r, h]

Out[1701]=

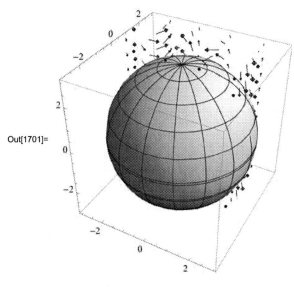

The surface area is

In[1703]:= $\mathbf{SArea} = \int_0^{\mathbf{Pi}} \int_0^{\mathbf{2\,Pi}} \mathbf{Norm[n[u,\,v]]\,du\,dv}$

Out[1703]= $4\,\pi\,r\,\text{Conjugate}[r]$

For a real number r, the conjugate of r is r and hence the preceding output is $4\,\pi\,r^2$.

Example 16.11. Consider the parametrized surface S defined by $G(u, v) = (u \cos v, u \sin v, v)$, where $0 \le u \le 1, 0 \le v \le 2\pi$.
a) Find the surface area of S.
b) Evaluate $\iint_S xyz\,dS$.

Solution:
a)

In[1704]:= **Clear[G, u, v]**
G[u_, v_] = {u Cos[v], u Sin[v], v}

Out[1705]= $\{u \cos[v], u \sin[v], v\}$

In[1706]:= **Clear[Tu, Tv, n]**
Tu[u_, v_] = D[G[u, v], u]
Tv[u_, v_] = D[G[u, v], v]
n[u_, v_] = Cross[Tu[u, v], Tv[u, v]]

Out[1707]= $\{Cos[v], Sin[v], 0\}$

Out[1708]= $\{-u\ Sin[v], u\ Cos[v], 1\}$

Out[1709]= $\left\{Sin[v], -Cos[v], u\ Cos[v]^2 + u\ Sin[v]^2\right\}$

The surface area $A(S)$ is given by

In[1710]:= **SArea = $\int_0^1 \int_0^{2\ Pi}$ Norm[n[u, v]] dv du**

Out[1710]= $\pi\left(\sqrt{2} + ArcSinh[1]\right)$

which is approximately equal to

In[1711]:= **N[%]**

Out[1711]= 7.2118

b) We define f:

In[1712]:= **Clear[f]**
f[x_, y_, z_] = x y z

Out[1713]= $x\ y\ z$

The surface integral of f is

In[1714]:= **$\int_0^1 \int_0^{2\ Pi}$ f[G[u, v][[1]], G[u, v][[2]], G[u, v][[3]]] Norm[n[u, v]] dv du**

Out[1714]= $-\dfrac{1}{16}\pi\left(3\sqrt{2} - ArcSinh[1]\right)$

Or numerically,

In[1715]:= **N[%]**

Out[1715]= -0.659983

■ Exercises

1. Plot the parametrized surface $G(u, v) = (e^u \sin v, e^u \cos v, v)$ over the domain $D = \{(u, v) \mid -1 \le u \le 1,\ 0 \le v \le 2\pi\}$.

2. Plot the parametrized surface $G(u, v) = (3 \sin u \cos v, \sin u \sin v, \cos v + 3 \cos u)$ over the domain $D = \{(u, v) \mid 0 \le u \le 2\pi,\ 0 \le v \le 2\pi\}$.

3. Consider the parametrized surface $G(u, v) = (e^{-u} \cos v, e^u \sin v, e^u \cos v)$.
a. Find $\mathbf{T}_u$, $\mathbf{T}_v$, and $\mathbf{n}$.
b. Find the equation of the tangent plane at $(0,\ \pi/2)$.
c. Plot the tangent plane and surface.

4. Consider the parametrized surface S: $G(u, v) = (u - v, 3u + v, u^2 - 2uv + 6v^2)$, where $0 \le u \le 1, 0 \le v \le 1$.

a. Find the surface area of S. (Use **NIntegrate** for faster integration.)

b. Evaluate $\iint_S (3x + 2y^2 - z^2) \, dS$.

▪ 16.5 Surface Integrals of Vector Fields

Students should read Section 16.5 of Rogawski's *Calculus* [1] for a detailed discussion of the material presented in this section.

An orientation of a surface S is a continuously varying choice of the unit normal vector $\mathbf{e}_n(P)$ at each point of the surface. Thus, $\mathbf{e}_n$ is given by either

$$\mathbf{e}_n(P) = \frac{\mathbf{n}(P)}{\|\mathbf{n}(P)\|} \quad \text{or} \quad \mathbf{e}_n(P) = -\frac{\mathbf{n}(P)}{\|\mathbf{n}(P)\|}$$

If $\mathbf{F}(x, y, z)$ is continuous at all points of a parametrized surface S, then the *surface integral* of $\mathbf{F}$ over S is given by

$$\iint_S \mathbf{F} \cdot d\mathbf{S} = \iint_S (\mathbf{F} \cdot \mathbf{e}_n) \, dS$$

where $\mathbf{e}_n$ is the unit normal determined by an orientation. The surface integral of $\mathbf{F}$ is also called the *flux* of $\mathbf{F}$ across S.

The surface integral of $\mathbf{F}$ over a parametrized surface S given by $G(u, v) = (x(u, v), y(u, v), z(u, v))$, where $(u, v) \in D$, is given by

$$\iint_S \mathbf{F} \cdot d\mathbf{S} = \iint_S (\mathbf{F} \cdot \mathbf{e}_n) \, dS = \iint_D \mathbf{F}(G(u, v)) \cdot \mathbf{n}(u, v) \, du \, dv$$

Example 16.12. Find $\iint_S \mathbf{F} \cdot d\mathbf{S}$, where $\mathbf{F}(x, y, z) = \langle xz, z, yx \rangle$ and S is given by $G(u, v) = (u - v^2, uv, u^2 - v)$, $0 \le u \le 2$, and $1 \le v \le 3$.

Solution:

```
In[1716]:= Clear[F, G, x, y, z, u, v]
          F[x_, y_, z_] = {x z, z, y x}
          G[u_, v_] = {u - v^2, u v, u^2 - v}
```

Out[1717]= $\{x z, z, x y\}$

Out[1718]= $\{u - v^2, u v, u^2 - v\}$

```
In[1719]:= Clear[Tu, Tv, n]
          Tu[u_, v_] = D[G[u, v], u]
          Tv[u_, v_] = D[G[u, v], v]
          n[u_, v_] = Cross[Tu[u, v], Tv[u, v]]
```

Out[1720]= $\{1, v, 2u\}$

Out[1721]= $\{-2v, u, -1\}$

Out[1722]= $\{-2u^2 - v, 1 - 4uv, u + 2v^2\}$

```
In[1723]:= Flux = ∫₀² ∫₁³ F[G[u, v][[1]], G[u, v][[2]], G[u, v][[3]]] . n[u, v] dv du
```

Out[1723]= $-\dfrac{6928}{15}$

Example 16.13. Find $\iint_S \mathbf{F} \cdot d\mathbf{S}$, where $\mathbf{F}(x, y, z) = \langle x^2, z^2, y + x^2 \rangle$ and S is the upper hemisphere $x^2 + y^2 + z^2 = 4$ with outward normal orientation.

Solution: First, we find the parametric equation of the cylinder. This can be given by $x = 2 \cos u \sin v$, $y = 2 \sin u \sin v$, and $z = 2 \cos v$, where $0 \le u \le 2\pi$ and $0 \le v \le \pi/2$.

For the hemisphere to have the outward orientation, we note that $\mathbf{n} = \mathbf{T}_v \times \mathbf{T}_u$. With this in mind we compute the flux of $\mathbf{F}$ across S through the following steps.

In[1724]:= **Clear[F, G, x, y, z, u, v]**
F[x_, y_, z_] = { x², z², x² + y + z³}
G[u_, v_] = { 2 Cos[u] Sin[v] , 2 Sin[u] Sin[v] , Cos[v] }

Out[1725]= $\left\{ x^2, z^2, x^2 + y + z^3 \right\}$

Out[1726]= {2 Cos[u] Sin[v], 2 Sin[u] Sin[v], Cos[v]}

In[1727]:= **Clear[Tu, Tv, n]**
Tu[u_, v_] = D[G[u, v], u]
Tv[u_, v_] = D[G[u, v], v]
n[u_, v_] = Cross[Tv[u, v], Tu[u, v]]

Out[1728]= {-2 Sin[u] Sin[v], 2 Cos[u] Sin[v], 0}

Out[1729]= {2 Cos[u] Cos[v], 2 Cos[v] Sin[u], -Sin[v]}

Out[1730]= $\left\{ 2 \cos[u] \sin[v]^2, 2 \sin[u] \sin[v]^2, 4 \cos[u]^2 \cos[v] \sin[v] + 4 \cos[v] \sin[u]^2 \sin[v] \right\}$

In[1731]:= **Flux** = $\int_0^{Pi/2} \int_0^{2 Pi}$ **F[G[u, v][[1]], G[u, v][[2]], G[u, v][[3]]] .n[u, v] ⅆu ⅆv**

Out[1731]= $\dfrac{28 \pi}{5}$

■ Exercises

1. Find $\iint_S \mathbf{F} \cdot d\mathbf{S}$, where $\mathbf{F}(x, y, z) = \langle e^z, z, yx \rangle$ and S is given by $G(u, v) = (uv, u - v, u)$, $0 \le u \le 2$, and $-1 \le v \le 1$, and oriented by $\mathbf{n} = \mathbf{T}_u \times \mathbf{T}_v$.

2. Find $\iint_S \mathbf{F} \cdot d\mathbf{S}$, where $\mathbf{F}(x, y, z) = \langle z, x, y \rangle$ and S is the portion of the ellipsoid $\frac{x^2}{16} + \frac{y^2}{9} + \frac{z^2}{4} = 1$ for which $x \le 0$, $y \le 0$, and $z \le 0$ with outward normal orientation.

3. Let S be given by $G(u, v) = \left(\left(1 + v \cos \frac{u}{2}\right) \cos u, \left(1 + v \cos \frac{u}{2}\right) \sin u, v \sin \frac{u}{2} \right)$, $0 \le u \le 2\pi$, and $\frac{-1}{2} \le v \le \frac{1}{2}$.
a. Plot the surface S. (S is an example of a *Mobius strip*.)
b. Find the surface area of S.
c. Evaluate $\iint_S (x^2 + 2 y^2 + 3 z^2) \, dS$.
d. Find the intersection points of S and the xy-plane.
e. For each of the points on the intersection of S and the xy-plane, find the normal vector $\mathbf{n}$.
f. Show that $\mathbf{n}$ varies continuously but that $\mathbf{n}(2\pi, 0) = -\mathbf{n}(u, 0)$. (This shows that S is not orientable and hence it is impossible to integrate a vector field over S.)

Chapter 17   Fundamental Theorems of Vector Analysis

Useful Tip: If you are reading the electronic version of this publication formatted as a *Mathematica* Notebook, then it is possible to view 3-D plots generated by *Mathematica* from different perspectives. First, place your screen cursor over the plot. Then drag the mouse while pressing down on the left mouse button to rotate the plot.

NOTE: In order to perform the operations of curl and divergence on vector fields discussed in this section using *Mathematica*, it is necessary to first load the **VectorAnalysis** package:

In[1732]:= **Needs["VectorAnalysis`"]**

The Fundamental Theorem of Calculus for functions of a single variable states that the integral of a function $f(x)$ over an interval $[a, b]$ (domain) can be calculated as the difference of its anti-derivative $F(x)$ at the endpoints (boundary) of the interval:

$$\int_a^b f(x)\, dx = F(b) - F(a)$$

This integral relationship between domain and boundary can be generalized to vector fields involving the operations of curl and divergence and is made precise by three theorems that will be discussed in this chapter: Green's Theorem, Stoke's Theorem, and Divergence Theorem.

■ 17.1 Green's Theorem

Students should read Section 17.1 of Rogawski's *Calculus* [1] for a detailed discussion of the material presented in this section.

Let $\mathbf{F}(x, y) = \langle P(x, y), Q(x, y)\rangle$ a vector field continuous on an oriented curve C. Recall that the *line integral of* $\mathbf{F}$ along C is denoted by

$$\int_C \mathbf{F}(x, y, z)\cdot d\mathbf{s} = \int_C P\, dx + Q\, dy$$

If $\mathbf{c}\,(t) = \langle x(t),\ y(t),\ z(t)\rangle$ is the vector equation of the curve C, then

$$\oint_C P\, dx + Q\, dy = \int_a^b \left(P(x(t), y(t))\frac{dx}{dt} + Q(x(t), y(t))\frac{dy}{dt}\right) dt$$

The following is a generalization of the Fundamental Theorem of Calculus to two dimensions, which relates a double integral over a region with a corresponding line integral along its boundary.

Green's Theorem: If C is a simple closed curve oriented counterclockwise and D is the region enclosed, and if P and Q are differentiable and have continuous first partial derivatives, then

$$\oint_C P\, dx + Q\, dy = \iint_D \left(\frac{\partial Q}{\partial x} - \frac{\partial P}{\partial y}\right) dA$$

Refer to your textbook for a detailed discussion and proof of Green's Theorem.

Example 17.1. Compute the line integral $\oint_C e^{2x+y}\, dx + e^{-y}\, dy$, where C is the boundary of the square with vertices $(0, 0)$, $(1, 0)$, $(1, 1)$, $(1, 0)$ oriented counterclockwise.

Solution: We will use Green's Theorem. Thus, we need to verify that the hypotheses of Green's Theorem hold. To this end, we define the function P and Q and compute their partial derivatives.

In[1733]:= `Clear[x, y, P, Q]`
`P[x_, y_] = E^(2 x+y)`
`Q[x_, y_] = E^(-y)`

Out[1734]= e^{2x+y}

Out[1735]= e^{-y}

In[1736]:= `D[P[x, y], x]`
`D[P[x, y], y]`
`D[Q[x, y], x]`
`D[Q[x, y], y]`

Out[1736]= $2 e^{2x+y}$

Out[1737]= e^{2x+y}

Out[1738]= 0

Out[1739]= $-e^{-y}$

The partial derivatives are continuous inside the square and the curve is oriented counterclockwise. Thus, the hypotheses of Green's Theorem are satisfied. Note that the region D enclosed by C is given by $0 \le x \le 1$ and $0 \le y \le 1$.

In[1740]:= $\int_0^1 \int_0^1 (D[Q[x, y], x] - D[P[x, y], y]) \, dy \, dx$

Out[1740]= $-\dfrac{1}{2} (-1 + e)^2 (1 + e)$

In[1741]:= `N[%]`

Out[1741]= -5.4891

NOTE: If we were to solve this using the definition of line integral as discussed in Chapter 16 of this text, we would then need to consider four pieces of parametrization of C and then sum the four integrals. Toward this end, let us use C_1 for the lower edge, C_2 for the right edge, C_3 for the top edge, and C_4 for the left edge of the square. Here are the parametrizations followed by their line integrals.

```
In[1742]:= Clear[x1, x2, x3, x4, y1, y2, y3, y4, t, F, c1, c2, c3, c4]
        F[x_, y_] = {P[x, y], Q[x, y] }
        x1[t_] = t
        y1[t_] = 0
        c1[t_] = {x1[t], y1[t]}

        x2[t_] = 1
        y2[t_] = t
        c2[t_] = {x2[t], y2[t]}

        x3[t_] = 1 - t
        y3[t_] = 1
        c3[t_] = {x3[t], y3[t]}

        x4[t_] = 0
        y4[t_] = 1 - t
        c4[t_] = {x4[t], y4[t]}
```

Out[1743]= $\{e^{2x+y}, e^{-y}\}$

Out[1744]= t

Out[1745]= 0

Out[1746]= $\{t, 0\}$

Out[1747]= 1

Out[1748]= t

Out[1749]= $\{1, t\}$

Out[1750]= $1 - t$

Out[1751]= 1

Out[1752]= $\{1 - t, 1\}$

Out[1753]= 0

Out[1754]= $1 - t$

Out[1755]= $\{0, 1 - t\}$

In[1756]:= $\int_0^1 F[x1[t], y1[t]].c1'[t] \, dt + \int_0^1 F[x2[t], y2[t]].c2'[t] \, dt +$

$\int_0^1 F[x3[t], y3[t]].c3'[t] \, dt + \int_0^1 F[x4[t], y4[t]].c4'[t] \, dt$

Out[1756]= $-1 + \dfrac{1}{e} + \dfrac{-1 + e}{e} + \dfrac{1}{2}\left(-1 + e^2\right) - \dfrac{1}{2} e \left(-1 + e^2\right)$

```
In[1757]:= N[%]
```

Out[1757]= -5.4891

■ **Exercises**

In Exercises 1 through 4, use Green's Theorem to evaluate the given line integral.

1. $\oint_C y^2 \sin x \, dx + x \, y \, dy$, where C is the boundary of the triangle with vertices $(0, 0)$, $(1, 0)$, $(1, 1)$, oriented counterclockwise.

2. $\oint_C 2 \, x^2 \, y \, dx + x^3 \, dy$, where C is the circle $x^2 + y^2 = 4$, oriented counterclockwise.

3. $\oint_C \left(x^2 + y^2\right) dx + y \, e^x \, dy$, where C is the boundary of the region bounded between the parabola $y = 5 - x^2$ and the line $y = 2 \, x - 3$, oriented clockwise.

4. $\oint_C \frac{x}{x^2+y^2} \, dx - \frac{y}{x^2+y^2} \, dy$, where C is the boundary of the quarter-annulus situated between the circles $x^2 + y^2 = 1$ and $x^2 + y^2 = 9$ in the first quadrant (see plot below), oriented counterclockwise.

5. Let $\mathbf{F}(x, \, y) = \left(2 \, x \, y + y^3, \, x^2 + 3 \, x \, y + 2 \, y\right)$. Use Green's Theorem to demonstrate that the line integral $\int_C \mathbf{F}(x, \, y, \, z) \cdot d\mathbf{s} = 0$ for every simple closed curve C. What kind of a vector field do we call $\mathbf{F}$?

■ 17.2 Stokes's Theorem

Students should read Section 17.2 of Rogawski's *Calculus* [1] for a detailed discussion of the material presented in this section.

Let $\mathbf{F}(x, \, y, \, z) = \langle F_1, \, F_2, \, F_3 \rangle$ be a vector field. The curl of $\mathbf{F}$, denoted by curl($\mathbf{F}$) or $\nabla \times \mathbf{F}$, is defined by

$$\text{curl}(\mathbf{F}) = \nabla \times \mathbf{F} = \begin{vmatrix} \mathbf{i} & \mathbf{j} & \mathbf{k} \\ \frac{\partial}{\partial x} & \frac{\partial}{\partial y} & \frac{\partial}{\partial z} \\ F_1 & F_2 & F_3 \end{vmatrix} = \left\langle \frac{\partial F_3}{\partial y} - \frac{\partial F_2}{\partial z}, \, \frac{\partial F_1}{\partial z} - \frac{\partial F_3}{\partial x}, \, \frac{\partial F_2}{\partial x} - \frac{\partial F_1}{\partial y} \right\rangle$$

Here, we are using the *del* or symbol ∇ (nabla) to denote the vector operator $\nabla = \left\langle \frac{\partial}{\partial x}, \, \frac{\partial}{\partial y}, \, \frac{\partial}{\partial z} \right\rangle$.

The *Mathematica* command for computing the curl of a vector field $\mathbf{F}$ is **Curl[F,coordsys]**, where **coordsys** is the coordinate system of the vector field. This is demonstrated in the next example.

The following is a generalization of the Fundamental Theorem of Calculus three dimensions, which relates a surface integral involving curl with a corresponding line integral along its boundary.

Stokes's Theorem: If $\mathbf{F}(x, \, y, \, z)$ a vector field with continuous partial derivatives and if S is an oriented surface S with boundary ∂S, then

$$\oint_{\partial S} \mathbf{F} \cdot d\mathbf{S} = \int\!\!\int_S \text{curl}(\mathbf{F}) \cdot d\mathbf{S}$$

If S is closed, then it has no boundary and hence both integrals are equal to 0.

NOTE: Recall that if the surface S is given by $G(u, \, v) = (x(u, \, v), \, y(u, \, v), \, z(u, \, v))$, where $(u, \, v) \in D$, then $\int_S \text{curl}(\mathbf{F}) \cdot d\mathbf{S}$ is given by

$$\int\!\!\int_S \text{curl}(\mathbf{F}) \cdot d\mathbf{S} = \int\!\!\int_D \text{curl}(\mathbf{F}) \, (G(u, \, v)) \cdot \mathbf{n}(u, \, v) \, du \, dv$$

Refer to your textbook for a detailed discussion and proof of Stokes's Theorem.

Example 17.2. Find the curl of the vector field $\mathbf{F}(x, y, z) = \left\langle x \sin(y\,z),\, e^{x/y}\,z,\, y\,x^2 \right\rangle$.

Solution: We use the **Curl** command:

```
In[1758]:= Clear[F, F1, F2, F3, x, y, z]
        F1 = x Sin[y z]
        F2 = E^x/y z
        F3 = x^2 y
        F = {F1, F2, F3}
```

Out[1759]= $x \sin[y\,z]$

Out[1760]= $e^{x/y}\,z$

Out[1761]= $x^2\,y$

Out[1762]= $\left\{ x \sin[y\,z],\ e^{x/y}\,z,\ x^2\,y \right\}$

```
In[1763]:= Curl[F, Cartesian[x, y, z]]
```

Out[1763]= $\left\{ -e^{x/y} + x^2,\ -2\,x\,y + x\,y\,\cos[y\,z],\ \dfrac{e^{x/y}\,z}{y} - x\,z\,\cos[y\,z] \right\}$

NOTE: We obtain the same answer for the curl of **F** using the explicit formula:

```
In[1764]:= curl = {∂y F3 - ∂z F2, ∂z F1 - ∂x F3, ∂x F2 - ∂y F1}
```

Out[1764]= $\left\{ -e^{x/y} + x^2,\ -2\,x\,y + x\,y\,\cos[y\,z],\ \dfrac{e^{x/y}\,z}{y} - x\,z\,\cos[y\,z] \right\}$

Or equivalently,

```
In[1765]:= CurlF = {D[F3, y] - D[F2, z], D[F3, x] - D[F1, z], D[F2, x] - D[F1, y]}
```

Out[1765]= $\left\{ -e^{x/y} + x^2,\ 2\,x\,y - x\,y\,\cos[y\,z],\ \dfrac{e^{x/y}\,z}{y} - x\,z\,\cos[y\,z] \right\}$

Example 17.3. Let $f(x, y, z)$ be a function of three variables with continuous first and second partial derivatives and let $\mathbf{F} = \nabla f$ be the gradient of f. Find the curl of the vector field $\mathbf{F}$.

Solution:

```
In[1766]:= Clear[f, F1, F2, F3, x, y, z]
        F1 = D[f[x, y, z], x]
        F2 = D[f[x, y, z], y]
        F3 = D[f[x, y, z], z]
        F = {F1, F2, F3}
```

Out[1767]= $f^{(1,0,0)}[x,\,y,\,z]$

Out[1768]= $f^{(0,1,0)}[x,\,y,\,z]$

Out[1769]= $f^{(0,0,1)}[x,\,y,\,z]$

Out[1770]= $\left\{ f^{(1,0,0)}[x,\,y,\,z],\ f^{(0,1,0)}[x,\,y,\,z],\ f^{(0,0,1)}[x,\,y,\,z] \right\}$

Then the curl of **F** is

In[1771]:= **Curl[F, Cartesian[x, y, z]]**

Out[1771]= $\{0, 0, 0\}$

To see why the curl is zero, let us examine each partial derivative used in computing the curl of **F**.

In[1772]:= **D[F3, y]**
D[F2, z]

Out[1772]= $f^{(0,1,1)}[x, y, z]$

Out[1773]= $f^{(0,1,1)}[x, y, z]$

NOTE: Here, $\mathbf{f}^{(0,1,1)}[\mathbf{x}, \mathbf{y}, \mathbf{z}]$ stands for the second partial derivative f_{yz}. Thus, the two partial derivatives that appear in the x-component of the curl of **F** are equal and hence their difference is zero. Similarly, we have

In[1774]:= **D[F3, x]**
D[F1, z]

Out[1774]= $f^{(1,0,1)}[x, y, z]$

Out[1775]= $f^{(1,0,1)}[x, y, z]$

and

In[1776]:= **D[F2, x]**
D[F1, y]

Out[1776]= $f^{(1,1,0)}[x, y, z]$

Out[1777]= $f^{(1,1,0)}[x, y, z]$

Example 17.4. Compute $\oint_{\partial S} \mathbf{F} \cdot d\mathbf{S}$, where $\mathbf{F}(x, y, z) = \langle xyz, z + 3x - 3y, y^2 x \rangle$ and S is the upper hemisphere of radius 4.

Solution: Note that ∂S is a circle of radius 4 lying on the xy-plane. Hence, ∂S can be parametrized by the curve $c(t) = (x(t), y(t), z(t))$ where

$$x = 4\cos t, y = 4\sin t, z = 0, \text{ where } 0 \le t \le 2\pi$$

We then use this parametrization to evaluate the line integral $\oint_{\partial S} \mathbf{F} \cdot d\mathbf{S} = \int_0^{2\pi} \mathbf{F}(x(t), y(t), z(t)) \cdot c'(t) \, dt$:

In[1778]:= **Clear[F, x, y, z, t, c, curlF]**
F[x_, y_, z_] = {x y z, z + 3 x - 3 y, y² x}
x[t_] = 4 Cos[t]
y[t_] = 4 Sin[t]
z[t_] = 0
c[t_] = {x[t], y[t], z[t]}

Out[1779]= $\{x\,y\,z,\ 3\,x - 3\,y + z,\ x\,y^2\}$

Out[1780]= $4\,\text{Cos}[t]$

Out[1781]= $4\,\text{Sin}[t]$

Out[1782]= 0

Out[1783]= $\{4\,\text{Cos}[t],\ 4\,\text{Sin}[t],\ 0\}$

In[1784]:= $\displaystyle\int_0^{2\,\text{Pi}}$ **F[x[t], y[t], z[t]].c'[t] dt**

Out[1784]= $48\,\pi$

Next, we use Stokes's Theorem to obtain the same answer via the corresponding surface integral. The parametrization of the upper hemisphere of radius 4 is given by $S(u, v) = \{x(u, v), y(u, v), z(u, v)\}$, where

$$x = 4\cos u \sin v,\ \ y = 4 \sin u \sin v, \text{ and } z = 4 \cos v, \quad \text{where} \quad 0 \le u \le 2\,\pi, 0 \le v \le \pi/2$$

We now compute the normal of the upper hemisphere:

In[1785]:= **Clear[S, u, v, Tu, Tv, n]**
S[u_, v_] := { 4 Cos[u] Sin[v], 4 Sin[u] Sin[v], 4 Cos[v] }
Tu[u_, v_] := D[S[u, v], u]
Tv[u_, v_] := D[S[u, v], v]
n[u_, v_] = Cross[Tv[u, v], Tu[u, v]]

Out[1789]= $\{16\,\text{Cos}[u]\,\text{Sin}[v]^2,\ 16\,\text{Sin}[u]\,\text{Sin}[v]^2,$
$16\,\text{Cos}[u]^2\,\text{Cos}[v]\,\text{Sin}[v] + 16\,\text{Cos}[v]\,\text{Sin}[u]^2\,\text{Sin}[v]\}$

The curl of **F** is

In[1790]:= **curlF[x_, y_, z_] = Curl[F[x, y, z], Cartesian[x, y, z]]**

Out[1790]= $\{-1 + 2\,x\,y,\ x\,y - y^2,\ 3 - x\,z\}$

Thus, the surface integral is given by

In[1791]:= $\displaystyle\int_0^{\text{Pi}/2}\int_0^{2\,\text{Pi}}$ **curlF[S[u, v][[1]], S[u, v][[2]], S[u, v][[3]]] .n[u, v] du dv**

Out[1791]= $48\,\pi$

This answer agrees with the one obtained using the line integral definition.

Example 17.5. Find the flux of the curl of the vector field $\mathbf{F}(x, y, z) = \langle x^2,\ z^2,\ y + x^2 \rangle$ across S, where S is the part of the cone $z^2 = x^2 + y^2$ for which $1 \le z \le 4$ with outward normal orientation.

Solution: First, we will need the following parametric equations to describe the cone S: $x = u \cos v$, $y = u \sin v$, and $z = u$, where $0 \le v \le 2\pi$ and $1 \le u \le 4$.

For the cone to have outward orientation, we set $\mathbf{n} = \mathbf{T}_v \times \mathbf{T}_u$ (right-hand rule) since $\mathbf{T}_v$ points in the horizontal direction around the cone and $\mathbf{T}_u$ points in the direction along the length of the cone.

In[1792]:= `Clear[F, S, u, v, Tu, Tv, n]`
`F[x_, y_, z_] = {x² + y², x + z², 0}`
`S[u_, v_] := { u Cos[v] , u Sin[v] , u }`
`Tu[u_, v_] := D[S[u, v], u]`
`Tv[u_, v_] := D[S[u, v], v]`
`n[u_, v_] = Cross[Tv[u, v], Tu[u, v]]`

Out[1793]= $\{x^2 + y^2, x + z^2, 0\}$

Out[1797]= $\{u \operatorname{Cos}[v], u \operatorname{Sin}[v], -u \operatorname{Cos}[v]^2 - u \operatorname{Sin}[v]^2\}$

We now compute the flux of curl ($\mathbf{F}$) across S through the following steps.

In[1798]:= `curlF[x_, y_, z_] = Curl[F[x, y, z], Cartesian[x, y, z]]`

Out[1798]= $\{-2 z, 0, 1 - 2 y\}$

In[1799]:= $\textbf{Flux} = \int_1^4 \int_0^{2 \, \text{Pi}}$ `curlF[S[u, v][[1]], S[u, v][[2]], S[u, v][[3]]].n[u, v] ⅆv ⅆu`

Out[1799]= -15π

■ Exercises

NOTE: In order to perform the curl operation in *Mathematica*, it is necessary to first load the **VectorAnalysis** package. See instructions given at the beginning of this chapter.

In Exercises 1 and 2, find the curl of the given vector field.

1. $\mathbf{F}(x, y, z) = \left\langle \ln\left(x^2 + y^2 + z^2\right), x/z, e^x \sin(yz) \right\rangle$

2. $\mathbf{F}(x, y, z) = \left\langle -\dfrac{x}{\left(x^2+y^2+z^2\right)^{3/2}}, -\dfrac{y}{\left(x^2+y^2+z^2\right)^{3/2}}, -\dfrac{z}{\left(x^2+y^2+z^2\right)^{3/2}} \right\rangle$

In Exercises 3 and 4, verify Stokes's Theorem for the given vector field $\mathbf{F}$ and surface S.

3. $\mathbf{F}(x, y, z) = \left\langle x^3 e - 3 x y + z^3, 2 z^3 - x z^2 + y^4, 6 y + 2 z^3 x^2 \right\rangle$ and S is the part of the paraboloid $z = x^2 + y^2$ for which $z \le 9$ and with outward normal orientation.

4. $\mathbf{F}(x, y, z) = \langle x y z, x y, x + y + z \rangle$ and S is the elliptical region in the plane $y + z = 2$ whose boundary is the intersection of the plane with the cylinder $x^2 + y^2 = 1$ and with upward normal orientation.

In Exercises 5 and 6, use Stokes's Theorem to compute the flux of the curl of the vector field $\mathbf{F}$ across the surface S.

5. $\mathbf{F}(x, y, z) = \left\langle \tan(x y z), e^{y-xz}, \sec(y^2 x) \right\rangle$ and S is the upper hemisphere of radius 4.

6. $\mathbf{F}(x, y, z) = \left\langle x^2 z, x y^2, z^2 \right\rangle$ and S consists of the top and four sides of the cube (excluding the bottom) with vertices at $(0, 0, 0)$, $(1, 0, 0)$, $(0, 1, 0)$, $(1, 1, 0)$, $(0, 0, 1)$, $(1, 0, 1)$, $(0, 1, 1)$, $(1, 1, 1)$.

■ 17.3 Divergence Theorem

Students should read Section 17.3 of Rogawski's *Calculus* [1] for a detailed discussion of the material presented in this

section.

Let $\mathbf{F}(x, y, z) = \langle F_1, F_2, F_3 \rangle$ be a vector field. The divergence of $\mathbf{F}$, denoted by div($\mathbf{F}$) or $\nabla \cdot \mathbf{F}$, is defined by

$$\text{div}(\mathbf{F}) = \nabla \cdot \mathbf{F} = \frac{\partial F_1}{\partial x} + \frac{\partial F_2}{\partial y} + \frac{\partial F_3}{\partial z}$$

where $\nabla = \left\langle \frac{\partial}{\partial x}, \frac{\partial}{\partial y}, \frac{\partial}{\partial z} \right\rangle$.

The *Mathematica* command for computing the divergence of a vector field $\mathbf{F}$ is **Div[F,coordsys]**, where **coordsys** is the coordinate system of the vector field. This is demonstrated in the next example.

The following is another generalization of the Fundamental Theorem of Calculus three dimensions, which relates a triple integral of a solid object involving divergence with a corresponding surface integral along its boundary.

Divergence Theorem: Let W be a region in $\mathbb{R}^3$ whose boundary ∂W is a piecewise smooth surface, oriented so that the normal vectors to ∂W point outside of W, and $\mathbf{F}(x, y, z)$ be a vector field with continuous partial derivatives whose domain contains W. Then

$$\iint_{\partial W} \mathbf{F} \cdot d\mathbf{S} = \iiint_W \text{div}(\mathbf{F}) \, dV$$

Refer to your textbook for a detailed discussion and proof of the Divergence Theorem.

Example 17.8. Find the divergence of the vector field $\mathbf{F}(x, y, z) = \left\langle x \sin(yz), e^{x/y} z, yx^2 \right\rangle$.

Solution:

```
In[1800]:= Clear[F1, F2, F3, x, y, z]
        F1 = x Sin[y z]
        F2 = E^(x/y) z
        F3 = x^2 y
        F = {F1, F2, F3}
```

Out[1801]= $x \sin[y z]$

Out[1802]= $e^{x/y} z$

Out[1803]= $x^2 y$

Out[1804]= $\left\{ x \sin[y z], e^{x/y} z, x^2 y \right\}$

Then the divergence of $\mathbf{F}$ is

```
In[1805]:= Div[F, Cartesian[x, y, z]]
```

Out[1805]= $-\dfrac{e^{x/y} x z}{y^2} + \sin[y z]$

NOTE: Again we obtain the same answer for the divergence of $\mathbf{F}$ using the explicit formula:

```
In[1806]:= D[F1, x] + D[F2, y] + D[F3, z]
```

Out[1806]= $-\dfrac{e^{x/y} x z}{y^2} + \sin[y z]$

Example 17.9. Find $\iint_S \mathbf{F} \cdot d\mathbf{S}$, where $\mathbf{F}(x, y, z) = \left\langle x, y^2, y + z \right\rangle$ and $S = \partial W$ is the boundary of the region W contained in the cylinder $x^2 + y^2 = 4$ between the plane $z = x$ and $z = 8$.

Solution: If S is the boundary of the solid W, then W is given by

$$W = \left\{ (x, y, z) : -2 \le x \le 2, \ -\sqrt{4 - x^2} \le y \le \sqrt{4 - x^2}, \ x \le z \le 8 \right\}$$

In[1807]:= `Clear[F, divF, x, y, z]`
`F[x_, y_, z_] = {x, y`^{2}`, y + z}`
`divF = Div[F[x, y, z], Cartesian[x, y, z]]`

Out[1808]= $\left\{ x, y^2, y + z \right\}$

Out[1809]= $2 + 2 y$

By the Divergence Theorem, we see that $\iint_S \mathbf{F} \cdot d\mathbf{S}$ is given by

In[1810]:= $\int_{-2}^{2} \int_{-\sqrt{4-x^2}}^{\sqrt{4-x^2}} \int_{x}^{8}$ `divF dz dy dx`

Out[1810]= 64π

- ## Exercises

NOTE: In order to perform the divergence operation in *Mathematica*, it is necessary to first load the **VectorAnalysis** package. See instructions given at the beginning of this chapter.

In Exercises 1 and 2, find the divergence of the given vector field **F**.

1. $\mathbf{F}(x, y, z) = \left\langle x\,y\,z, \ x^2 + y^2 + z^2, \ x\,y + y\,z + x\,z \right\rangle$

2. $\mathbf{F}(x, y, z) = \left\langle e^{x\,y} \cos z, \ e^{y\,z} \sin z, \ z^2 \right\rangle$

In Exercises 3 and 4, verify the Divergence Theorem for the given vector field **F** and solid region W.

3. $\mathbf{F}(x, y, z) = \left\langle x^2\,y, \ y^2\,z, \ z^2\,x \right\rangle$ and $W = \left\{ (x, y, z) : x^2 + y^2 + z^2 < 1 \right\}$ is the unit ball.

4. $\mathbf{F}(x, y, z) = \langle e^x \cos y, \ e^x \sin y, \ x\,y\,z \rangle$ and W is the region bounded by the paraboloid $z = x^2 + y^2$ and $z = 4$.

In Exercises 5 and 6, use the Divergence Theorem to calculate the flux of the vector field **F** across the surface S.

5. $\mathbf{F}(x, y, z) = \left\langle x\,e^z, \ y^2, \ y + z\,x \right\rangle$ and S is tetrahedron bounded by the plane $3\,x + 4\,y + 5\,z = 15$ and the coordinate planes in the first octant.

6. $\mathbf{F}(x, y, z) = \left\langle x\,y\,z, \ x^2 + y^2 + z^2, \ x\,y + y\,z + x\,z \right\rangle$ and S is the unit cube with vertices at $(0, 0, 0)$, $(1, 0, 0)$, $(0, 1, 0)$, $(1, 1, 0)$, $(0, 0, 1)$, $(1, 0, 1)$, $(0, 1, 1)$, $(1, 1, 1)$.

Appendices - Quick Reference Guides

■ A. Common Mathematical Operations - Traditional Notation versus *Mathematica* Notation

The following list demonstrates how to translate common mathematical operations described using traditional notation into *Mathematica* notation. In many instances *Mathematica*'s palettes (see Section 1.5) will allow the user to input commands using traditional notation without having to convert to *Mathematica* notation.

Operation	Traditional Notation	*Mathematica* Notation
Define a function	$f(x) = x^2$	$f = x\,^\wedge 2$ or $f[x\_] = x\,^\wedge 2$ or $f[x\_] := x\,^\wedge 2$ (delayed assignment)
Evaluate a function	$f(1)$	$f\ /.\ x \rightarrow 1$ or $f[1]$
Square root	$\sqrt{f(x)}$	**Sqrt[$f[x]$]**
Absolution value	$\|f(x)\|$	**Abs[$f[x]$]**
Limit	$\lim\limits_{x \to a} f(x)$	**Limit[$f[x]$, $x \rightarrow a$]**
Derivative	$f\,'(x)$	$f\,'[x]$ or **D[$f[x]$, x]**
Second derivative	$f\,''(x)$	$f\,''[x]$ or **D[$f[x]$, $\{x, 2\}$]**
Indefinite integral	$\int f(x)\,dx$	**Integrate[$f[x]$, x]**
Definite integral (Exact)	$\int_a^b f(x)\,dx$	**Integrate[$f[x]$, $\{x, a, b\}$]**
Definite integrate (Approximate)	$\int_a^b f(x)\,dx$	**NIntegrate[$f[x]$, $\{x, a, b\}$]**
Pi	π	**Pi** or π (from palette menu)
Euler number	e	**E** or e (from palette menu)
Imaginary number	i	**I** or i (from palette menu)
Infinity	∞	**Infinity** or ∞ (from palette menu)
Sine function	$\sin x$	**Sin[x]**
Inverse sine function	$\arcsin x$ or $\sin^{-1} x$	**ArcSin[x]**
Exponential function	e^x	**E$^\wedge$x** or **Exp[x]** or e^x (from palette menu)
Natural logarithm (base e)	$\ln x$	**Log[x]**
Logarithm (base a)	$\log_a x$	**Log[x, a]**
Define i-th element of a sequence	$x_i = a$	$x[i] = a$ or $x_i = a$ (from palette menu)

▪ B. Useful Commands for Plotting, Solving, and Manipulating Mathematical Expressions

Mathematica Command	Description
Plot[f[x], {x, a, b}]	Plot a function $f(x)$ on the interval $[a, b]$
Plot3D[f[x, y], {x, a, b}, {y, c, d}]	Plot a two-variable function $f(x, y)$ on $[a, b] \times [c, d]$
ParametricPlot[{x[t], y[t]}, {t, a, b}]	Plot parametric equations $x = f(t)$, $y = g(t)$ on $[a, b]$
PolarPlot[f[θ], {θ, a, b}]	Plot polar function $r = f(\theta)$ on $[a, b]$
ContourPlot[f[x, y], {x, a, b}, {y, c, d}]	Plot contour of $f(x, y)$ on $[a, b] \times [c, d]$
ContourPlot[F[x, y] == 0, {x, a, b}, {y, c, d}]	Plot implicit function $F(x, y) = 0$ on $[a, b] \times [c, d]$
Solve[f[x] == g[x], x]	Solve an equation $f(x) = g(x)$ for x
DSolve[F(x, y, y' (x)) == 0, y[x], x]	Solve a differential equation $F(x, y, y'(x)) = 0$ for $y(x)$ with initial value $y'(0) = a$
Part[*expr,i*] or *expr*[[*i*]]	Refer to i-th element of list *expr*
N[*expr*] or **N[*expr,n*]** (*n*-digit precision)	Numerical approximation of a quantity *expr*
Simplify[*expr*]	Reduce an expression *expr* to most simple

▪ C. Useful Editing and Programming Commands

Mathematica Command	Description
SHIFT+ENTER	Evaluates input
%	Refers to previous output
%%	Refers to second previous output
%k or **Out[k]**	Refers to output line k
In[k]	Refers to input line k
CTRL+L	Reproduces the previous input
CTRL+SHIFT+L	Reproduces the previous output
?Plot	Lists all *Mathematica* commands containing the expression **Plot** (or any other specified command)
(* *expr* *)	Insert comment *expr* (unevaluated)
If[*test,expr,else*]	Evaluate *expr* if *test* is true; otherwise, evaluate *else*
Do[*expr*,{i,min,max,step}]	Evaluate *expr* through loop i running from *min* to *max* with increment *step*
While[*test, expr*]	Evaluate *expr* while *test* is true; otherwise stop

■ D. Formatting Cells in a Notebook

Mathematica organizes a notebook in terms of data boxes called cells. The size of a cell is indicated by the corresponding size of the right bracket symbol attached to the right hand margin of each cell. A new cell can always be created by moving the cursor to any position between cells and begin typing. To edit a cell, just move the cursor to the desired position within that cell.

Each cell can be formatted to perform a specified function. By default, a new cell is always formatted as an input cell, which are used to evaluate *Mathematica* expressions. *Mathematica* outputs are contained within output cells, naturally. Other cell formats included title, section, subsection, text, formula, etc. The format of a cell is indicated by the left-most box on the toolbar. To change its format, first highlight the cell by clicking on the right bracket symbol attached to it. Then click on the indicator box and choose the desired format.

■ E. Saving and Printing a Notebook

Saving or printing a notebook can be accomplished by going to the File menu and selecting the desired option. To print a portion of a notebook that has been highlighted, choose the Print Selection option instead. To save your Notebook in other formats such as PDF, print it by selecting the desired format as the output source.

References

1. J. Rogawski, *Calculus: Early Transcendentals*, 2nd Edition, W.H. Freeman and Co., New York, 2012.